It's Gonna Be OK™:
Proven Ways to Improve
Your Child's Mental Health

by Dr. Roseann Capanna-Hodge

Dedication

To all my fellow special needs mamas:

The journey is long and hard, but the rewards are all the sweeter.

We walk this road together.

No one told us that when we had kids, we would be up all night worrying about our babies!

Only another special needs mama can understand the worry we face about our kids at the bus stop, at lunch, and/or in the class. Will they learn? Will they be liked? Will they turn in their homework? Will they get into trouble?

Will this therapy work?

We understand the torture of going to a special education or 504 meeting like no other ... I mean, a root canal is easier!

We know the fear that washes over you when the teacher, principal, or guidance counselor calls, because you know it means there are more problems that no one seems able to fix.

Yet after all is said and done, we get to watch as our kids laugh and smile just as much—if not more—than any other kid their age ... because of the love and care we provide them.

The most important thing after our kiddos is this: our relationships with one another. We want our babies to have someone to sit with at lunch in the same way we know we need other moms in our corner who get our daily struggles and joys. Our special needs kids make it clear who our real friends are.

We aren't those ladies at the bus stop who talk about how perfect Johnny didn't make the travel soccer team because we are trying every diet, supplement, and holistic therapy we can fit in between karate and tutoring.

We mamas do what it takes ... because who else is going to help our kids be the rock stars they are?

If you have an out-of-the-box kiddo, or a child with different needs, and you are simply an imperfect, extraordinary mom like me, then you understand this journey ... and you know

IT *IS* GONNA BE OK!

I am with you in mind, body, and spirit every step of the way.

Roseann Capanna-Hodge

Endorsements

"Of all the experts I met along the way on my child's healing journey, Dr. Roseann is one of my favorites. She made me feel so validated and helped me deepen my own healing alongside my son's with natural therapies." - Miranda Hope, granddaughter of Bob Hope and TEDx Speaker

"There may be a lot of mental health and parenting experts out there, but I trust Dr. Roseann's advice to help children, teens, and families." - Cynthia Henry Thurlow, Nurse Practitioner, Women's Health Expert, TEDx Speaker with 8 Million Views

"As the parent of a teenager, I found Dr. Roseann's techniques for naturally dealing with mental health issues to be both effective ... and full of heart. In combination with the solid, proven science behind diet and gut health influencing mental health, Dr. Roseann is blazing an important, new path for today's youth, parents, and teachers!" - Vincent Pedre MD Bestselling author of Happy Gut -- The Cleansing Program to Help You Lose Weight, Gain Energy, and Eliminate Pain

"Dr. Roseann is one of the foremost experts on childhood behavior. I trust her advice, and I know that whatever she recommends, it is based on recent research and works to improve behavior, thinking, and attention in children and teens in the safest, most effective way possible. Every parent needs to read this book!" - Robin McManne, Founder of Parenting for Connection, Parenting Expert

"I wish I had this book on hand when my teens were struggling, because Dr. Roseann walks you through, in a step-by-step manner, how to reduce and reverse symptoms naturally and effectively without dangerous medications." - Dr. Debi Silber, Founder, The Post Betrayal Transformation Institute

"Dr. Roseann is the authority on children's mental health, and she is changing the way we view and treat mental health in a time when families and their children are in crisis." - Maria Rickert Hong, Author of Almost Autism

"This is the essential guide every special needs parent should have on hand to turn their child's learning, attention, and behavior around." - Amber Trueblood, LMFT Parenting Expert

"Dr. Ro is my go-to PANS/PANDAS/AE and Lyme mental health expert for helping stuck kids get unstuck." - Dr. Tom Moorcroft, DO Founder of Origins of Health and PANS/PANDAS/AE and Lyme and Tick-borne Disease Expert

"One of my favorite things about Dr. Roseann is that, in addition to being a walking encyclopedia of children's mental health, she makes serious topics fun and actionable in an incredibly personable and loving way. If you're going through something challenging with your child, this is the woman you want by your side." - Dr. Cleopatra Kamperveen, Founder, The Fertility & Pregnancy Institute, Research Scientist and USC Tenured Professor

"If your child or teen is struggling with attention, behavior, learning, or stress, this book is the trusted resource you want to have on your nightstand." - Dr. Daniel Cardellichio, Functional Physician

"Dr. Roseann is showing parents that they can change their children's mental health in a powerful but easy-to-follow way through lifestyle changes that any parent can add into their daily routine." - Beth Lambert, Director of Epidemic Answers and Author of A Compromised Generation

Contents

Foreword

I know you're a busy parent, just like me. We all have so much competing for our time and attention, especially if we have a child suffering from ADHD, autism, anxiety, depression, OCD, or behavioral problems.

If your child has any mental health concerns, investing in this book is one of the very best things you can do to help him or her with any issue related to attention, worry, behavior, learning, or mood.

As a holistic pediatrician, I know firsthand the truth of what Dr. Roseann teaches—that with an integrative and functional medicine approach, mental health problems are reversible!

Dr. Roseann's unique and cutting-edge approach teaches parents how to reduce and reverse their children's mental health symptoms with heart and humor. She is a licensed child psychologist and expert in her field, and I completely trust her advice to help parents of special needs children.

I know that whatever Dr. Roseann recommends, it is based on the most up-to-date research … that it works … and that it truly helps.

I am an internationally recognized holistic pediatrician, pediatric functional medicine expert, and mom to two thriving kids. I have helped thousands of kids by getting to the root cause of their health concerns (ranging from frequent colds and ear infections to asthma and eczema to autism, ADHD, PANS/PANDAS, anxiety, depression, and autoimmune illnesses) while helping their parents understand how to help their children thrive—body, mind, and spirit.

Dr. Roseann is a licensed psychologist, pediatric mental health expert, and founder and director of The Global Institute of Children's Mental Health who has pioneered a holistic approach to reversing mental health using neurofeedback, biofeedback, psychotherapy, nutrition, and natural therapies. I met Roseann through an amazing community of health and wellness professionals who are working to change health across the globe at JJ Virgin's Mindshare collaborative. I now know Roseann personally as a dear friend and professionally as a pediatric mental health colleague, and I know firsthand the profound changes parents and children can achieve by utilizing her approach.

And now, you can learn that approach with this book.

One of my favorite things about Dr. Roseann is that she not only has energy and enthusiasm, but that she can make even the most serious topics fun, understandable, and doable.

Long before the pandemic, kids were facing an epidemic of childhood mental health disorders. This is a situation that has only worsened with the pandemic. Now, our kids are in a serious crisis. Parents are struggling with what to do and how to help their kids.

It's Gonna Be OK™: Proven Ways to Reverse Your Child's Mental Health is needed now more than ever. It gives parents the tools they need to take action today—to take important-but-simple steps to help their children and teens reduce stress, improve learning, and reverse mental health problems.

This book is filled with evidence-based holistic therapies that every parent can use to support the challenges and distresses their children are facing. Dr. Roseann walks you through her process step-by-step, so that you know why and how to unwind your child's mental health concerns in an achievable and sustainable way.

Now, as a pediatrician, I get to share with you Dr. Roseann's book—my number one special needs parent resource. Every parent of a child who struggles socially, emotionally, behaviorally, or academically should have it as their go-to-resource. It is filled with hope, research-based techniques, and actionable steps to change the trajectory of your child's life.

With Dr. Roseann's help, it really will be OK.

Elisa Song, MD

Holistic Pediatrician and Pediatric Functional Medicine Expert

Founder, Healthy Kids Happy Kids

Introduction

As the daughter of Italian immigrants, I grew up with a holistic foundation that I have always incorporated into my work as a psychologist. In my almost three decades of helping children, teens, and families heal from mental health issues, I have never seen a crisis in children's mental health like I'm seeing now. It is truly why I *am* on a mission to *"change the way we view and treat children's mental health,"* and writing this book is part of that mission. My goal is to help parents understand that they can reduce and reverse their child's mental health issues with proven natural therapies.

Watching so many distressed parents at the end of their rope being told by doctors to feed their kids more medication, despite it clearly not working, compelled me to find another way. Off I went to the microfiche (did I mention this was a long time ago?!) in the basement of the library, and to my surprise, I quickly found a ton of research about neurofeedback and various other evidence-based holistic treatments. What I discovered is that there *is* another way, besides medication and talk therapy, to help kids get focused, be calm, and learn better. In fact, there were a *lot* of other ways, and a lot of research to support them, but they had all been discouraged in favor of a "magic" little pill.

Throughout the 30 years since then, I've used those therapies to help thousands of children and young adults reverse the most challenging conditions such as ADHD, autism, anxiety, depression, concussion, learning disabilities, Lyme Disease, and PANS/PANDAS using proven holistic therapies.

I've traveled the world to share what I've learned, and because of the lives that have been changed because of it, I've been featured on CBS, NBC, the New York Times, Forbes, Parents Magazine, Money, and Healthline, and I've reached over two billion people worldwide in dozens of media outlets.

In January 2020, right before the pandemic, I founded The Global Institute of Children's Mental Health. It was born out of a realization that over my 30-year career, I watched as year after year, children began exhibiting the signs of anxiety at an earlier age. With the average age of onset of an anxiety disorder now at six years old, I realized that I needed to help children and families on a global level, not just one at a time in my office.

Today, kids are struggling to make friends, getting bombarded with hours of schoolwork, and are increasingly stressed and anxious while dealing with physical illnesses like PANS/PANDAS and Lyme Disease.

My mission to change the way we view and treat children's mental health extends to both parents and professionals. For professionals, I wrote the first book EVER on teletherapy activities, the ***Teletherapy Toolkit™***. **It guides therapists in facilitating change virtually.** I am also teaching parents that they can reverse their child's mental health via my **Get Unstuck Program™**, in which I provide step-by-step personal guidance.

And I know what I'm doing really is making a difference… *Forbes* called me, "A thought leader in integrative children's mental health," because I am moving the dial by getting parents and professionals to think differently about what they can do to change their child's mental health via proven holistic techniques and therapies that are backed by research.

I made the commitment to "doing better" by starting a global conversation on children's mental health and teaching parents how to reverse symptoms. As a pediatric mental health expert, I am working hard to bring awareness to the modern-day concerns affecting children, explaining how everything from eco-anxiety (worries about climate change) to re-entry panic syndrome (the impact COVID-19 fears have on embracing our "new normal") are affecting children on a global scale.

I wholeheartedly believe that the more we talk about mental health challenges, the more people can find help for themselves. I know that when parents understand how they can change their child's mental health, they will go from wondering "if" holistic techniques will work to "when." I want every parent to be filled with the same hope for healing their child's issues as they had for their bright future on the day their child was born.

It's Gonna Be OK!™ gives them the tools to get started today.

Chapter 1 - What Is Symptom Reversal?

If you have a child who struggles with learning, paying attention, and/or dealing with stress, your life is likely packed with sleepless nights of worry-filled tossing and turning as you catastrophize everything from who he or she sat next to at lunch that day to whether or not s/he will make it in college. You're probably used to being dragged into school for meetings about behavior on the bus or in the classroom, failure to turn in homework, trouble getting along with other kids, falling behind in school, and so on. And maybe, because of all this, you're worn out and close to giving up hope; the idea of your child's learning, social, or behavioral issues getting better seems like a fairy tale.

You are not alone. When parents walk through my door, they are battle-weary, worried, and out of hope. They've explored everything they can think of to find answers and get help for their kiddos: asking the school for assistance, talking to the pediatrician, putting their baby on medication, and of course, driving countless miles to see every therapist in town. Despite their efforts, nothing works to create lasting change.

James's Story

James, a super-bright, slightly hesitant and shy 12-year-old was well-liked and well-behaved at school. His grades were good, but despite being so bright, he held himself back from new things and group activities and had only a couple friends. On most school days, he complained of a tummy ache, but his parents, Joanna and Mitch, were unable to find the source and suspected it might just be a case of nerves. They never once got a call from the school, so they thought things were ok.

When James went into the fourth grade, they noticed him biting his nails. Often worried over writing assignments, he consistently asked, *"Is this good enough?"* His work was near perfect, but nonetheless, James would fret over every line in every paragraph, and frequently erase and rewrite to get things *"right."*

Joanna and Mitch spoke to his fourth-grade teacher, who said, *"James is doing great. He is so bright. I don't think you should worry."* They would come to hear the same from pretty much all his teachers. Since nothing "major" was going on, even his pediatrician didn't have much to offer. Anxiety and stress never came up.

But by the time James entered the seventh grade, he was so anxious that he wasn't sleeping. He had headaches to accompany his recurring stomach aches, and his grades were all over the place.

At this point, it was obvious that James was experiencing anxiety, so Joanna and Mitch went to the psychiatrist their physician recommended and were mortified when only medication was offered. They knew there had to be another way.

That is when they discovered neurofeedback and psychotherapy. They learned that all the physical symptoms James experienced were manifestations of his anxiety—it was his body's way of communicating its stress. That chronic stress built up over time, and James simply could no longer keep up with school, sleep, and management of his worried thoughts.

After treatment, James's anxiety stopped. As Joanna and Mitch put the pieces together, they were able to see all the ways James had always been anxious. The nail biting, stomach aches, headaches, shyness, and resistance were all behavioral signs that he was a stressed and anxious kid, despite his doing well in school and being a well-liked overall sweetheart.

The truth is, James had been suffering a long time before Joanna and Mitch got him help—before his anxiety really began to show itself at school and before it fully destroyed his self-esteem. His parents felt pretty darn bad that they had missed it, but they were relieved they hadn't put him on the medication rollercoaster they were all too familiar with having heard the stories from family members and their friends' kids.

Finally, James's anxiety was able to be reversed, and they all felt for the first time that things were going to be ok.

You Mean You Can Reverse Symptoms?

When I say, *"symptom reversal,"* many parents look at me and ask, *"What does that mean? Is that even possible?"* Most parents simply desire the comfort of not having to constantly worry about their child, because he or she is happy, accepted by others, and self-confident. All parents just want things to be better for their kid, which means they likely haven't even thought about actually *reversing* focus, anxiety, or mood problems.

We have all been told what is possible with medication. Yet they are empty promises, because even after being medicated, children remain behind in school, exhibit irritability, or continue to suffer in some way or another, right? Heck, if we're honest, the whole family suffers. Everyone hopes the meds will work like magic, but alas, they don't. In fact, they make things worse.

I am here to tell you something you may have never heard:

There *is* a difference between *treating* symptoms and *reversing* them. When we just treat them with medication, we never really get to the core of the problem. We are simply putting a Band-Aid on the issue, and that never works as a long-term solution. After all, what exactly are you treating, and how do you know for certain that you have the right diagnosis and treatment?

With our current model of whack-a-mole diagnostics and treatment, you simply don't.

As parents, we put so much effort into trying to survive—to live with the issues our children have—but they never get truly better when we medicate without understanding the why behind them.

When we use neuroscience, we can get to the *right* diagnosis and then the *right* treatment at the *right* time. (Yes, there is a such a thing.)

And when we shift our efforts to addressing the root causes of the problems, we can actually reverse the issues and symptoms they experience.

Yes, mental health issues *can* be reversed.

Imagine watching your child grow at a normal rate, instead of standing back and witnessing all the other kids changing as much as two times the rate as yours (even if you haven't experienced this yet, it often catches up with them, as it did in James's case).

Symptom reversal allows your child to change and grow alongside their peers, too. Getting them unstuck makes all the difference.

[Would you like to GET STARTED right away? Grab my free Mental Health Symptom Reversal Quickstart Guide at www.drrotips.com/quickstart.]

How Do Parents Describe Symptom Reversal?

When you hear parents of a special needs child describe "symptom reversal," you "get" it in a way only another special needs parent can truly understand. You understand what only another special needs parent understands about how it feels when a child reduces that irritability, stress, and disorganization … when grades get better, the sibling brawls lessen, and there is no longer a flood of tears before school every morning because the day's socks just aren't right.

Here is how some of the parents I've worked with describe symptom reversal:

"Seeing your child reduce and reverse symptoms that get in the way of connecting, succeeding, and thriving means everything. I mean how could it not?! For a parent who sees her child struggle, suffer, or come up against bigger challenges than other children have to deal with, reversing symptoms means giving that child a leg up on having a good life. And in the end, that is all any parent ever wants and all we strive to do."

"Reversing symptoms means everything. It means that the veil is lifted, and the constant struggle, big or small, just isn't there. For things to just be a little bit easier—for the child to not have so many disorganized thoughts and be able to independently carry through on his assignments and follow directions—really means the world to a parent. Finding that thing or combination of things to make things just a little easier for a child is something a parent would do a thousand times over."

"It's not only seeing your child improve in so many ways, but creating that big shift that changes the trajectory of a child's life, so he or she can be happy."

"Symptom reversal is about taking all the little steps that get you moving along, or really starting to strip away all layers to the problems that are holding my kid back."

"Taking all the little steps—from nutrition to starting psychotherapy to getting the right treatment—makes the difference. It took a long time, but my daughter has really been able to overcome the limitations that she had because of her dyslexia and her ADHD. And now, she's in high school, and she's looking at going to college. She's happy, confident, and doing so well in school."

"To see your child gain that light back in her eyes … laugh, and just walk a little taller.

To truly overcome those things that hold her back … dyslexia, ADHD, anxiety, depression, trauma, or whatever it is … that is what reversing mental health symptoms means to me."

As parents, we all want our kids to feel good about themselves and be accepted … to be independent … for their lives to be easier than the uphill battle many of them experience when they are uncomfortable in their skin.

Getting the right diagnosis and using the right combination of treatments and techniques in the right order *will* reduce and reverse symptoms.

This book is a guide for all parents to start unwinding the behaviors and issues that are holding your children back—to get them unstuck. No matter what you struggle with, at the end of the day, when you incorporate the eight pillars into your child and family's life, it *will* be OK!

In the next chapter, you will understand why holistic therapies that have been around for decades are proven to be safe, effective, and natural treatments for physical and mental health. And in this book, you will learn how you can use these proven therapies to reduce and reverse mental health problems and see your child feel calm, alert, and good about him or herself again … or maybe for the first time.

Chapter 2 - Proven Holistic Therapies

If you're familiar with holistic therapies, you know how powerful they are in getting us out of our heads, improving how we feel, and reducing pain. For those who aren't, though, it's common to be a little skeptical. If that's you, you may wonder why we as a society don't use them more, if they're so great. That is a fair question, but before we jump into why holistic therapies aren't used enough, let's first explore what I consider the top five (of millions) reasons we *should* use them.

5 Reasons Using Holistic Therapies Is Important in Reducing Your Child's Mental Health Symptoms

Reason 1: The research backs up the benefits.

"Once I saw the research on neurofeedback, I wanted to know why everyone wasn't doing it! Then, I got mad that I hadn't been told about it." - Mom of child with ADHD

We tend to think of "holistic" or "natural" therapies as treatments that have little validity and don't work. That just isn't the case. There is *a lot* of research to back up the efficacy of holistic therapies.

Treatments such as neurofeedback, biofeedback, nutrition, exercise, meditation, and psychotherapy have decades of scientific research that clearly demonstrate their effectiveness in the treatment of a host of mental health issues and stress-related conditions.

Reason 2: They are safe and natural.

"I think we're in a society where medication is so normalized, and children are so overmedicated, that it's considered very normal. And I'm telling you, I've been told, 'Put them on that.' No thank you. I trusted my gut, knowing there was another way." - Mom of child with dyslexia and anxiety

I invite you to ask yourself this question:

Can I treat my child's issues with evidence-based therapies that are safe and natural?

We know that our child's/teen's brain is developing, and it is so important to use effective treatments that support focus, mood, and positive behavior. It is also equally important to use *safe* treatments. As much as traditional medicine and big pharma wants us to believe that psychiatric medications are safe, there are risks associated with them that should be considered every time you give your child medication for focus, mood, anxiety, or any other behavioral or emotional issue.

Is there a place for medication? In my thirty years of experience, when it comes to children, the answer is rarely. Without exception, *every single* psychiatric medication available has a long list of side effects. We should *always* look to the research for what works and start with treatments that are safe and natural. Even in scratching the surface of your Google MD education, you begin to realize that there really are well-researched options available to help reduce and reverse your child's mental health symptoms sans medication.

Reason 3: They produce lasting change.

"When I changed my thinking from an external focus of medication to an internal focus, I realized that there was actually so much we could do to give [our child] what she needed to change how she learned and manage stress throughout her life." - Mom of teen with anxiety

One of the most surprising realizations for parents along their child's healing journey is how effective proven holistic therapies can be, and second, how they produce *lasting* results. When we intervene with nutrition, stress management, and changes in how we parent, we literally can not only rewire our child's brain, but we can create changes at the genetic level that positively impact our kids' and future generations.

Our genetics don't have to define us or our lifestyle, and the interventions we implement can create epigenetic changes, which is truly mind-blowing.

Reason 4: They support "checking under the hood."

"Well, with mainstream medicine, they just deal with symptoms—little, individual symptoms that never seem to connect. The holistic route takes the whole system into account; it really has made a big difference in my son's whole life." - Parent of teen with learning disabilities, ADHD, anxiety, and depression

Our allopathic medical model is set up to chase down symptoms without thinking about how things are connected. That means a lot of visits with medical and mental health professionals and a whole lot of guessing.

With mental health, the standard of care is to come in for a sit-down intake which encompasses a review of your symptoms and how they affect your life. No QEEG brain map or lab work to look at neurotransmitters, nutrient deficiencies, or anything medically related that could be causing emotional or behavioral distress.

When people come to my Ridgefield, CT center or work with me virtually, we "check under the hood," so we can make sense of the symptoms and behaviors and connect them to what we know about the brain. Only with the right diagnosis can we get the right treatment ... right? Somehow, this commonsense notion has been lost. A person's diagnosis is directly related to the skill and experience of the mental health provider seen, which is why people often spend years chasing down the right diagnosis before finally getting the right help.

Symptoms are connected and don't occur in isolation, so the specialist model of chasing down each symptom never works. I remember one client whose son had a known case of food poisoning, and for the next months, went from being a happy, energetic, and good student to a teen who had sleep and stomach issues that caused him to miss a lot of school, which he was failing. Despite his obvious food poisoning, his doctors said, *"We can't find anything, so it must be stress. Go see a psychiatrist."* Uh, really?! Yep!

Thankfully, when Nancy told me this, I said, *"What does your gut say?"* And she replied that it had to be connected to the food poisoning, because it all started literally that day. She cancelled the psychiatrist appointment and decided to go to the integrative medicine physician I referred her to who did one test and found the DNA of a parasite. After 12 days of the right treatment, Nancy's son's symptoms completely reversed.

While I wish I could say Nancy's is a rare story, I see this lack of connecting the dots and "checking under the hood" every single day. Thankfully, there is another way, and we are going to dive deep into it in this book (and you can learn even more through our Get Unstuck Program™ at www.getunstuckprogram.com).

Reason 5: We want our kids to learn skills, not take pills.

"I didn't want to change who my daughter was; I wanted to give her strategies as opposed to pills." - Mom of a child with OCD and anxiety

I get it—we wish our kids could just take something that would eliminate their pain and frustrations. It just isn't that easy, as much as we wish it was. When we give children psychiatric medication, we fail to provide them with the tools they need not just today, but in their future.

In order for kids to be resilient to stress, they need to *learn* different behaviors. They need to learn how to manage their emotions and uncomfortable feelings and how to tolerate and recover from stress. They need to learn how to be resilient. These are the life skills that secure happiness, maintain relationships, and build careers. A Resiliency Mindset™ is all about how one views, manages, and recovers from stress, and that involves having a regulated nervous system and learned ways of coping with stress.

A pill isn't magic nor often effective in regulating the nervous system so kids and teens can gain the attention and cognitive skills to *learn* another way to respond to stressors. Changing how they act so they learn to behave and think differently is where the magic happens. A pill won't teach them how to get along with others, recognize when their body tells them they are stressed or upset, or how to persist through a really boring task. That only comes with direct teaching. And just like if you were weak in math (that's me!), if you struggle with managing frustrations, following directions, and/or putting the brakes on, you can learn another way. With mental health, a licensed therapist can help a child or teen and his or her parents turn those behaviors around, get unstuck, *learn* new ways of coping, and most importantly, feel good about themselves.

5 Reasons We Don't Use Proven Holistic Therapies Enough

At this point, you're starting to think differently, right? Your mind is opening up. You are curious. Then, you let your left brain creep in, and you ask, *"If these therapies are so great, why isn't everyone using them?"*

It's an understandable question. The truth is, parents *are* using holistic therapies—research shows that they just aren't telling their pediatricians about it. And people are using these therapies more and more.

We already know that kids are struggling with physical illness, behaviors, and mental health issues, and that parents are desperately searching for something that can truly help their children. Holistic therapies have a proven track record. Following are five main reasons why the word just isn't getting out.

Reason 1: We do what our doctor or therapist tells us.

"When you go to a medical doctor, he/she pretty much immediately sends you to a psychiatrist. I think people simply don't know that there are other options. I know I didn't until I looked." - Father of two children with ADHD

The biggest reason we aren't using holistic therapies is simple: we just don't know about them. We rely so much on the advice of trusted professionals like our child's pediatrician. The problem is, pediatricians are overloaded. It is hard for them to stay current on all the treatments available. They have their hands full, and I get it.

Even though treatments like neurofeedback are rated at the same efficacy level as psychostimulants for the treatment for ADHD, that information just isn't reaching parents (American Academy of Pediatrics, 2012). Despite the widespread knowledge about how many of these treatments work, doctors tend to recommend medication, and sometimes, talk therapy. Even tried-and-true changes in nutrition to improve mental health get overlooked. Keep in mind that most physicians never take a course on nutrition (yep, it's true!), so they just aren't going to push what a game-changer diet modification can be. Ultimately, if your child's pediatrician or therapist isn't telling you about how diet (eating only nutrient-dense foods), neurofeedback, and/or changes in sleep hygiene can help your child, you simply won't know about it. And even if you do, you'll be wary about trusting it.

Reason 2: We don't know enough about them.

"They don't know what they don't know, and because of stigma, it seems invalidating." - Mom of a child with ADHD

Even when parents hear about things like an anti-inflammatory diet, neurofeedback, or ERP for OCD therapy, they don't *know* how it can help their child. Despite the push toward holistic therapies in the modern world, you might not have a provider or friend who can talk to you about it. The internet is fabulous, but it is a black hole. To put it simply, we are much more likely to listen to a trusted friend or provider.

The good news is there *is* information that can help you out there. This book (and our **Get Unstuck Program**™ at www.getunstuckprogram.com) will help you take the steps toward change. My mission is to cut through all the information and research to give you the essentials that support just how effective natural therapies can be. This way, you can feel confident making the choice to follow the research to help heal your child's issues instead of embarking on the medication rollercoaster.

Reason 3: We don't know where to start and/or are overwhelmed by the options.

"You know it takes a lot of research to be able to find what it is you need to fix yourself and help

your child. Yet I would do anything to help my son." - Mom of child with social anxiety

I remember running an ADHD parent support group for a large ADHD organization, and even though it was supposed to be a general support group, it became a "My-Child's-ADHD-Medication-Causes-X-Side-Effect Group." To hear how much the kids suffered from medication rebound effects and side effects was heartbreaking. How hard the after-school period became as the kids (and parents!) exhibited agitation, hyper behaviors, and a worsening of lack of focus. Those parents were so afraid to pull their children off of their ADHD medication(s) because their *"grades were better,"* even though their kids were a hot mess at home and parenting felt like a nightmare. The notion of where to start with a holistic therapy was so overwhelming for them that many ultimately decided to keep their kids on medications that were actually worsening things. For them, having a house built out of a deck of cards felt easier than laying a new foundation, because they were just overwhelmed.

Sometimes, we become immobilized when we are overwhelmed, which isn't so abnormal. The problem is, we are constantly choosing grades over the social and emotional development of our children, which causes a breakdown of family harmony sooner or later. It's easy for parents to feel overwhelmed, because there are a LOT of options, and knowing which treatment is best for your child may be the biggest hurdle.

This book provides you with the road map to get started, and getting started somewhere is all it takes. Remember, little waves create big waves!

Reason 4: No one talks about how effective they are.

"Until people have a tragedy or real crisis on their hands, they don't search this stuff out. It wasn't until we hit bottom that I began asking my friends and found Dr. Ro." - Mom of a teen with PANS, anxiety, depression, and suicidal thoughts

When our children are struggling, it is typically a private matter. There is still a lot of stigma around having mental health or behavioral issues. While we may post "ISO a good plumber" on social, few will post, "ISO a great therapist for my anxious teen." Parents may not feel comfortable sharing their child's health journey for many reasons. Plus, fears about privacy, judgement, and trust are real concerns in today's world of 'perfect' people.

That in turn means we aren't sharing what works with other parents who need it as much as you did. If I could scream it from the rooftop, I would. Oh wait, I do! People are using natural therapies more and more, they just aren't talking about it because of the stigma around mental health.

But who hasn't added a smoothie to their regimen, tried meditation, or used some lavender oil? Well, those are all evidence-based approaches to supporting physical and mental health.

So, how can parents find the natural support they need for their child? Ask your friends or an open provider, or search the internet, for evidence-based and natural ways to treat anxiety, attention problems, behaviors, etc. I can tell you my clients frequently get my name from four or five friends or providers before they actually get to me, and they always say, *"I wish I got here sooner."* Remember, you just need to start somewhere—so look for natural solutions and take action. Whether you take small steps or big ones, start taking them. You're reading this book because it's time for change … because you know what you are doing for your child right now isn't working.

Every time I am on television or featured in an article, my goal is the same: to change the way we view and treat children's mental health. That means I am committed to teaching you how YOU can turn things around for your child, and hopefully, your family.

Reason 5: We are afraid.

"First and foremost, parents are scared. They go to their doctor and school for advice. And they are always being told, especially if it is ADHD, that medication is the best option for them. So, you try, and try, and then try something else, and nothing seems to make a difference. It just breaks your heart." - Mom of a child with ADHD

The number one reason my families are afraid to use proven holistic therapies is that they have tried so many other therapies that haven't worked, and they are afraid to try again. Another *"Maybe this will work …"* is almost too much to bear.

Yet, when things begin to change for the better, their *"Yes, this works!"* feels amazing!

Most of us special needs parents took a bumpy ride to find that right combination of treatments and techniques to get our child smiling and talking again. So please, hang in there! There is no magic wand, but there is a clear step-by-step system that uses only natural and evidence-based therapies to reduce and reverse mental health symptoms.

There *is* a way to get unstuck.

I am hoping you've had some "aha" moments reading this far, and that you are beginning to believe that things really can get better for you, your child, and your family. In the next chapter, you'll hear Paul's story, and about how his mom, Jennifer, got sick and tired of trying the same ineffective therapies over and over. With the help of her friend, though, she found a path that turned things around for her son.

Chapter 3 – Modern Mental Health: Whack-a-Mole

Paul's Story

Paul, a very bright boy who came to our center about eight years ago, had zero motivation. His grades were horrible; he was perpetually in trouble for not listening and was even getting on the nerves of the few friends he had. After struggling for years at school with getting his ideas down on the page and turning in his work, he basically gave up.

High school was really hard for him, because he couldn't rely solely on his intelligence—he actually had to turn stuff in. When his parents checked his grades in the portal, they would come to find that while Paul did his work, it would often be found crumpled at the bottom of his bag or sitting in his Google Drive. No matter what system they put in place or tutor they asked for help, Paul could never find a way of doing things on his own. This led to a lot of heated arguments at home and zero positive change.

His parents tried *everything*. You know … medication, therapy, meetings at school … but his grades just kept going down the toilet. They were worried what might happen to their son if he didn't make it to college. They questioned if he could even learn a trade, because his grades were constantly up and down even with a tutor by his side. He could barely remember to flush the toilet, let alone be sent off to school to live independently.

Feeling like she was at the end of her rope, Paul's mom, Jennifer, remembered her friend telling her about some brainwave retraining called "neurofeedback" that had helped her own daughter's ADHD and anxiety years earlier. At the time, Jennifer remembered thinking that, if this "neurofeedback" thing was so good, surely her doctor would've told her about it. Instead, though, they had entered the early stages of "medication Russian roulette" that became their life for the next three years.

Paul went on to try one medication after another, each accompanied by a promise from his psychiatrist that it would *"help him focus and do better in school."* Not only did that never happen, but Paul's mental health actually declined. He became really depressed and experienced sleep problems. It was like the light had gone out of his eyes.

That was Jennifer's tipping point. Grades were one thing, but seeing him so sad and not like himself was something else. She knew she had to find another way.

She reached out to her friend, who was happy to share how doing neurofeedback at our center changed her daughter Emma's life forever. Years earlier, Emma had struggled with focus and was crippled by anxiety. But now, she is a confident young woman who is comfortable on her own and has friends and good grades.

Jennifer was afraid to hope … but she couldn't help but wonder if it could work for Paul, too.

We began. With the brain map ("checking under the hood"), I could literally see what was interfering with Paul's attention and executive functioning! That meant no more guessing, because we could see the areas that were overworked and underworked and how the brain "talked" to itself, which all affected how Paul processed and paid attention. It made sense that this very bright teenager had such a hard time starting and finishing tasks, because those areas in his brain just didn't turn on in the same way as others. His processing was as slow as a slug; he just needed time, which was a luxury he didn't have as a teenager in high school. Come to find out, by the time Paul realized what it was he had to do, the rest of the kids had already started, so he often just gave up.

Paul began neurofeedback and worked with an executive function coach who showed him how to actually think differently about starting a task. She broke down that process, teaching him to visualize the end product and then work backwards. With ADHD and executive functioning issues, Paul never knew where the pieces fit in the thousand-piece puzzle, so what he learned with the coach was huge! He began starting with the image of the thousand-piece puzzle, and *then* put the pieces in.

Neurofeedback got his brain to alert differently, and coupled with the guidance he received in thinking differently, produced some dramatic changes. He was not only paying attention on his own, but he was taking action. Little by little, you could see Paul's wheels turning as he applied what he learned without someone having to be all over him "like white on rice."

Within weeks, Jennifer actually got a call from Paul's science teacher who asked what was going on, because Paul was paying attention in class! He wasn't just passing, but getting As and Bs! Paul was motivated and able to complete his assignments without his parents having to constantly monitor him, which also decreased the arguing.

As a mom, the hardest thing to deal with is having everyone so miserable at home, so for Jennifer, this was a huge relief!

I'm happy to say that Paul went to college, graduated, and is now in graduate school. His joy for life and excitement for learning comes through every time he messages me.

And that's one of the things I love most about neurofeedback: once you teach the brain how to get into a healthy rhythm, it stays there ... which is exactly what happened with Paul. He is now self-confident, independent, and most importantly, happy.

Chapter 4 - The 8 Pillars of Mental Health Symptom Reduction and Reversal

Five diagnoses, Five Opinions ... Finn's Story

Finn came to the center with five diagnoses and at least five different professional opinions as to what was wrong. He had OCD, acid reflux, anxiety, ADHD, ODD, recurring strep, and chronic ear infections. His parents had taken him to no less than a dozen doctors, and at the time, he was seeing seven specialists for his various issues.

His parents, Nora and Jim, continuously asked, *"Aren't these things connected? Because nothing seems to work!"* The answer they received over and over again: *"Of course not. Some of these things are just comorbid conditions that occur together a lot, but aren't related."* It didn't make sense to Nora and Jim, so they searched away, quickly becoming Google MDs.

They read about things like "root causes," and how it was important to understand that you can make sense of a laundry list of conditions by connecting them to their source or sources. Intrigued, they continued their Google sleuthing and learned about PANS and PANDAS—conditions that cause children to display a range of mental health behaviors with a sudden onset of a problem(s) after exposure to an infection or environmental toxins. The exposure creates a misdirected immune response, and the body turns against itself, leading to behaviors such as rage, problems focusing, regressive behaviors, obsessions, compulsions, anxiety, depression, etc.

And the lightbulb went off!

Finn was developing pretty typically until the chronic ear infections and strep in preschool. From there, his behavior started to change. He became demanding and easily irritated when he never was before. He became angry. The bedtime routine his parents had established of walking him upstairs and staying in his room until he fell asleep was cute until it became apparent that he couldn't sleep without it. His anger would flare if the routine wasn't followed, and Finn's parents quickly learned the importance of a growing boy being able to get to sleep on his own.

Finn also became obsessive, questioning everything; *"Mom, where are you going? How long will you be gone? What happens if you die?"* He exhibited a constant and increasing need for reassurance, which became difficult to manage and have patience for.

The psychologist they were seeing at the time declared Finn was suffering from anxiety. It took another four therapists before they received the proper diagnosis of OCD. That process of searching, misdiagnosis, more searching, repeat, before finally getting the accurate diagnosis went on for seven years.

Before they knew it, Finn was 12, and despite all they had been through in trying to get their son help, his parents had to figure out on their own that he was clearly suffering from PANS. It should also be noted that none of their seven providers agreed with a PANS diagnosis—the family had to seek out a PANS specialist for that. Not a one had suggested the diagnosis to them.

At first, they were relieved that it was a medical condition causing all of Finn's mental health and behavioral issues. But then, they were angry. For seven years, they had searched for help, guidance, and care, and had gotten nothing. Instead, they were sent down the wrong road countless times, dealing with ineffective therapies and medications every single time. And each of those journeys ended with the same heartbreak. Along the way, they continuously lost a little bit of Finn throughout their quest for healing.

When they came to me, I helped them peel back all the layers they were still sorting through. I guided them through the 8 Pillars of Symptom Reduction and Reversal. They listened and learned, patiently implemented, and saw gradual, steady changes in Finn's behavior and health.

While Nora and Jim admitted to holding their breath at times as they waited for the other shoe to drop, they trusted and moved forward, doing the work as a family and healing wounds. Over time, the old Finn was back! He went on to graduate high school and attend college. All three are now vocal advocates not only for PANS/PANDAS education, but for parents being the CEOs of their family's health.

[If you're ready to embrace your CEO role and want to GET STARTED right away, grab my free Symptom Reversal Quickstart Guide at <u>www.drrotips.com/quickstart</u>.]

Now, let's talk about the pillars.

The Synergy of the 8 Pillars

While your story may not be just like Finn's, the journey is often the same … being left to blindly guess at what might be wrong with your child, following a treatment plan that never seems to work, and repeat … off to the next treatment. Why, you ask?

Here is the secret no one is telling you:

>*To reduce and reverse symptoms, you need to change your lifestyle.*

There is no magic bullet. It requires adjusting several things all at one.

And that is precisely what this book, *It's Gonna Be OK!* and my program, the **Get Unstuck Program**™ (<u>www.getunstuckprogram.com</u>), is all about. This book is a deep dive into the "why" behind each of the eight pillars, so you can understand how they all work together to reduce and reverse mental health symptoms. I give you the exact road map of getting started on the journey toward your child being calm, alert, and feeling good about him or herself.

And the beautiful thing is, what you learn won't just help your child … it will help *the whole family*, and even future generations … because *using the eight pillars can actually impact your epigenetics.*

Take a look at the **8 Pillars of Symptom Reduction and Reversal:**

- Stress Management

- Nutrition

- Nutrient Deficiencies

- Genetic Mutations

- Detoxification

- Sleep

- Proven Brain-Based Solutions

- Parenting

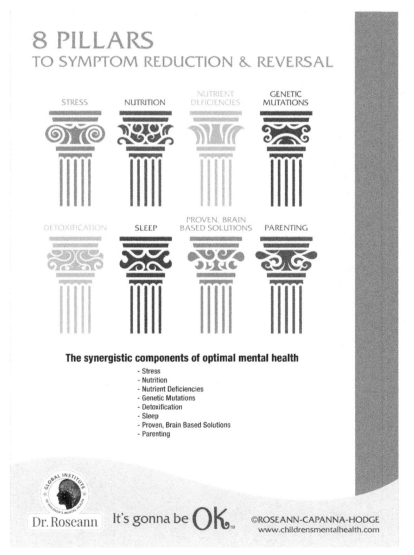

Dr. Roseann-Capanna-Hodge

Family Lifestyle Changes and Parent Self-Care

Each of these pillars are super-important stand-alone treatments, but it is their combination and integration into your family's life that is so critical for real and lasting change.

Think of it this way: we all wish we could go to the gym one time and be super-fit, right? But that isn't how muscles form. Muscles form over time, requiring effort and dedication to building them. We must apply that same philosophy to mental health issues, as well—applying the eight pillars to your child's and family's life takes mindful effort. And just as it is in fitness, the more you do it, the easier it becomes, and the more you come to appreciate how effective these healing principals are with *any* health issue.

In other words, the pillars bring wellness and vitality to life… and they deserve and require time and attention.

When we start anything new, often the biggest hurdle is getting started. Right now, you may feel like you have tried a lot (and I bet you have!), but you probably haven't added the eight pillars into your child's and family's life. I get it! As a special needs mom myself, I have been there. It can become really hard to "see" success.

But when you follow the eight pillars, you will reduce symptoms and bring health to your family.

Yes, they will help your child. And making changes to your family's health means you're taking care of *yourself*, too … maybe for the first time in a long time.

Your self-care is essential in your child's healing journey. When the captain goes down, so does the ship! During times of crisis, we parents (especially mamas!) put ourselves last, often neglecting our own care. Stop thinking it is selfish to take a bath, go for a walk, or spend time with your bestie. At minimum, we need to care for our nervous system so we can be the model of health and stress management for our kids.

By incorporating the eight pillars into your family life, you can take care of your babies and yourself, too.

But the reality is that self-care is about taking care of ourselves in interest of our own wellness, so we can feel good. So commit to 10 minutes a day of doing something to quiet your brain and body. A few ideas: mediation, yoga, **or intently practicing gratitude using our** *It's Gonna Be OK!™ Gratitude and Giggles Journal*: www.itsgonnabeok.com/journal.

Stress: The Derailer

Let me tell you, stress can derail any healing, therapy, or treatment, period! I dig deeper into this topic in the next chapter, but know that our body is designed to deal with stress first and healing second. You can try to outwit stress, but trust me, your body will hold it and divert its resources to go after any other unknown stress or potential "threat."

When your child is struggling, stress builds up in the body and can and will prevent symptom reduction and reversal. The good news is we can harness the power of neuroscience and use what we know to combat stress and get the body working, so your child can process more easily and feel calm, focused, and happy!

The Mind-Body-Spirit Connection

You may have heard it before—the mind and body are connected. But who is really teaching you about how our physical and mental health have a bi-directional relationship? You can't have one without the other.

Enter spiritual health. This is about our belief system and connection to a higher power, and we need it, too.

For optimal physical and mental wellness and greater resilience, all three of these aspects of our self are interconnected and work in unison. Each part supports the other, which means there are *so many* ways to improve our brain and mental health by deepening the mind-body-spirit connection.

When we teach children to connect to their bodies, they have greater emotional regulation, connectedness, empathy, and ultimately, self-confidence and self-esteem. When children know themselves and their body and feel connected to a higher power, they are so much more capable and confident and certainly less stressed and more resilient.

Self-Regulation and Resilience

You may already recognize that your child has a hard time monitoring and managing his or her behaviors, emotions, and thoughts, as well as altering them in accordance with the changing demands of a situation. Your son or daughter may react more strongly to things than others or be slower to catch on to learning. Thus, you find yourself telling him or her things that even your younger child has already figured out, but that he or she just can't seem to master.

This occurs when one is weak in self-regulation.

Self-regulation is our ability to put our brakes on and stay the course in pursuit of a goal or task completion. When it comes to controlling our behaviors, self-regulation is about pumping those brakes and/or shifting gears whenever a situation requires it. It means being in a balanced emotional state, so you don't react too strongly (or not strongly enough) in more challenging situations. It means remaining calm under pressure. It also means getting through tasks even when we don't enjoy them.

So many children with social, behavioral, learning, and attentional issues struggle with self-regulation, which causes them to over-rely on their parents and teachers for help. Having a clinical or neurological issue and/or having limited opportunities for independent practice are two reasons children and adolescents struggle with self-regulation.

Conditions such as ADHD, anxiety, autism, learning disabilities, etc. impact how the brain regulates its brainwaves, which affects how one self-regulates behavior and emotions. These conditions can make it harder for one to apply the brakes in situations of low interest or when they are overstimulated. They can also interfere with one's ability to even recognize the need to. Problems with self-regulation not only make us more reactive to things in our environment and stressors, but they also make it difficult to recover from stressors and have resilience. And while there are so many benefits of improving a child's self-regulation skills, the biggest may be the improvement of resilience (or stress tolerance).

The good news is that, with intervention, children can improve their ability to self-regulate behaviorally and emotionally.

Resiliency is one of *the* most important factors in mental health. How we view, manage, and recover from stress directly relates to how stress affects us. When we have a Resiliency Mindset™, we are happier and less likely to feel the effects of all kinds of stressors, even big ones. And really, we just don't view stressors the same way, which means we aren't activated and irritated as easily, either.

In a world filled with stress, more and more children are having trouble with self-regulation and managing it. And without an ability to regulate behaviors and emotions, not only will they experience more stress, but they are more likely to react negatively to stress. And the way the nervous system works, the more it reacts to something, the more likely it is to repeat that behavior … good or bad.

But when we teach the brain to self-regulate, one can focus better and be calm. That means your child will be more connected, a better independent problem-solver, and happier, because his or her brain and body can regulate instead of react. When the nervous system is calm, it can *learn* to react in a healthy way.

And as parents, we can guide them.

Children learn to regulate their emotions and behaviors through a process of trial and error. How they approach problem-solving and learn from their mistakes and the reactions they get from others has a lot to do with how they learn to self-regulate. Like toddlers who rely on their parents to help them navigate situations that require behavioral, emotional, and social regulation, these skills can be learned over time. Unfortunately, in our high-stress world, children have become less resilient, because there are so many stressors taxing their nervous system: sensory experiences, academic pressure, toxins, and a stressed-out world filled with stressed-out people.

In order to teach self-regulation skills, it is incredibly important for parents to let kids explore their environment and attempt problem-solving on their own. At the same time, parents should guide and provide positive feedback at a child's attempt to manage his or her own behaviors and emotions. For example, *"I saw that was very frustrating for you, but you waited your turn, and look what a great time you time you had!"*

Even when we try our best, sometimes our children are too activated to absorb our role modeling and direct teaching. The good news is when we calm the nervous system, our children are able to learn.

Dysregulation and the Nervous System

When you have a stress hyperactivation of the nervous system™, your frontal lobes shut down, and it becomes virtually impossible to have rational thoughts. (Yep, that is why your child or teen is like a tyrant when he or she is "in the red.") The brain is designed to go 'offline,' so you can act without bothering to think.

Our autonomic nervous system exists to help us manage stressors. A healthy, regulated autonomic nervous system will demonstrate regular oscillations between the sympathetic (energizing) and parasympathetic (relaxing) branches of the brain. A healthy nervous system will idle closer in the calmer, more "chilled-out" parasympathetic state and activate to the sympathetic dominant state when faced with a stressor. Even after dysregulating circumstances, like an activity that increases your heart rate, a "near death" experience, or some other jolting incident, your autonomic nervous system should return to normal as you calm down.

The thing about stress is that it can be real or imagined. Our kids' nervous systems are increasingly prone to stress-hyperactivated states due to genetic mutations, poor nutrition, heightened stress in the world around them, greater device usage, less play and down time, and a host of other contributors.

For some, chronic stress states can cause a "flight, fight, or freeze response," causing the nervous system to get stuck in one of these states as the sympathetic and parasympathetic systems become unbalanced. This leads to dysregulation.

Behaviorally, you will notice your child shut down, fly into a rage, or avoid things and people altogether. He or she might react strongly to things you would never expect—touch, sounds, food textures, things not going his/her way, and a host of other things that don't make logical sense.

Most individuals are born with a healthy nervous system and regulated brainwave functioning. But conditions such as excessive stress can make the nervous system over-responsive, which can lead to over-thinking and worry. And, when an excessive amount of worry creeps into your daily life, it often makes it hard to sleep, concentrate, and/or perform daily tasks by blocking your ability to self-regulate.

A regulated nervous system is crucial to our ability to take action, learn, and respond to whatever life throws at us.

Medications

I don't want this book to be all about why you shouldn't use medication. Rather, I aim for it to be a reliable source of evidence-based treatments that help turn children's and teen's behavior around ... really, to change the trajectory of their lives.

Even though medication has its benefits for those with a true chemical imbalance, the problem is that the standard of care in mental health is to *guess* at issues sans lab work or use of proven tools such as QEEG brain mapping. When this happens, we are failing to "check under the hood," choosing instead to prescribe psychiatric medications to children with a trial-and-error approach. Moreover, we are giving children medication that might be an "off-label" use, and almost without exception, there is at least one adverse effect due to medication toxicity. This puts parents in the awful position of having to make a risk-versus-benefit decision.

This book and our **Get Unstuck Program**™ (www.getunstuckprogram.com) are all about showing you a different way, because I am dedicated to sharing the research behind neuroscience and what it can do.

The most common psychiatric medication given to children is psychostimulant medication for ADHD and therefore bears discussion, as it is frequently thought of as "safe."

Adderall is FDA-approved for Attention-Deficit Hyperactivity Disorder (ADHD) in both children and adults. It is designed to help improve concentration and focus. It is also FDA-approved for the sleep disorder narcolepsy, which causes excessive sleepiness and can be quite debilitating (even causing sleep paralysis and loss of muscle control) in order to increase alertness.

With long-term usage, the brain can become reliant on the chemical support due to changes in dopamine activity that can impact the brain's reward center and alter one's ability to experience pleasure without the psychostimulant. The FDA notes that Adderall may be habit-forming, and this medicine is a drug of abuse.

As a stimulant, when Adderall wears off, it can leave one feeling fatigued and unmotivated. When stopped abruptly, temporary symptoms of withdrawal may occur. Therefore, individuals who would like to come off Adderall should always consult with their physician.

Adverse reactions from stimulants are common and include irritability, depression, appetite suppression, weight loss, and headaches. It is important to tell your doctor if you or your family have a history of depression, anxiety, mental illness, bipolar disorder, psychosis, problems with aggression, or suicidal thoughts or actions, as Adderall can exacerbate these issues. Adderall and Adderall withdrawal can lead to depressive or bipolar episodes of suicidal thoughts.

Cleary, the decision to start your child on this medication is not one to be taken lightly. I also hear from a lot of parents that they didn't even know there was another way.

There is, and that is what this book is about. There are in fact *many* other ways… and they are safe, natural, and effective. Let's let the research guide us, so you can see how using neuroscience to inform our interventions and initiate symptom reduction and reversal is most certainly possible.

If you'd like to learn even more about how natural, evidence-based approaches to health will blow your mind, replenish your hope, and motivate you to spring into action, I would love to walk and coach you through the 8 Pillars in my **Get Unstuck Program**™ (www.getunstuckprogram.com), which includes weekly calls and videos.

Dr. Roseann-Capanna-Hodge

Chapter 5 - The Effect of Stress on the Brain and Body

Pillar 1: Stress

Every day, we fight against stress. Now, you may think, *"Well, we all have it … so what?!"* While that is true, we also know that stress takes a toll on our physical and mental health, and that includes our children's.

Let's talk specifics about the toll stress has on the average American. According to the American Psychological Association 2019 Stress in America™ survey, stress has been at a constant level with an increase in specific sources of stress. In 2019, the majority of Americans experienced significant stress about healthcare, the election, and mass shootings. While stress related to work and money may still be common sources for most, in 2019, mass shootings were the most prevalent source of daily stress cited by U.S. adults across different racial and ethnic groups.

In 2019, I spoke a lot about children having eco-anxiety and concerns about climate change and global warming—the same stress affecting 56% of Americans. Discrimination as a source of daily stress is now on the rise, with one-quarter of adults (25%) in 2019 citing it as a *"significant"* source of stress. The American Psychological Association 2020 Stress in America™ survey found many of the same concerns. Now, with the impact of COVID, 19% of adults say their mental health is worse than last year.

Most people know that high levels of stress are unhealthy and recognize that they need more emotional support. In the 2019 Stress in America™ survey, 59% of adults said they, *"could have used more emotional support than they received in the past year, marking the highest proportion of adults who indicate this since APA first asked this question in 2014."*

The question is, then, what is the impact on our children?

Research has found that almost fifty percent of school children report and show signs of stress (Valizadeh, Farnam & Farshi, 2012). Children display their stress in a variety of ways, including experiencing worry, accelerated heart rate, being afraid, having chills, feeling sad, and experiencing headache and tiredness (Valizadeh, Farnam & Farshi, 2012). Chronic stress is impacting our children's physical (Bernard, 2002) and mental health, as well as learning (Vogel & Schwabe, 2016).

Parents of special needs children face even greater stress than parents of typical children (Hayes, & Watson, 2013), and that stress builds and leads to chronic or toxic levels of stress. In addition, the greater the levels of poverty or worries about income, the greater the impact of parenting stress (U.S. Department of Health and Human Services, 2011-2012).

The American Psychological Association 2020 Stress in America™ survey found that parents are of course struggling during the pandemic. We've had to take on additional responsibilities, and it's easy to feel overwhelmed and isolated. With the strain on family and general disruption of education, seven in ten parents (70%) say family responsibilities are a significant source of stress in their daily life. When it comes to their children's school and their additional homeschooling responsibilities, the majority (63%) say the COVID-19 pandemic made the 2019-20 school year extremely stressful for them.

I can tell you that I have never seen parents as exhausted and overwhelmed as I do right now. For some, homeschooling has shined a light on their child's issues in a way that has scared them. Seeing their kids struggle with focus, stress tolerance, and learning independently has surprised, heck, *shocked* many parents. More than any other year, I've had parents return to my center who I'd seen years ago, but they didn't take action. Yet after seeing their children struggle despite medication and talk therapy, they seek out another way again. While it isn't unusual for parents to try meds first and then come to me, 2020 provided them with clarity around the need to get unstuck in a way that is natural, effective, and builds independence.

Chronic stress can and does impact us and our children in so many ways. In my 30 years of working with children, I have seen a dramatic decrease in stress tolerance—the ability to stay calm and react without high emotionality or behaviorally when under stress. Why is that important?

Again, it's about resiliency. Today's children aren't able to tolerate stress as well as previous generations. Resiliency in the face of adversity or times of stress is a key component to the mental well-being of children throughout their life. Resilience is all about viewing stress differently, managing stressors, and recovering quickly when things are hard—skills that are typically even harder for kids with special needs. Fostering resilience and building that Resiliency Mindset™ is so critical for mental health.

There are so many reasons children are more easily stressed and frustrated these days, including a decrease in free play activities, less social interaction, less sleep, poor diet and food quality, increased developmentally inappropriate educational demands and activities, increased child and parent stress, and increased mental and physical health problems. With so much affecting our children right now, they just don't have the skills to manage stress ... but they *can*.

Understanding what stress is and what it does to the brain and body is CRITICAL in removing barriers to healing. Most of you will wonder why you didn't learn about this from your physicians or mental health provider. My answer is that, sadly, we have accepted chronic stress as a part of our lives.

But stress doesn't have to be runaway train. There are so many things you can do for yourself, your child, and your family.

Jack's Story

My friend Amanda came to me one day about her son Jack. He is one of those super-sweet and charming kids who happens to also be a good student. But Amanda shared that Jack was throwing up every single night. They had been to at least a half-dozen doctors trying to get to the bottom of what was going on, but no one could figure it out. He was happy and had lots of friends, but his mom wondered if stress and anxiety could be the source. After all, although he was naturally bright, there is a lot of pressure for kids to keep up. Even though Jack didn't say he was anxious, his mom realized that his stomach aches were likely a sign that he was (at minimum) stressed out. Amanda also wondered if neurofeedback could help him. So, Jack began a course of neurofeedback to help tame his nerves and stop his anxious stomach.

Luckily for Jack, from the day he began, he stopped throwing up! Amanda was right—the stomach aches and body tension were clear indicators of anxiety that many physicians missed. Amanda also began to notice that Jack became more affectionate with the members of his family. He just seemed to be his best self—calm, focused, and able to get through his work more quickly.

Fast forward seven years later: Jack is off to college on a full scholarship, and most importantly, is a happy and healthy young adult!

What Is Stress?

Not all stress is the same. It can be real or imagined, good or bad—unfortunately, our body doesn't know the difference. If our brain perceives something as stressful, it impacts us the same way physiologically regardless. And while normal levels of stress are okay, most children and adults experience chronic levels, which impact our brain and body. Remember, it is that stress hyperactivation of the nervous system that leads to anxiety, OCD, and depression. No one can live in a chronic stress state without it having a physical or psychological impact.

Let's talk about the different kinds of stress that impact our daily lives.

Normal Stress

Stress is a healthy and natural response to challenges or frustrations—your body's response to an external trigger. For example, people may experience normal stress in social situations such as reading out loud in a classroom. A healthy nervous system reacts to stress, moves toward a sympathetic state, and then rebalances itself as it goes back to a more relaxed, parasympathetic-dominant state. Stress grows from external pressures and expectations, which makes coping with a situation challenging. Stressed adults often know the cause; children may not. Symptoms of this type of stress typically dissipate once the temporary stressful situation resolves.

Acute Stress

Acute stress is the most common form of stress. In this case, we experience an immediate and brief perceived threat, either physical, emotional, or psychological. Acute stressors can be anything from remembering you left your phone at the coffee shop to the bell ringing at school or getting in trouble at home. How a child reacts to acute stressors varies depending on his or her level of stress tolerance.

Episodic Acute Stress

People who frequently experience acute stress have episodic acute stress. Children who live with chronic violence or in areas of unrest may experience repeated abuse, bullying, racism, and/or other situations that consist of repeated acute stressors causing episodic acute stress. These intense and prolonged periods of stress can take quite a toll on a child's mental and physical health. My experience is that these children don't regulate as well and experience higher rates of behavioral and emotional symptoms, including anger, irritability, short temper, impatience, and/or low frustration tolerance, worry, sadness, physical tension, and somatic complaints. These kids lack a Resiliency Mindset™ and don't view, manage, or recover from stress in the same way as others.

Chronic Stress

Chronic stress is that every day constant stress that builds and builds over time and disrupts our functioning. It creates a constant hum or irritation during which we feel we are unable to stop thinking and physically relax. The day-to-day grind builds tension within our bodies and negatively impacts our physical health and bodily processes. Children under chronic stress can display the same type of behaviors as kids who experience episodic acute stress. What is surprising to parents is that chronic stress can build in our day-to-day life. One does not have to endure a major event of acute stress to get dysregulated. Developmentally inappropriate education, learning challenges, social pressures, poor food quality, sensory issues, and other stressors common with children are just some of the long list of contributors to chronic stress. Chronic stress can lead to anxiety, OCD, depression, attention problems, chronic pain, and somatic complaints.

Toxic Stress

Toxic stress is any type of prolonged activation of the stress response systems that can disrupt the development of brain architecture and other organ systems and increase the risk of stress-related disease and cognitive impairment well into the adult years.

What Causes Stress in Children and Teens?

Stress comes in many shapes and forms. There are common stressors that impact us as a culture, too. Research has found that almost fifty percent of school children report and show signs of stress (Valizadeh, Farnam & Farshi, 2012).

Sources of childhood stress and anxiety include, but are not limited to, genetic predispositions, situational stressors, environmental issues, and comorbid conditions such as autism, ADHD, sensory processing disorder, learning disabilities, and medical issues. Thus, a family history of anxiety can make your child more likely to be diagnosed with anxiety whether from genetic inheritance or exposure to familial stress-management behaviors.

Simply put, kids learn behaviors from us.

Since parents set the stress management example, practicing and modeling self-care is important. It not only benefits us, but our children, too, as they learn how to manage their own stress by watching us. (Gulp! Don't feel guilty. View it as an opportunity to help "stress inoculate" your kids.)

The most common stressors children and teens experience include:

- Schoolwork or grades

- Not being able to keep up with peer learning expectations

- Taking tests or giving a presentation

- Poor learning environment or method of instruction

- Having a teacher who doesn't understand or like them

- Having learning, attentional, or emotional issues that interfere with schoolwork, relationships, and/or managing responsibilities

- Health problems or injuries

- Sensory processing issues

- Lack of sleep

- Poor diet

- Environmental toxins

- EMF exposures

- Juggling responsibilities such as school, work, or sports and overpacked schedules

- Typical problems with friends

- Managing social interactions at school and on the bus

- Peer group pressures

- Bullying

- Changes within a family, including new siblings

- Seeing parents go through a divorce or separation

- Changing schools, moving, or dealing with housing problems or homelessness

- Changes or big events (even fun ones)

- Going through body changes (both sexes)

- Safety concerns (living in an unsafe home or neighborhood)

- Parent instability or mental health issues

- Parents having their own problems

- Ill-suited parenting styles

- Money problems

- World events or the news

- Watching scary movies or reading a scary book

- Negative thinking

- Fears

- Uncertainty

(Medline, June 2020)

Signs of Stress in Children

Children display stress differently than adults, and they don't have the language skills to connect what their body is expressing to their emotions. They aren't going to look at you and say, *"Hey, I am feeling sad and angry, and I'd like to see a therapist."* Instead, they are going to throw a tantrum or stop talking to everyone. Behavior is the language of kids and teens. That's why you are much more likely to see their stress manifest in their behaviors. And trust me, the signs are there—you just need to know what to look for. Watch for a worsening of a pre-existing condition or behaviors and/or the onset of a new behavior. For example, if your child suddenly begins developing stomach aches at night, consider stressors that might be causing them.

Nico's Story

Nico was a sweet boy with dyslexia who got along well with everyone. He also was a rule-follower who became easily stressed by other kids *not* following them.

When Nico's mom Amy (who was a good friend of mine) said Nico didn't want to go to school, I was shocked. This kid loved school! I asked if she had noticed any changes in him, and she said he was having nightmares. I encouraged her to talk with Nico and engage him with open-ended questions to find out if anything was different at school.

 It turned out that a new student in his small class was not only breaking the rules, but was also super loud. Despite complaining to the teacher, Nico felt stuck, and that's why he didn't want to go to school anymore.

Amy spoke to Nico's teacher, and the other student was moved. She had a big talk with Nico about how some kids were impulsive, and that just means we need to love them more. Nico felt good about the move and discussion, and more importantly, his sleep improved immediately. He no longer complained about school, and their check-ins about his feelings were good. For Amy, it was only in looking back that she realized his nightmares were a sign that something was bothering him. This is an important reminder that, even if your kid is struggling, he or she might not say anything to you, but his/her behavior always will.

Behavioral or Emotional Signs of Stress

- Difficulty concentrating/filtering noises

- Problems with starting or completing tasks

- Regressive behaviors

- Behavioral changes such as moodiness, anger, aggression, or a short temper

- Aggressive or emotional outbursts

- Anger, crying, whining over minor issues or for no apparent reason

- New or recurring fears (fear of the dark, being alone, of strangers)

- Separation anxiety or clingy behavior

- Problems getting along with others, including siblings

- Loss of emotional control

- Increased temper tantrum, long tantrums, or slow recovery from tantrums

- Development of a nervous habit, such as nail biting, hair pulling, finger snapping, shirt biting, etc.

- Withdrawal from family or friends

- Extended time spent in alone (in bedroom, etc.)

- Reduced communication

- Increased behavioral issues at school

- A change in school behavior or performance

- Refusal to go to school or ride the bus

- Lying or taking of items

- Oversensitivity

- Frequent (and easy) crying

- Emotional lability (up and down emotionally)

- Anger or rage

- Long tantrums or meltdowns

- Lack of self-confidence

- Fearfulness

- Phobias

- Separation anxiety

- Constantly seeking approval

- Rituals, compulsions, obsessions

- Perfectionistic tendencies

- Rigidity

- Negative talk or a tendency to think the worst

- Sensory processing difficulties

- Social avoidance or difficulties

- Attention or focus problems

- Distraction by worried thoughts

- Fear of speaking in public or to strangers

- Low frustration tolerance

- Frequent erasing of work

- Not turning in schoolwork

- Test anxiety

- Avoiding new experiences

- Saying "no" all the time

- Worries about things in the future

- Hyperverbal looping of worries (i.e., asking "Why did she do that?" over and over)

Physical Signs of Stress

- Stomach aches or headaches

- Gastrointestinal distress

- Constipation or diarrhea

- Joint pain or chronic pain

- Teeth grinding

- Hair pulling

- Involuntary tics or motor movements

- Excessive fatigue

- Decreased or increased appetite

- Red face in social situations

- Excessive sweating

- Hives or skin conditions (unexplained)

- Hair loss (unexplained)

- Bedwetting

- Sleep problems - falling asleep and staying asleep

- Nightmares

- Holding of bladder or bowels

- Frequent urination

- Hyperactive behavior

Differentiating Between Stress and Chronic Stress

Ok, so stress is bad. You get that. But how does everyday stress turn into chronic stress for kids?

Everyday stress is short-term and often brief, whereas chronic stress occurs over long periods of time. An example of an acute stress would be an argument with a sibling that doesn't last very long. Chronic stress occurs when a child argues with siblings constantly and over a long period of time.

Our bodies are more capable of handling brief acute periods of stress than prolonged periods of chronic stress. In fact, the body is actually quite good at quickly recovering from acute stress, as it is designed to manage stress-triggered physiological reactions with increased blood pressure and heart rate that spike temporarily and then return to normal after a period of time. That CNS activates and goes into a sympathetic dominant state before calming to its baseline parasympathetic state when healthy. And remember, resilience is all about how quickly we recover from stress.

In contrast, chronic stress is more harmful, because over time, it causes our body to overwork *all the time*, suspending us in that sympathetic dominant state, which leads to a long list of physical and mental health problems (Hammen, Kim, Eberhart & Brennan, 2009; Mariotti, 2015; McEwen, 2011). Prolonged periods of stress also break down our stress recovery (resilience), making it more difficult for us to snap back from any type of stressor, normal or acute.

So, let's say a child with an attention problem occasionally needs redirection. His body gets a stressful alert from an adult, and he goes back to his normal state. In contrast, the very unfocused or impulsive child with ADHD receives the stressful alert differently. The constant redirections are practically a startle to his system and typically lead to secondary anxiety. In fact, I rarely see a QEEG brain map from a child with ADHD who isn't also dealing with anxiety.

Maybe right now you are thinking, *"My super-unfocused kid who can't even remember to put his clothes in the hamper is stressed?! What about me?! I'm the one who has to remind him!!!"*

Well, it is BOTH of your nervous systems that become stress hyperactivated. When you have to be your kiddos frontal lobes, you're going to *really* start losing patience with each other. Heck, you might even grow to dislike the sight of each other! That long-term, constant (or chronic) stress can really wear you down physically while breaking down your relationship with your child.

How Is Stress Different from Anxiety?

Chronic stress is something you and your child are already living with, right? Wondering when it flips to clinical anxiety? Well, despite what the DSM (Diagnostic and Statistical Manual of Mental Disorders) tells us, there isn't a set time (i.e., exactly at the six-month mark). It is more about how the symptoms interfere with your child's daily life.

Essentially, any time stress is marked and occurs over prolonged periods, it can become clinical anxiety. Clinical anxiety interferes with a person's ability to adequately function in some way. It interferes with emotional or behavioral regulation, communication, academics, social, home life, and/or activities of daily living. For example, it can prevent a child from concentrating in school or cause a teen to avoid talking to others. The source can be real or imagined, but regardless, it's a significant issue causing prolonged distress that interferes with a person's daily functioning.

With anxiety, our worried feelings or behavioral symptoms are disproportionate to the real or imagined stressor or issue. Since anxiety lingers, children, teens, and adults often experience looping or spinning thoughts.

Clinical anxiety causes one to worry about or experience anxiety around a variety of issues or a specific issue. Anxiety crosses into a disorder when it is irrational, overwhelming, and out of proportion with the challenge faced. There are different types of anxiety disorders, each of which is categorized based on the type of anxiety you have. They include generalized, social, phobia, substance-induced, medically induced, and so on. Key features of anxiety disorders are excessive anxiety and worry and struggles with controlling worried thoughts. Anxiety disorders often run in families and are affected by both genetics and environmental stressors.

It's important to know that, if you or your child are dealing with anxiety, it is no one's fault. In fact, in today's achievement-centered, perpetually connected society, anxiety has become a common struggle, especially for children and teens. Research indicates that 8.3 percent of teens aged 13-18 have an anxiety disorder classifying in the severe impairment range with the average onset age listed as six years old (Merikangas et., al, 2011). In the U.S., anxiety disorders are the most common mental illness, affecting 40 million adults age 18 and older, or (18.1% of the population every year) (National Institute of Mental Health, 2017).

Does that mean that every special needs child or a child with an issue is guaranteed to have clinical anxiety? No, but it is increasingly common amongst children and teens, and it seems rare to see one without it because of the pressures they face today. Anxiety disorders affect 7.1% of children aged 3-17 years (approximately 4.4 million) (CDC, 2020) and 25.1% of children between 13 and 18 years old (National Institute of Mental Health, 2017). That means one in four teens have an anxiety disorder, so even if your own kids don't, you can bet their friends, your niece, or your neighbors do.

Every once in a while, I'll get a child with executive functioning issues who is bright and as happy as can be. When I brain map him or her, s/he always has a ton of the "feel good" brain wave, alpha. These kids tend to be very creative—the skip-through-the-field-of-daisies kind of kids. Not a lick of anxiety in them!

[Not sure if your child is stressed or experiencing anxiety? Download my free Is it Stress or Anxiety? Checklist at www.drrotips.com/stressanxietychecklist.]

Angela's Story

I recall a beautiful girl, Angela, whose two physician parents weren't happy about having a theatrical, artistic teen who was an *"okay"* student. *"But Roseann, she is just so smart! What a waste for her to just be an artist!"*

Yes, sometimes even I have conversations like this with parents. And really, if we're honest, Angela's parents were just so mad at her. Their marriage was falling apart, and poor Angela became the vehicle of their dislike for each other.

Eager to see her improve her academics, they finally came to me saying, *"Roseann, we want you to tell us that it is okay to medicate her."* Yes, they actually said that to me! Uh, did they ever see my website or hear me speak?! I couldn't be more anti-meds if I tried!

These parents were the anxious ones, not Angela. Of course, against my recommendations, they put her on a psychostimulant. That first seven or eight months, her grades improved. But then, the anxiety started. Enter crying episodes, irritability, and grade slipping.

The family came back to me again to ask my opinion. Really, they were looking for the "magic-wand approach." My answer was the same as it had been before: neurofeedback, counseling for Angela, counseling for the now-divorced parents, and supplementations rather than the psychostimulant, because Angela's QEEG brain map was showing clear-cut anxiety. I also gave them a lot of education about not pathologizing kids who really are artists as opposed to lovers of intense academics. I mean, she was a solid B student, but that just wasn't good enough for these two M.D.s.

At that point, they added a mood stabilizer into Angela's regime, and she just fell apart emotionally and behaviorally. Sadly, the outcome of the "medication-highway-to-'fix'-my-kid approach" is pretty typical. But in Angela's case, they never had to go down that road. She was simply a kid with low-level ADHD, who was an artist. It was her parents trying to fit her into the wrong box that caused her to be anxious.

Stress and the Immune System

One of the most obvious ways stress impacts our health is by causing our immune system to not work properly, or even break down, leading to a greater frequency of everyday illnesses such as colds and more significant and chronic disease states such as cancer, diabetes, cardiac problems, etc. (Segerstrom & Miller, 2004). Chronic stress impacts how all our bodily processes work. The field that studies the impact of stress on the brain and body has led to a whole new field of study—psychoimmunology.

What Is Psychoimmunology?

Our immune system is a living organism that is impacted by factors within the body as well as external factors. It tries to achieve homeostasis through the management of and interaction with the central and peripheral nervous, endocrine, and immune systems, as well the outside environment and human behaviors, including lifestyle choices. What we do in our daily life of course has a direct impact on our health—specifically, our mental health.

Psychoimmunology helps us understand the connection between the mind and body and how the interplay between the two impacts our physical health. It is the study of the connection between psychological processes and the nervous and immune systems of the body (Zachariae, 2009). Over the last forty years, and the last decade in particular, psychoimmunology research has demonstrated the connection between the mind and body and how the interplay between the two have a direct impact on the physical health and disease states (Tausk, Elenkov, & Moynihan, 2008; Zachariae, 2009). It has helped us to understand that behavioral and psychological events can influence the immune system, and really, that our mind impacts our health.

We may not think about how the immune system and mental health are intertwined, but they are, and they impact your child's issues. It is easy to see how our immune system affects mental health in extreme cases, such as with PANS/PANDAS and Lyme, because individuals often have tics, OCD, anxiety, and depression. But immune system issues can creep up and cause brain fog, behavioral issues, and learning problems, too. Conditions such as PANS/PANDAS are on the rise, and I can tell you that it has become standard with the kids I work with to have some kind of immune system dysfunction. The question is, is it the chicken or the egg? Which came first? The stress or infectious disease, parasites, or environmental toxins?

How Stress Affects the Immune System

So, you're wondering why your child has ear infection after ear infection despite eating and sleeping well. Have you thought about his stress levels?

We know that stress, and more specifically, chronic stress, impacts our health and has a direct effect on how our immune system works and how it is able to manage infection and disease states. While stress alone doesn't cause the sickness, chronic stress weakens the immune system's ability to respond to infectious agents and cellular malfunctions, which makes us more vulnerable to infection and disease (Morey et. al, 2015; Viktoriya, 2019).

Chronic stress can also interfere with regular bodily processes that disrupt the homeostasis (or the balanced state) of the body, which impacts the immune system. And as you already learned, our body (more specifically, our immune system) works best when we are in homeostasis. Stress also impacts our body's resilience (or ability to recover quickly), since the immune system is suppressed as it tries to deal with stress or stressors. Basically, all of our resources get diverted as the body prepares to "go to war" against an unknown stressor, and when we get out of balance, infections and toxins can creep in and take hold.

It is important to understand the neuroscience of mental health, so we can get to those root causes and accurate diagnoses and treatments at the right time. We have to stop taking that "whack-a-mole approach" to mental health, because *the science is there* to guide us through reducing and reversing mental health symptoms. We have to look at how the immune system works to really understand how stress disrupts it.

The immune system's job is to protect us from attacks from foreign invaders. It is an intricate network of various systems, organs, cells, tissues, and proteins that work together. When the body experiences stress, the immune system kicks into action, and cells are mobilized into the bloodstream, potentially preparing the body for injury or infection during a "fight-or-flight response" to stress (Boggero et. al, 2015). Stress is known to cause the release of several stress hormones (cortisol, prolactin, growth hormone, glucocorticoid hormones, noradrenaline, and adrenaline) through activation of the hypothalamic–pituitary–adrenal (HPA) axis and cate-cholamines through the sympathetic nervous system (Marketon & Glaser, 2008). These stress hormones are released into the bloodstream and transported to various locations within the body.

These stress hormones have detrimental effects on immune function, including reduced NK cell activity, lymphocyte populations, lymphocyte proliferation, and antibody production and reactivation of latent viral infections (Marketon & Glaser, 2008). Stress impairs the immune system, decreasing white blood cell production and lowering production of antibodies. One of the most detrimental effects of prolonged stress is that it leads to high cortisol levels, which alters the effectiveness of cortisol to regulate both the inflammatory and immune response, because it decreases tissue sensitivity to cortisol (Segerstrom, 2006). Even children and teens can have high cortisol levels, which indicates that our CNS is stress hyperactivated. This stress hyperactivation of the CNS isn't only going to interfere with our immune system, either. It essentially hijacks our kids' rational brain, and therapy isn't going to work to "fix" it. (Parenting becomes a whole lot harder, too.)

Acute stress also increases blood levels of pro-inflammatory cytokines, which plays a role in inflammation—an increasingly identified factor in mental and physical health. Inflammation is a necessary and useful short-term response of our immune system to infection or inju-ry. On the flip side, systemic inflammation represents dysregulation of the immune system and increases risk for chronic diseases (Morey et. al, 2015). Pro-inflammatory cytokines are important not only to our immune function, but to our brain function, and they have been shown to communicate with the brain and affect neurotransmission, neuroendocrine activi-ty, and brain structure and functions, thereby inducing emotional, cognitive, and behavioral changes (Viktoriya, 2019).

Stress also impacts our gut health, and our microbiome has a bidirectional influence with our brain and immune system. Stress may induce alterations of the intestinal epithelium via the interaction of the neuroendocrine and immune system (Niess, Monnikes, Dignass, Klapp,

Arck, 2002). And the more we learn about the gut, the more we know how impactful it is on brain health.

I have worked with too many cases of PANS/PANDAS and Lyme and tick-borne disease to count. What I have learned is that those kids and adults can't heal without regulating their nervous system—or as I like to say, without calming it the heck down! Many parents get tripped up with questions like, *"Did the infection come before the chronic stress? How can we delineate between the two in today's intense world?"* We can't, but what I can tell you is that every person with a chronic disease state has a stress hyperactivated nervous system, and without daily stress management, healing isn't going to happen.

Charlotte's Story

Charlotte tried many treatments for her strep and anxiety, but none ever seemed to stick. She had great doctors and psychotherapists, and the whole family altered their diet and took every supplement known to man.

Still, the moment Charlotte had any stress or even the tiniest cold, it was like they took 20 steps backward, and her anxiety and insomnia would skyrocket for weeks.

After hearing me on a podcast, Charlotte's dad, Dan, knew what Charlotte needed to do—get her brain out of that constant, flight-fight-freeze mode. We worked with Charlotte remotely, teaching her how to regulate her nervous system using biofeedback and a specific kind of PEMF. She became keenly aware of all the signs her body would give her that her stress levels were rising, and when they did rise, she employed what she learned. This broke her constant flare cycle of stress, anxiety, and illness.

Charlotte was able to return to college and graduate, and now, she works as a nurse.

How Stress Affects the Developing Brain of Children

Not only does early life stress influence the developing immune system and brain, but maternal stress also has a huge impact on child neurodevelopment (De Asis-Cruz J, Krishnamurthy D, Zhao L, et al., 2020; Talge, Neal, & Glover, 2007). Both the brain and immune system are evolving organisms that are not fully formed at birth, but rather continue to develop in response to environmental factors (Danese & Lewis, 2016). That means there is much we can do to positively influence the development of our child's brain and immune system. It also means that since these systems are developing, they are also highly susceptible to stressors, so we need to address maternal mental health.

Even though there are hundreds of stressors that have different effects, the timing of when these stressors occur can have the biggest impact on brain development. *"When stress occurs early in life, it can have profound and lasting effects on brain organization and function"* (Gee & Casey, 2015). During times known as "sensitive periods" in brain development, there is heightened neuroplasticity, which makes the brain especially amenable to environmental influence. For children, the most sensitive period in brain development is in infancy and adolescence, so we must be even more mindful of positive influences during that time. We know that early trauma is linked to later and more significant mental health disorders (Carr et. al 2013) and poorer mental health treatment outcomes (Ford & Kidd, 1998). Chronic early life stress is also linked to later inflammation (Danese & Lewis, 2016), and again, inflammation is linked to mental health issues in both children and adults.

De Asis-Cruz J, Krishnamurthy D, Zhao L, et al., 2020 found that *"Maternal psychological distress during pregnancy is associated with adverse obstetric outcomes and neuropsychiatric deficits in children."* And with stress on the rise, we need to teach women in particular how to manage their own stress to create what my dear friend, fertility expert and scientist Dr. Cleopatra Kamperveen, always calls *"superbabies."* It has been her life's work to teach women how to not only be fertile, but to have healthy babies, in part through her Primester Protocol™ system. And guess what? Moderating stress is one of its key components!

I'll say it again: daily stress management is key in regulating the CNS, thereby creating homeostasis (or balance) that leads to physical and mental wellness.

How Does the Central Nervous System Respond to Stress?

The body's stress response is there to protect us from actual stressors. The problem is that in today's stressful world, our nervous system never seems to catch a break—we are *constantly* bombarded with stress.

You are beginning to understand that stress impacts every system and function in our body and creates an environment ripe for disease, both physical and mental, to take hold. Right? But how does the body actually respond to stress?

First, brain structures jump into action and prepare for a crisis, which triggers the fight-or-flight response. That stress then triggers a cascade of hormones that produce physiological changes within the central nervous system (CNS). The body will then shift into a primitive survival fight-or-flight mode when it has a real or perceived stressor and move all its resources toward fighting off or fleeing from an "enemy" (Rosen & Donley, 2006).

The **hypothalamic pituitary adrenal (HPA)** axis is our central stress response system and involves the interaction and interplay between the hypothalamus, pituitary gland, and adrenal glands. It is this system that triggers stress hormones that impact the autonomic nervous system, which regulates how we respond to stress. The **autonomic nervous system** has two components, the **sympathetic nervous system** and the **parasympathetic nervous system**. The sympathetic nervous system controls our stress responses, and the parasympathetic nervous system works to calm us. After a threat passes, our parasympathetic system works to return our body to homeostasis. Each is very important, and they must be in balance for our body to react and recover from stress.

We always hear about the emotional center of our brain, our **limbic system**, but our whole brain is involved in how we manage stress and emotions and which behaviors follow. The limbic system is composed of four main parts: the hypothalamus, the amygdala, the thalamus, and the hippocampus. The amygdala and hippocampus play a major role in emotional regulation and our stress response and are part of the hypothalamic pituitary adrenal (HPA) axis. Our brain's emotional center, the **amygdala**, perceives danger, and then, it instantly sends a distress signal to the hypothalamus, which acts like a command center and communicates with the rest of the body through the autonomic nervous system. The amygdala gets activated not only when we are fearful, but when things are uncertain (Rosen & Donley, 2006), and in today's world filled with such uncertainty, it's no wonder that stress, anxiety, and clinical mental health conditions are on the rise. The **hypothalamus**, also part of our limbic system, activates our sympathetic nervous system, which signals the adrenal glands to release hormones called adrenalin (epinephrine) and cortisol. We need these hormones to fight off "enemies." While these chemical reactions are happening, the amygdala (our emotional center) overrides the prefrontal cortex when involved with the fight-or-flight system. The prefrontal cortex is the center for critical and rational thought while the amygdala commands our emotional reactions. Without good prefrontal control, the amygdala hijacks the brain, and we react in less rational ways as the brain goes into survival mode.

This HPA axis loop is absolutely a necessary bodily function, but the problem is, constant stressors, real or imagined, trigger the CNS to react less strongly to stimuli. This hyperactivation of the sympathetic nervous system results in the release of excitatory neurotransmitters, norepinephrine and epinephrine, further contributing to the nervous system remaining or getting stuck in a hyper state. It is that chronic stress state that is perhaps the most significant barrier to healing, often leading to physical and mental health issues, especially anxiety, OCD, and depression.

The good news is, when you break the hyperactivation, you can do the therapeutic work to change behaviors and communication patterns. That is how you reduce and reverse mental health!

The Effect of Stress on the Brain

Stress can not only impact the chemical and cellular functioning within the brain, but it can also lead to structural changes in different parts of the brain (Yaribeygi et. al, 2017). We know that chronic stress has a shrinking effect on the prefrontal cortex, the area of the brain responsible for memory and learning (McEwen, 2017).

Chronic stress changes the neural networks, or how the brain talks to itself and regulates (Jankord, & Herman, 2008). Our neural networks determine how we respond to data input and process higher-level information. When our neural networks don't work the way they are supposed to, our processing is labored, and we can't regulate our responses the way we should.

With neurofeedback, we work on restoring the neural networks. That is why calmness and processing is improved—because it works on restoring the brain's own ability to regulate itself and its responses to stressors and stimuli.

Chronic stress also impacts the structure of the amygdala, as it may increase its size, which can make the brain more receptive to stress. Constant cortisol output is believed to create a pathway between the hippocampus and amygdala, which then makes the brain even more likely to remain in a state of fight or flight (Bergland, 2014).

Chronic stress impacts how the amygdala processes emotional information, and research has shown that anxious children can't recognize facial expressions as well as their non-anxious peers (Easter et al., 2005). Activation of the amygdala has been implicated in every kind of anxiety, including social anxiety and difficulty with public speaking as well as emotional reactivity in general and PTSD specifically (Etkin & Wagner, 2007).

Chronic stress is associated with just about every major mental health condition there is. High levels of cortisol due to chronic stress states are linked to depression, anxiety, focus problems, and thinking problems (Mah, Szabuniewicz, & Fiocco, 2016). The role of chronic stress as the source (or at least in the exacerbation of) mental health has long been underestimated. Despite decades of research that shows the reduction of mental health symptoms with lifestyle adjustments and therapies, little has been done to change the medical model of pushing medication.

The good news is that, if you are reading this, you already know you can positively impact your child's mental health and actually change how his or her brain develops and functions by implementing the stress-reducing strategies in this book and in my **Get Unstuck Program**™ (**www.getunstuckprogram.com**).

How Stress Affects Learning and Memory

Chronic stress impacts both the function and the structure of one of the most important brain structures involved in memory—the **hippocampus**. Cellular and chemical function in the hippocampus are directly impacted by prolonged stress states. When under stress, the neural networks just don't communicate in the same way, which means our kids can't think straight. Their brain is stress hijacked! Stress also impacts other structures involved in the memory system, including the amygdala and prefrontal cortex (Sandi & Pinelo-Nava, 2007).

Chronic stress can impact short-term, working, and long-term memory, as well as specific types of memory such as declarative or textbook type learning (Tatomir, Micu, & Crivii, 2014). I know I typically see a real decline in learning when a child or teen is anxious, and that is because of the impact of stress on our neural networks.

Stress also impacts our hormones, and we need good hormone functioning for both the encoding and retrieval of information. When we are in a chronic stress state, our memory is impacted. Memory begins with simply paying attention, but when we are stressed, we become distracted by looping, worrisome thoughts, which impacts what we remember. If we aren't paying attention, then we simply won't be able to encode or store the information, which means there won't be anything to retrieve (Wolf, 2007).

Many kids with anxiety are actually falsely diagnosed with ADHD, because on the surface, they struggle with attention. But the root cause is different. In fact, at least 40 to 50% of the children who come to me as ADHD are in reality dealing with anxiety or OCD as the main problem. And because of that, they can't focus. These are the same kids and teens who react so horribly to ADHD meds they are often prescribed—because psychostimulants actually ignite their anxiety. That is why "checking under the hood" is so critical ... the right diagnosis leads to the right treatment.

The Effect of Stress on the Body

Every system in the body is impacted by stress, which means it can affect your body in many different ways. Initially, it may be hard to make the connection, because the effects of chronic stress build over time as opposed to showing immediately.

Stress can have a short-term and permanent effect on everything from your heart, muscles, endocrine system, gut health, and microbiome to your nervous system. Stress can disrupt hormones, sleep, and your emotional well-being. It is one of the leading contributors to chronic pain, autoimmune disease, and other chronic diseases such as cancer (Antoni & Dhabhar, 2019; Karl et. al, 2018; Stojanovich & Marisavljevich, 2008; Steptoe & Kivimäki, 2012). When we are stressed, our cortisol levels rise and remain elevated for several hours after, which makes us feel uncomfortable and can lead to unhealthy ways of "managing" stress (like drug or alcohol use).

It is important to not ignore your child's somatic complaints. Instead, consider stress a potential cause. As you have read in my anecdotes, I can tell you that every single person who walks in my door has a physical issue related to stress. When it comes to our kids, stress is typically the first sign of something bigger.

It is safe to assume that every single child on the globe has some sort of stress. So, let's be *proactive* in teaching them ways to manage it and build resilience. If we are, our mental health crisis will lessen.

EFFECT OF STRESS
ON THE BRAIN AND BODY

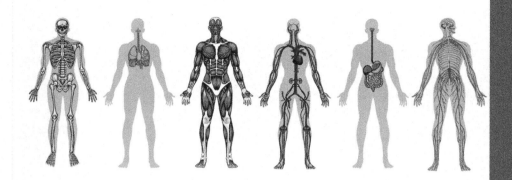

Musculoskeletal System
- Muscle tension
- Joint pain
- Changes blood flow to muscles
  in our arms and legs

Respiratory System
- Reduced oxygen to cell
- Shortness of breath and increased
  rapid breathing

Cardiovascular System
- Increased heart rate and BP
- Inflammation in the circulatory system
- Increased cholesterol levels

Endocrine System
- Impaired communication between
  the immune system
  and the HPA axis
- Increased steroid hormones production
  (glucocorticoids), which includes cortisol

Hormone & Reproductive Systems
- Can create hormone fluctuations
- Estrogen levels impacted
- Impact sperm production and maturation
- Conception and postpartum

Gastrointestinal System
- Increased gastrointestinal pain, bloating,
  nausea, & constipation
- Causes blood to flow away from the gut,
  slowing digestion and impacts what
  nutrients the intestines absorb

Nervous System
- The sympathetic nervous system (SNS)
  contributes to the "fight-or flight response"
  and signals the adrenal glands to release
  the hormones adrenaline and cortisol
- After the stress, the body returns to the
  unstressed state which is facilitated by the
  parasympathetic system (PNS).
- Continuous activation of the nervous system
  affects bodily symptoms

Immune System
- Suppressed immune function due to
  increased inflammation

Dr. Roseann It's gonna be OK™

EFFECT OF STRESS
ON THE BRAIN

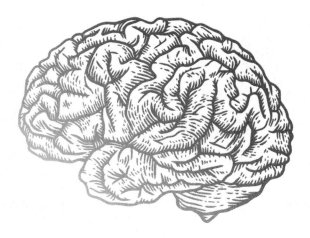

Cortisol levels spike
- Too much cortisol interferes
  with neurotransmitter function

Prefrontal cortex shrinks
- Impacts attention, learning & memory

Cellular changes
- Affects the hippocampus, which is part
  of the limbic system and is responsible for
  motivation, emotion, learning, and memory
- Autophagy of cells in hippocampus

Neurotransmitter changes
- Disrupts synaptic regulation
- Kills brain cells
- Reduces excitability of neurons
  and suppresses neuron regeneration

Amygdala
- Size increases and makes you more
  receptive to stress
- Activates Hypothalamic-pituitary-
  adrenocortical (HPA) axis
- Leads to constant activation
  of fight-flight-freeze response

Dr. Roseann | It's gonna be OK.™

©ROSEANN-CAPANNA-HODGE
www.childrensmentalhealth.com

SIGNS OF
CHRONIC STRESS

Cognitive symptoms:
- Memory problems
- Focus and concentration difficulties
- Poor judgment
- Racing thoughts
- Constant worrying
- Obsessive compulsive thinking
- Negative thinking

Emotional symptoms:
- Unhappiness/Lack of pleasure
- Anxiety
- Agitation
- Emotional reactivity
- Moodiness, irritability, or anger
- Easily frustrated or overwhelmed
- Loneliness and isolation
- Problems with memory
  or concentration

Physical symptoms:
- Aches and pains
- Chronic pain
- Diarrhea or constipation
- Stomach aches
- Nausea, dizziness
- Headaches
- Rapid heart rate or high BP
- Chest pain
- Frequent illness or infection

Behavioral symptoms:
- Change in behavior
- Withdrawing from others or activities
- Procrastination
- Avoidant behaviors
- Impulsiveness
- Negative or inappropriate talk
- Use of substances for stress/coping
- Nervous or compulsive habits/behaviors
  (e.g. nail biting, handwashing)
- Over/under eating
- Sleeping too much or too little
- Sensory sensitivity

Dr. Roseann   It's gonna be OK™

©ROSEANN-CAPANNA-HODGE
www.childrensmentalhealth.com

Ways to Foster Resilience and Build Stress Tolerance in Children

So, we know our kids are stressed out, which can lead to changes in the brain that may or may not be reversible. The good news is that the brain doesn't stop forming until the mid-twenties, and the frontal lobes, or the brain's control center, are the last to develop. That means we have time to influence the brain and create healthy neural connections while improving its function and structure!

And that is why people come to my center every day to begin neurofeedback and biofeedback—because the impact of these therapies on not just brainwave activity, but on brain regulation and on the nervous system to get into a calm rhythm is powerful. Now, you understand how important it is for the central nervous system (CNS) to be in a balanced, homeostatic state … a calm, parasympathetic-dominant state.

We know that kids who lack resilience, or the ability to recover from stress quickly, are prone to greater mental health difficulties (Michl et. al, 2013). These kids tend to ruminate, or get stuck, on the perceived stressor. Their thinking and behaviors get stuck, and they can't shift easily, which makes them much more likely to have clinical depression, anxiety, and OCD. And boy, are they tough to parent.

The good news is that through lifestyle changes, parents can do a lot to reduce stress, improve their child's brain health, and ultimately reduce and reverse symptoms. Pair that with new learning through parenting and therapy, and things can change dramatically for a child.

Leo's Story

According to Leo's parents, Leo was *"a pain in the butt who never listened and just didn't seem to care."* They had taken him to no less than seven therapists, yet the only change they saw was *"in our bank account."*

When Leo was really little, his therapists would sometimes involve his parents in Leo's therapy sessions, but now that he was thirteen, *"It was Leo's session."* They didn't know what was happening in the sessions, and tempers were flaring all around. They were desperate for help, living in constant fear that Leo would *"do stupid stuff and get in trouble."* Their concerns were valid; Leo was pushing toward unhealthy boundaries and lying a lot.

We started with remote neurofeedback and parent coaching. They needed to learn how to set boundaries with Leo as he became more alert and calmer, and they all needed to learn a new way to communicate. Leo's parents had to stop thinking the other shoe was going to drop, get their stuff together, and set positive expectations for their son. They all had to break out of that negative expectation cycle, and they did! They worked at it consistently, and soon, things began to improve as everyone learned how to better listen and speak with one another … most of the time! They also learned how to move forward without holding past behaviors against one another.

How The REPS Protocol™ Can Help Lower Stress

So how do you lower stress levels all around—your own, your child's, and your family's? Well, let me walk you through my four-part process (I teach this to members of organizations, too!) via my **REPS Protocol**™!

The key here is to practice it yourself, model it, and then, teach your child or teen how to do the same. We can't just expect things to happen in this world without a little elbow grease, right? But don't worry … when we follow the REPS Protocol™, *it feels good* … so it becomes an easy habit to incorporate into our daily routine!

The REPS Protocol™

- **Respiration**

- **Envisioning**

- **Positivity**

- **Stress Management**

With **Respiration**, I teach the importance of breathwork in calming the brain and body. From a neuroscience perspective, breathwork impacts the autonomic nervous system (ANS), which receives information from the environment and other parts of the body (often at a subconscious level) and regulates the activity of the organs. The ANS is composed of the parasympathetic and sympathetic systems, both of which have a direct impact on how we manage stress. The body's fight-or-flight response is controlled by the sympathetic nervous system. The other part is the parasympathetic nervous system, which works to relax and slow down the body's response.

When you're stressed or anxious, your breathing can become irregular, and shallow breath affects our ANS. When we breathe deeply, we allow for more carbon dioxide to enter our blood, which quiets down parts of the brain like the emotional centers that handle your anxiety response: the limbic system and the amygdala. On the other hand, slow, deep breathing functionally resets the autonomic nervous system. It is then that we can connect our breath to our body and learn how to pay attention to those cues that it is giving us about stress.

It really doesn't matter what kind of breathing technique you use (there are many), as long as it is a diaphragmatic, or deep belly, breath. My favorite is the 4-7-8 breath (you can learn more about how to do a 4-7-8 breath in the next chapter). It works in making your exhale a few counts longer than your inhale, which causes the vagus nerve (which goes from the neck down through the diaphragm) to send a signal to your brain to increase your parasympathetic nervous system and decrease your sympathetic nervous system, thereby more quickly leading to a calmer state.

With the next step, **Envisioning**, I teach the power of visualizing positive outcomes. Being mindful of our surroundings and using visualization to reduce stress has become an increasingly popular technique (Goldin & Gross, 2010). The intentful practice of visualization is different from meditation. Visualization is a powerful way to not only get clarity on your goals, but to help manifest them. Successful people spend a lot of time visualizing what they want, because success doesn't just happen. They put a lot of effort behind their actions, and it all starts with visualizing successful outcomes.

I am sure right now you're thinking, *"Well, of course, Dr. Ro!"* but I am here to tell you that so many of our actions are based in fear. And our struggling kids don't always see a positive outcome. They see only a negative.

Those who visualize first hone in on their authentic purpose, and then, they create goals around it. They "see" and "feel" what they want and spend time every day visualizing that outcome.

Help your child to actually experience his or her desired outcome in his/her mind. Encourage her to put herself where she wants to be and incorporate a sensory component of smell, feeling, and touch. Guide her in focusing on what she can control right now and connect to that moment even though she is visualizing a positive future event. Paired with action around her goals, she can move toward positive outcomes.

Whether you have a goal to better manage stress or address a specific issue, intentful visualization is a great way to create positive momentum by getting to the core of the issue and its resolution. This is also a such a powerful tool for us special needs parents who feel hopeless about getting our kids unstuck—try visualizing a resolution to each individual symptom or issue.

Step three involves embodying **Positivity** in your thinking and words. Are you a glass-half-full or a glass-half-empty type of person? Research is very clear that those with a positive outlook are happier and live longer. While some are born with a positive disposition and others are not, a sunny outlook can be developed with intention and practice.

The goal here is to catch your child being negative, and simply flip his or her internal and external dialogue. Didn't get the color paper she wanted, and now she's upset? Try and say, *"This is great! They have the purple one. I can't wait to see your awesome creativity come out with this."* Your child may not stop her behavior at first, but over time with your positive role modeling and reinforcement of the desired, more regulated behaviors, she will. Be patient, because those subtle changes in how you view things help you to remain positive in any situation and absolutely build a Resiliency Mindset™ while reducing stressful reactions. Our subconscious brain will believe whatever we tell it, so let's tell it positive things and envision successful outcomes.

The final step is making time every day for Stress Management. Calming that nervous system down allows one to literally think. We know what it is like to be in stress overload and not be able to think clearly, so why do we expect something different from our kids?

When your stress is at maximum capacity, your frontal lobes go "offline," and it is almost impossible to have a rational thought, let alone react rationally. That over-activated nervous system causes children to go into a flight-fight-freeze response and explains those frequent reactions to seemingly minor things … sound, the tone of their brother's voice, or not winning a card game. So, nurturing your nervous system is critical to being able to think and react in a calm manner while controlling the anxious (and even panicked) feelings and behaviors. The daily practice of breathwork, meditation, biofeedback, neurofeedback, and yoga are proven and natural techniques and therapies that children and adults can use to effectively calm their brain and body down, so they can restore their attention, mood, and thinking, and make strides in how they respond to stress.

Proven Ways to Help Your Child Reduce Stress

Phew! We've talked a lot about the neuroscience of stress, and I'm confident that you can really see what it does to our children's thinking and behavior. Hopefully, you also feel empowered to create lasting change for both your child and yourself!

Children can learn healthy ways to respond to and cope with stress. You can help in the following ways:

- Follow the eight pillars.

- Make lifestyle changes.

- Practice good sleep hygiene and get at least eight hours of sleep a night.

- Eat an anti-inflammatory diet.

- Use magnesium and other supplements that support stress relief.

- Reduce environmental toxins.

- Incorporate detoxification methods into your daily life.

- Exercise daily.

- Take time every day to be quiet, so the nervous system can regulate.

- Use essential oils such as lavender to calm the nervous system.

- Limit electronics.

- Make your home a calm, safe, and secure place.

- Encourage communication.

- Connect as a family.

- Make time for family fun and laughter.

- Use emotional language.

- Give lots of hugs.

- Use positive language and encouragement.

- Parent using loving limits with an emphasis on learning.

- Be a role model for stress management.

- Expect and plan for stress with changes or new situations.

- Build independence by giving your child opportunities where he or she can have choices and control.

- Incorporate daily stress-management techniques.

- Teach your child problem-solving skills.

- Use meditation, biofeedback, neurofeedback, and yoga.

- Help your child connect to his/her emotions, and build a toolkit to manage uncomfortable emotions.

- Create boundaries with toxic family members or friends who bring stress into the home.

- Always watch for behavioral signs of stress.

While I could have devoted an entire chapter to the importance of movement and exercise in mental health, I'll summarize it in just a paragraph: it is *pivotal* in all aspects of physical and mental health and most certainly in reducing stress effectively and naturally. Movement helps attention, cognition, behavior, our immune system, our cardiac function, improves detoxification, and so many other functions. Exercise reduces symptoms of ADHD (Hartanto, Krafft, Iosif, & Schweitzer, 2016; University of California - Davis Health System 2015), mood (Sharma, Madaan & Petty, 2006); stress and anxiety (Stubbs et al, 2017).

With virtual education and working from home, we are sitting for long periods of time. We need movement more than ever to help get oxygen to the brain, regulate our sensory system, get those feel-good endorphins going, reduce blue-light exposure, and counter spine compression from being slumped over our devices. My colleague, founder of The American Posture Institute Dr. Krista Burns, refers to the decline in cognitive and attention we are experiencing due to such high device usage as "digital dementia," and I really can't think of a more appropriate term for what everyone is feeling during this pandemic. Adding in daily exercise such as walking and yoga along with brain-based exercises such as Brain Gym activities will improve stress, attention, and thinking.

Exercise can and should be a part of your daily life to help mitigate the effects of stress. Pairing it with the REPS Protocol™ is an easy way to prioritize physical and mental health. Implementing tiny habits is important for you and your family, as it is those consistent small habit change that create lasting change.

When we follow the REPS Protocol™ process, we recognize that our children need to learn new ways to cope with and manage uncomfortable feelings. We don't want them to avoid their feelings, but rather deal with them independently. If your child or teen struggles with this type of processing, they can learn these skills over time with direct instruction and a whole lot of repetition and TLC.

Shifting your thinking from *"I want a quick fix; s/he should know this by now"* to *"I can invest my time in teaching my child this positive and effective way of processing"* is a hurdle, but you can overcome it, too! Once you get the neuroscience behind how stress affects the brain and body, and you remove that frustration and blame, then you can move forward with a mind toward teaching your child.

I have the privilege of teaching this process to parents every day and watching the lightbulb go off as they become filled with hope. It all just clicks: their child's brain and body are hijacked, and their thinking, communication, and behavior reflects that. They aren't doing anything on purpose, and there *is* a step-by-step approach to unwinding that stress and behaviors!

Using it, you change behavior not just now, but in the future. You help get everyone unstuck.

Dr. Roseann-Capanna-Hodge

Chapter 6: You've Got to Eat Right to Think Right

Pillar 2: Nutrition

In addition to being able to control our mindset—what we think in any given moment—we also have the ability to control what we put in our mouths. And that's important, because what we ingest has a big impact on how our brain and body work.

To put it simply, the brain and body need fuel—and not just any fuel, but high octane! Without it, they might still run, sure … but not as well, especially with all the stress our kids face today. Despite knowing we feel better when we eat whole foods, we seem to have somehow forgotten that eating nutrient-dense foods can and does impact the way our brain and body work. And it's no different for our kids.

I hope you just had another "lightbulb" moment.

The fact is, eating whole foods is even *more* important to our kids, because a child's brain is *still developing*. Our brain continues to develop until our mid-twenties, which is when our super-important frontal lobes fully develop.

Here's the thing: our genetics don't define us. We *can* influence our genetics and how our brain works with nutrients from food. Metabolites of vitamins A and D, fatty acids, some plant sterols, fiber, and zinc are nutrients that influence DNA transcription directly (Cousins, 1999). Transcription is the process in which a gene's DNA sequence is copied or transcribed into an RNA molecule. *"Genetic information flows from DNA into protein, the substance that gives an organism its form"* (Encyclopedia Britannica, 2019). Not all the genes in your body are turned on at the same time, nor are they in the same cells or parts of the body. It might be surprising, but *what we eat can directly influence genetic expression.*

This is pretty powerful when you think about it! YOU have the ability to influence your child's genes with food, and there is SO MUCH YOU CAN DO!

Karen's Story

Karen is a mom of three children who each have varying degrees of autism. None of them ate much, but her youngest, Eric, was the biggest obstacle to healthy eating. He ate only 11 foods, each of which were all white … typically the least nutrient-dense foods you can eat.

Karen spent years going from one doctor to the next, including physical, speech, and eating specialists. Eventually, she knew she had exhausted all the traditional therapies without results. So, she became Dr. Google, teaching herself about nutrition and strategies for overcoming food resistance. With each of her children eating different foods and having various food "quirks," making even one meal was already a difficult feat. But as she became empowered with the knowledge that kids often gravitate toward foods that give them a sugar rush (that also create inflammation), she decided to start concentrating on unprocessed real foods that were packed with healthy fats and nutrients.

At first, Karen tried to swap out unhealthy for healthier options, but that didn't fly with her tough crew (especially Eric, who really fought back!). However, she had learned that you can actually retrain a child to eat in 10 days. Utilizing a mixture of behavioral planning and varied (tasty!) food options, she knew her kids' hunger would motivate them to expand their palates.

She admits the first was a miserable week, with each of her children reacting differently but none going along with the changes easily. There were times she was about to throw in the towel, but then, just a week in, her biggest resistor, Eric, began resisting less. He had a strawberry, then a black bean pasta, and then bone broth.

And it wasn't just that Eric and her other two children were eating better; Karen noticed they were acting differently, too. They were sleeping better, and their behaviors lessened.

It is hard to describe the mix of joy and relief Karen reported. But then, there was anger. Why hadn't *any* of the professionals she had sought out told her about the importance of food choices? Why hadn't anyone assisted her with ways for getting her kids to eat healthy? She also wondered what else she could be doing that she didn't even know about.

That was the beginning of a family health and healing journey that helped her kids not only become better eaters, but great eaters and lovers of whole foods. Plus, as Karen learned more about therapies like brain gym and biofeedback, she began putting the pieces together as each reduced behaviors. Karen herself lost weight, slept better, and regained energy, too.

Why Is an Anti-Inflammatory Diet Important?

An anti-inflammatory diet can go a long way in improving both brain and body. It is one of the key components, if not *the* key component, of a symptom-reversal plan. A nutrient-dense diet full of antioxidant-rich foods and healthy fats powers the body and curbs inflammation, which research has increasingly tied to a variety of health conditions, including mental health issues.

Ultimately, incorporating an anti-inflammatory diet into your lifestyle is something anyone can do, and it can have a big impact, quickly. Remember, YOU have the power to change your child's mental health, and *nutrition is one of the best ways to get your child unstuck.*

Inflammation: The Good and The Bad

So, why all the concern about inflammation? Inflammation is not always bad; in fact, it is part of the body's immune response and necessary in order to heal wounds and fight off pathogens. Most of the time, the inflammatory process is controlled and self-limited (meaning it doesn't go on forever).

Inflammation exists to help us—it's the body's attempt to protect itself. It removes harmful stimuli and protects the body from infection, illness, and injury. As part of the body's inflammatory response to help fight infection, there is an increase in the production of white blood cells, immune cells, and substances called "cytokines."

There are two kinds of inflammation that can impact our health: acute and chronic.

Acute inflammation comes on rapidly, usually within minutes, but is generally short-lived. With acute inflammation, mechanisms spring into action to destroy invading microbes before switching gears to cart away dead cells and repair damaged ones. This cycle returns the affected area to a state of balance, and inflammation dissipates within a few hours to a few days as part of the healing process.

Chronic inflammation often begins with the same cellular response, but morphs into a lingering state that persists for months or years. In this case, it may stay active even after the initial threat has been eliminated. In other cases, low-level inflammation becomes activated even when there is no apparent injury or disease. It can become a low-level chronic irritant to the system, which can lead to pain, discomfort, and clinical issues.

In both cases, the immune system prompts white blood cells to attack nearby healthy tissues and organs. This attack on healthy tissues and organs begins a pattern of chronic inflammation that plays a central role in some of the most challenging diseases of our time, including autism, depression, mental health issues, rheumatoid arthritis, cancer, heart disease, diabetes, asthma, Alzheimer's disease, and PANS/PANDAS. These issues are all on the rise because inflammation is on the rise: there *is* a link between the two.

The good news is that we know what leads to chronic inflammation, so that means we can reduce it.

Chronic inflammation is heavily influenced by lifestyle choices, diet, and genetic history. We may think that genetics is something we can't control, but we *can* control diet and lifestyle, which influence our epigenetics—the likelihood of a gene expressing itself or not. How powerful is that?!

The most common causes of inflammation include:

- The Standard American Diet (SAD)
- Sugar and high-fructose corn syrup consumption
- Processed and packaged foods
- Excessive intake of alcohol
- Chronic stress
- Lifestyle
- High glucose and insulin levels
- Mitochondrial dysfunction
- Disease and infection
- Smoking
- Environmental toxins

- Inactive lifestyle
- Inadequate sleep

Signs of Chronic Inflammation

We all have some level of inflammation, but chronic inflammation can produce a host of symptoms that can really wear us down. Issues resulting from chronic inflammation may be difficult to identify, as a person may start off just feeling tired or generally unwell. It may feel like a mild cold, or that post-cold fatigue that just doesn't go away. It might even show as a little weight gain.

When symptoms are mild or worsen slowly over time, they can be difficult to chase down, which is a major reason many fail to make the connection to inflammation. Moreover, symptoms can range from mild to severe, and can change over time.

Symptoms of chronic inflammation may include:

- Fatigue
- Brain fog/attention issues
- Memory issues
- Pain
- Mouth sores
- Chest pain
- Abdominal pain
- Fever
- Rash or redness
- Joint pain
- Swelling
- Swollen glands
- Digestive issues
- Constipation or loose stools
- Regression or loss of some function

How an Anti-Inflammatory Diet Helps

Now, you realize that chronic low-level inflammation is problematic, and you may suspect that your child is impacted by inflammation. After all, we know there is a link between mental health issues and inflammation, so why would it be any different for your child? At a minimum, you may now realize he or she is likely not getting enough nutrients to power up his or her brain, right?

Following are some of the many ways an anti-inflammatory diet can help your child reduce and reverse his or her mental health issues.

An Anti-Inflammatory Diet … Reduces Inflammation.

I think you get it… a nutrient-dense diet reduces inflammation, and when we reduce inflammation, symptoms reduce and reverse. Yes! It is as simple as that.

An Anti-Inflammatory Diet Boosts Beneficial Bacteria and Supports Gut Integrity.

We want a happy gut. Good bacteria have so many beneficial effects on our nervous system, including helping us to remain calm and feel happier—and this diet supports the health of our microbiome (Du Toit, 2019). The microbiome is composed of bacteria, organisms, viruses, and microbes that reside in and on our bodies (Shreiner, Kao & Young, 2015). Our gut health impacts both our brain and body, and there is a strong connection between our gut and brain (University of Pittsburgh, 2020). The microbes in our body, and particularly our gut, contribute to metabolic functions, protect against pathogens, impact our immune system, and through these basic functions, affect directly or indirectly most of our physiologic functions (Shreiner, Kao & Young, 2015).

The gut and brain are connected by the autonomic nervous system's vagus nerve, which plays a huge role in how we manage stress. It works to slow the sympathetic stress response and push us into a calmer, parasympathetic dominant state. Our vagus nerve is what ties the all-important gut and brain electrical communications together, which influence the function and health of each other. The electrical activity in our gut is just as important as the electrical activity in our brain, and having a healthy gut is paramount in supporting brain functioning, including neurotransmitter activity.

Your gut health can impact how your body extracts nutrients from your diet and stores fat and modulates inflammation. The composition of the microbiome is impacted by diet, lifestyle, and environmental factors, all of which can be largely controlled by the individual (Shreiner, Kao, & Young, 2015; Telle-Hansen, Holven, & Ulven, 2018). We know that a good diet feeds good gut bacteria, whereas a poor diet has a negative impact, causing some strains to die off and others to flourish (Telle-Hansen, Holven, & Ulven, 2018; Truax et. al, 2018).

Processed foods can also interfere with the integrity of gut lining and allow toxins and pathogens to directly enter the bloodstream, so eating whole foods is critical to protect the junctures of the stomach lining (Lerner and Matthias, 2015).

An Anti-Inflammatory Diet Supports Insulin Sensitivity and Blood Sugar.

We often don't think about the food-mood connection, but what we eat *can* improve or worsen our mood. Foods that cause fluctuations in blood sugar impact our mood, attention, and stress level (Penckofer et. al, 2012). Eating anti-inflammatory foods such as healthy fats, fiber, and phytonutrients supports insulin sensitivity, which regulates blood sugar (Johnson, Hou & Li, 2017; Rehman, 2016). A diet high in sugar and sweeteners, as well as the typical Western diet, can have a negative impact on mood, learning, and mental well-being. We know these kinds of foods cause a disruption in blood sugar, which is linked to a variety of mental health issues (Penckofer et. al, 2012).

A growing body of evidence suggests a relationship between mood and variable blood sugar or glycemic levels. Symptoms of poor glycemic regulation have been shown to closely mirror mental health symptoms such as moodiness, irritability, anxiety, and focus problems. We may joke about being "hangry," but for many kids and teens, low blood sugar is a very real contributor to issues with mood and behavior. Research supports the relationship between high sugar consumption and common mental disorders, concluding that sugar intake from sweet foods and beverages has an adverse effect on not just short-term psychological health but on long-term, as well (Knüppel et. al, 2017).

Glucose is the primary source of energy for every cell in the body as well as in the brain—our most energy-demanding organ. It uses half of the body's glucose energy, so it needs a consistent and stable source. It makes sense then that when glucose levels are high or low, the brain is affected, and mental health symptoms result. Consistent protein consumption, which helps to create that stable source of glucose in the liver, is especially important for those with behavioral or mood issues.

An Anti-Inflammatory Diet Reduces Food Sensitivities and Allergies.

If you have a food allergy or sensitivity, trigger foods can activate your immune system and create an inflammatory response that can cause issues such as brain fog, attention problems, gut issues, skin conditions, etc. And boy, are these allergies and sensitivities on the rise! As our body's inflammation levels increase, we become even more sensitive to things in our environment and foods. With the rise of chronic inflammation, food intolerances and sensitivities have dramatically increased, too. That is why it is incredibly important to eat low-inflammatory foods, so mental health symptoms can reduce, and the brain and body can do what they are supposed to.

An anti-inflammatory diet eliminates common high-allergen foods such as gluten, dairy, and sweeteners and replaces them with nutrient-dense foods that enable your body to heal (Ionescu, 2014; Kitts et. al, 1997). Anti-inflammatory diets have been shown to improve skin conditions (Ionescu, 2014), asthma (Guilleminault et. al., 2017), and a host of other mental health and physical conditions, as well.

An Anti-Inflammatory Diet Provides Nutrition That Aids in Symptom Reduction and Reversal.

With one in two children today having physical or mental health problems, they need every nutrient they can get.

So many children are malnourished ... yes, malnourished! They aren't eating a variety of nutrient-dense foods that provide their body with the nutrients it needs to do its job. The truth is, a serving of broccoli here and there just isn't going to do it.

Ultimately, an anti-inflammatory diet provides the body with what it needs to heal itself—nutrients. It is a balanced approach to eating that incorporates healthy fats, fiber, vegetables, fruits, spices, and high-quality protein to give our children what they need to think, be calm, and feel good. It is what their central nervous system (CNS) needs to regulate and modulate all the stimuli that is constantly coming at them.

We've already established that the research is clear: an anti-inflammatory diet reduces mental health issues and physical problems (Anand, 2017; Minihane, 2015; Browning & Jebb, 2006; Godos et. al, 2020; Mascarenhas, 2019; Gomez-Pinilla & Nguyen, 2012; Mitchell & Goldstein, 2014; Manzel et. al, 2014). Therefore, it is a critical component in helping reduce and reverse your child's emotional, behavioral, cognitive, and learning challenges.

Will's Story

Will had always struggled with anxiety, but in his first year of college, the depression began. A great student, few were aware of the level of worry he had spinning through his brain at every given moment.

When Will came to me during his holiday break, he wasn't sure he could make it back. He was physically and mentally shot. He was exhausted and couldn't think straight. He also knew he had to be "all in" to the intensive treatment plan we created, which included diet changes, neurofeedback, and therapy, if there was even a small chance of his returning to school.

First, Will began following an anti-inflammatory diet known to improve anxiety and depression. Second, he came in almost daily for a regime of psychotherapy that addressed stress and anxiety coping mechanisms. Third, he underwent neurofeedback and biofeedback to support his nervous system's ability to get into a calmer, parasympathetic dominant state. He also began meditating.

Within a few days, Will and his mom (who joined Will in his new diet) reported feeling very different. Will was sleeping for the first time in months, feeling more energized, and thinking more clearly. Five weeks later, he had the lowest levels of stress and anxiety he had ever felt in his life! That constant, stress-related muscle tension he was used to was barely noticeable anymore.

In the end, because Will was so committed to doing the work that created change, he was able to apply the strategies he learned to lower his stress and return to school.

Anti-Inflammatory Diet Protocol

What Is an Anti-Inflammatory Diet?

An anti-inflammatory diet consists of foods that reduce inflammatory responses. This diet involves replacing sugary, refined foods with whole, nutrient-rich foods.

The great news? A person may be able to reduce his or her body's inflammatory response by implementing these healthful dietary changes! YOU, as the parent, have the power to help your child do so.

What Conditions Can an Anti-Inflammatory Diet Help?

- Auto-immune diseases, such as diabetes, Crohn's, Lupus, IBS
- Allergies
- Multiple sclerosis
- Anxiety
- PTSD
- Depression
- OCD
- Lyme and tick-borne disease
- PANS/PANDAS
- Autism
- ADHD
- Sensory processing
- Genetic and neurodevelopmental disorders
- Chronic pain
- Learning and processing disorders
- Neurodevelopmental disorders

(Anand, 2017; Minihane, 2015; Browning & Jebb, 2006; Godos et. al, 2020; Mascarenhas, 2019; Gomez-Pinilla & Nguyen, 2012; Mitchell & Goldstein, 2014; Manzel et. al, 2014)

Recommendations for Following an Anti-Inflammatory Diet Include:

- Drink LOTS of water.
- Include as much fresh food as possible (a minimum of nine servings a day).
- Minimize your consumption of processed foods and fast food.
- Eat fruits and vegetables (choose organic, non-GMO whenever possible).
- Eat blueberries, blackberries, and cherries.

- Eat dark-green leafy greens.

- Eat alliums: garlic, scallions, onions, and leeks, and cruciferous vegetables like broccoli, cabbage, cauliflower, mustard greens, and Brussels sprouts four times a week.

- Eat mushrooms such as shiitake, enokitake, maitake, oyster, and wild, as available.

- Add in healthy fats: raw and unsalted nuts (walnuts, pistachios, pine nuts, and almonds), avocado, extra-virgin olive oil, expeller-pressed grapeseed oil, flax, walnut, organic and expeller-pressed high-oleic sunflower or safflower oils, and coconut.

- Eat plant-based protein (beans, nuts, seeds, peas).

- Eat high-quality, organic, omega-3 enriched eggs.

- Eat wild-caught fish (not farm-raised varieties).

- Consume cold-water fish such as salmon, oysters, herring, mackerel, trout, sardines, and anchovies and low-fat fish such as sole and flounder.

- Eat meat that is organic, grass-fed, and antibiotic free.

- Eat high-fiber foods like raspberries, strawberries, blueberries, apples, pears, peas, broccoli, Brussel sprouts, cauliflower, carrots, squash, potatoes, kale, cabbage, kohlrabi, turnip greens, collard greens, spinach, swiss chard, beat greens, quinoa, oats, millet, brown rice, legumes, chia seeds, flax seeds, sunflower seeds, pinon nuts, almonds, and pistachios.

- When eating grains, make sure to choose organic, non-GMO, gluten-free whole grains.

- Add herbs and spices such as parsley, cilantro, turmeric, curry powder (which contains turmeric), ginger cinnamon, garlic (dried and fresh), chili peppers, basil, rosemary, and thyme.

- Enjoy plain dark chocolate in moderation (with a minimum cocoa content of 70 percent).

- Eat a variety of foods and ROTATE them.

POWER YOUR BRAIN
WITH FOOD

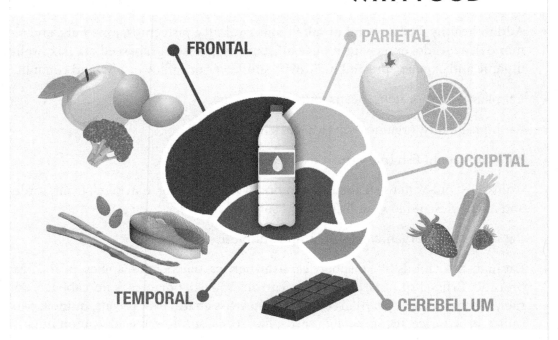

FRONTAL

PARIETAL

OCCIPITAL

TEMPORAL

CEREBELLUM

WHAT YOU EAT CAN AFFECT SPECIFIC AREAS OF YOUR BRAIN

FRONTAL LOBE

Water!	Dark Chocolate	Spinach
Apples	Eggs*	Peppers
Avocado	Flax Meal	Pistachios
Beans	Grass-Fed Meats	Probiotics
Beets	Green Tea	Pumpkin Seeds
Blueberries	Hemp Hearts	Raisins
Broccoli	Kale	Tomato
Celery	Leeks	Sunflower Seeds
Chard	Mushrooms	Walnuts
Chia Seeds	Olive Oil	Whole Grains
Coffee	Onions	
Dandelion greens	Salmon	

PARIETAL LOBE
Water!
Clementine
Grapefruit
Oranges

TEMPORAL LOBE
Water!
Asparagus
Almonds
Blueberries
Brussels
Cabbage
Carrots
Celery
Hazelnuts
Salmon
Turmeric
Walnuts

OCCIPITAL LOBE
Water!
Acai
Carrots
Cherries
Blackberries
Blueberries
Grapes
Strawberries

CEREBELLUM
Water!
Dark Chocolate!

Dr. Roseann   It's gonna be OK.™   ©ROSEANN-CAPANNA-HODGE
www.childrensmentalhealth.com

Foods to Avoid

The main foods that people following an anti-inflammatory diet should avoid include:

- Processed meats

- Sugary drinks

- Trans fats (fried foods)

- White bread

- White pasta

- Gluten

- Dairy products (milk, cheese, butter, ice cream)

- Transfats ("hydrogenated" or "partially hydrogenated oils" typically in vegetable shortenings, select margarines, crackers, and cookies)

- Margarine

- Vegetable oils (corn, safflower, soybean, peanut, and cottonseed oil)

- Processed snack foods (chips and crackers)

- High-sugar desserts (cookies, candy, ice cream)

- Excess alcohol

- Carbohydrates

*Wish you could easily find yummy anti-inflammatory recipes? Check out our *It's Gonna Be OK!™ Quick and Tasty Anti-Inflammatory Family Cookbook: www.itsgonnabeok.com/cookbook*.

Supplements

Supplements help fill gaps in your diet when you are unable to get your daily requirement of micronutrients due to illnesses that "rob" nutrients from the body, genetic issues that limit proper absorption, or "outside circumstances" that limit your ability to follow the anti-inflammatory diet.

Consider the following supplements:

- Magnesium
  (Moslehi et. al., 2012; Dibaba, Xun & He, 2014; Chacko et. al, 2014)

- Omega-3s
  (Calder, 2010; Simopoulos, 2002)

- Curcumin
  (Chacko, 2011; Chainani-Wu, 2003; Hewlings & Kalman 2017)

- Zinc
  (Prasad, 2014)

- Green Tea
  (Chatterjee, 2012

- Frankincense
  (Su et. al, 2015; Maroon et.al, 2010)

- Ginger
  (Hoseinzadeh et al, 2015; Rashidian et. al, 2014)

- Spirulina
  (Shih et. al, 2009; Nielsen et.al, 2010; Selmi et. al, 2011)

- Vitamin A
  (Reifen, 2002; Case Western Reserve University, 2017)

- B Vitamins
  (Folsom et.al, 2003: Chiang et. al, 2005)

- Vitamin C
  (Ellulu, 2015; UC- Berkley, 2008)

- Vitamin D
  (Cannell, 2015; Mangin et. al, 2014)

- Vitamin E
  (Nazrun et. al, 2012; Singh et. al, 2015)

- Alpha-Lipoic Acid
  (Moura, de Andrade, dos Santos, & Goulart, 2015)

How Am I Going to Get My Kids to Actually Eat This Stuff?

Ok, I get it … changing your kids' diet may feel overwhelming. You're probably thinking that your kid is already difficult, and now I'm telling you that you have yet another thing to battle with him about! Yes, I am.

But I wouldn't recommend it if I wasn't certain that it will make a difference in changing your child's behaviors that keep you up at night.

And although some parents do, I don't recommend changing every single part of your child's diet overnight. Start small. Just one small change, and go from there. (And make sure you are following the diet, too, because you deserve that same TLC.)

Finally, I won't leave you hanging! I'm about to share with you some of my best tips for swaying those picky eaters. And remember, *It's Gonna Be OK!*

Picky Eaters 101

Jimmy's Story

When Jimmy came to our center, his mom and dad were beyond worried about his health and anxiety. Their other two children were good eaters who consumed whatever Dave and Jenna prepared, but not Jimmy—he was eating only eight foods. Yep—eight! Jimmy struggled with being still and in school, and he had shiner-type bags under his eyes. His parents tried everything they could think of, but nothing changed. Jimmy remained unfocused at school and really struggled with learning.

When Jimmy's teacher called them with concerns about how *"zoned out"* he was, they went back to the doctors. When their primary care doctor recommended supplementing Jimmy's diet with one of those nutritional drinks (filled with sugar), they knew better and had enough. Luckily, they found me through friends.

After a QEEG brain map, we could see that there was a lack of nutrients getting to Jimmy's brain. He also exhibited poor gut health, which impacted protein reaching his brain, as well. We devised a treatment plan that included diet, lab work to examine his nutrient levels, and some breathwork to start.

With naturopathic care, Jimmy was able to get the nutrient support needed to help him eat better. He was especially low in zinc, which is tied to focus issues and reduced appetite. Within just a week of adding zinc to Jimmy's diet, he also added two new foods to his rotation. That means in just seven days, we added two new foods to his diet, which is something his parents hadn't been able to do in 10 years.

We added neurofeedback to Jimmy's health regime, and soon, he began to focus and stop the constant movement, all while eating too many foods to count. Jimmy eventually became an even better eater than his siblings and found a love of cooking, too.

Why Are Kids Picky Eaters?

Kids are picky eaters for a variety of reasons, including sensory, taste and textural experiences, allergies, and health and behavioral issues. Research from the University of Michigan (2020) found that a child who is highly pressured to eat may be a more finicky eater. In other words, the more parents try to control and restrict children's diets, the more children try to exercise their own control (which they otherwise rarely have in other areas) over what they eat, and often, they become even more resistant to foods. Essentially, early pressure to eat creates a lot of bad childhood memories that cause food resistance. The research found that it is more important to focus on pleasant experiences and less on forcing your child to eat. In the same research study, kids who received only low levels of parental pressure to eat were the least finicky eaters.

I always focus on giving kids healthy food options and having them help with the food preparation process to give them a sense of control. Plus, gaining independent cooking skills has the added bonus of being a big self-confidence booster.

If your child is resistant to eating because of sensory processing issues, it is important to connect with an occupational therapist to look at ways to stop food avoidance. OT's work with children to make them less sensitive to textures, and therefore, more open to new foods that meet their nutritional needs. They can teach you ways to help your children be less averse to textures, which will cut down on battles at mealtime.

It is possible that your child is a picky eater because s/he has low levels of zinc, as this has been associated with low appetite (Shay & Mangian, 2000). Adding in foods rich in zinc or a zinc supplement can have a dramatic effect on your child's appetite and reduce those picky eating behaviors.

Finally, having a child is stressful, right? Even more so when children are very restrictive eaters who consume less than 20 foods. This is backed by research, according to Dahlsgaard & Bodie (2019). Worrying about your child getting proper nutrition, particularly when the child has neurodevelopmental issues, is definitely hard. So, here are my favorite hacks to help your picky eater become more open to different foods.

Tips for Encouraging the Picky Eater

Shop with Your Kids

Get kids and teens excited about food by helping them shop for items *they* want to prepare. I like to lay the ground rules first by saying, *"We need protein, vegetables, fat,"* and so on. Thinking about what you want to make first is one way to approach it, but you can also look for something fresh and on sale and create from there. Having them take part in the selection process is empowering, and I have found that children are more likely to try something they have selected themselves.

Think About How Food Looks

When we go to a fancy restaurant, they don't just toss food on the plate in a big heap. They make it look just as good as it tastes. Add color by tossing in fruit, vegetables, or herbs your child likes, so it is more appealing visually, as well. Getting children to "plate" the food also makes them part of the process and encourages exploration.

Don't Force It

I always say to my kids, *"Try it, and if you don't like it, you don't have to eat it."* Nine times out of ten, they wind up liking it. Keep in mind that a child's fear around disliking new foods can be very real for some. By giving them choices, you reduce resistance, and hopefully, they'll be more likely to try again the next time.

Keep Exposing Your Child to New Foods

It takes nine to eleven times of being offered a new food for the average picky eater to actually try it. Now, you're thinking, *"Oh, that makes sense,"* right? So, be patient and try the same food more than once. You can experiment with preparing things a different way or mixing it with things they like.

Start with What They Like

Consider what your child already likes and find similar healthier alternatives. Even though some of the parents I work with choose to go "cold turkey" with their food makeovers, that doesn't work for everyone. If your child loves sandwiches, swap out the bread for an organic or gluten-free type, and buy nitrate-free meats. Trust me, there are some amazing products out there, and it really is very easy to get yummy and healthy "swapouts."

Infuse Flavor

I think one of the biggest fallacies about healthy eating is that the food doesn't taste good. For me and my family, it all starts with healthy ingredients and spices and herbs that infuse a lot of flavor. You don't need to be afraid of cooking! You can start with basic recipes that focus not just on nutrition, but flavor, too. Don't be afraid to be creative and explore different cuisines. Also, simple tweaks like marinating meat for two to three days really ups the flavor game.

Think about Texture and Spicing

More and more people have issues with textures due to sensory processing issues. For them, they react not to the food itself, but to the textures and feel of it. Some kids resist food out of fear that it will be uncomfortable. So, when it comes to meal planning, think about the textures your kids enjoy and build menus based on that. That doesn't mean you never add spices and textures if they can't stand them. You simply want to meet them where they are and build from there to keep them comfortable.

Rotate Your Foods

When you eat the same things all the time, you can easily get bored with food. And when that happens, the pallet narrows, and eating habits can become quite restrictive, causing resistance. Plus, when you don't rotate your foods, you can develop food sensitivities, which leads to inflammation that can also derail your health.

Let Your Kids Cook

I don't remember a time when my kids didn't cook! As soon as they could hold themselves up, they helped me add spices to food. And when they could stand and hold utensils, they could cut foods and help me prep. It is really pretty simple, and when children help prepare their own meals, they're just much more likely to eat the food. It's a great opportunity to help them develop their own relationship with and excitement about food and to enjoy a wonderful experience together.

Don't Keep Junk Food in the House

Here is the deal: If you don't have junk food in the house, no one can eat it. It is as simple as that. When you have tasty and healthy food at your disposal, that is what your family will eat. And don't worry; they will not starve!

Be a Role Model

If you want your kids to eat healthy, then you have to, too. That means you don't get to have your "special drawer." Show your kids that you too love eating chicken, fish, veggies, avocado, and so on, and they will join you.

Expose Your Child (and Their Friends) to New Flavors

One of my favorite tricks was to make some of my best dishes when my kids' friends were visiting. Their friends (even the picky ones) would love the food so much that my kids would beam with pride. That pride came to apply to our healthy eating, too, and I loved hearing them say, *"Dude, you gotta try this,"* to their buddies.

Give Choices

You can't force kids to eat spinach (okay, I do use a little hypnosis for that!), but you can give them a couple of things to choose from. When we give kids choices, they feel empowered and in control. And kids are always striving for autonomy, so why not give them the power to make healthy food choices? When they feel like they are in control, they are more likely to eat things they might not normally.

Start Them Young

Who says you have to feed young children boring flavors? They can eat spiced and tasty food, too! When I gave my infant rice pasta, I added in puréed spinach and garlic. I clearly remember him humming with delight as he ate. We don't start out giving our kids French fries and hot dogs, do we? No! We feed them vegetables and fruits because they are filled with nutrients. So, move from puréed foods to sautéed vegetables and meats with onions and garlic. There is no need to make separate meals consisting of processed garbage! Just start them young, and watch how it creates a love of healthy food.

Talk Food Science

My kids know what nutrients are contained in most foods. Ever since they were little, I made a game of sorts out of guessing which nutrients were in the food I was making. It gave them a deeper connection to the food and helped establish the "why" behind eating healthy. I didn't have to yell, "You need more vegetables," because they knew what vitamins A, C, D, and E did for the body and brain, and they knew they came from the food. Remember, you don't have to be a scientist to figure out the nutrients in foods—that's what Google is for!

Focus on Nutrient-Dense Food

Most kids are eating a lot of fillers—sugars, juices, sodas, candy, sweets, bread, cereals, and so on—instead of nutrients. When you focus on giving your kids foods that are packed with nutrients, proteins, and fats, their bodies will get what they need. Even better, they'll begin craving the good stuff instead of the junk. I can honestly say that if my kids have the choice between a cookie or a steak, they will pick the steak every time. (See the list of nutrient-dense foods provided above for ideas).

Add Smoothies to Their Diet

Smoothies can be a powerhouse of nutrition, and kids usually love them! Not only are they tasty, but you can sneak in some really good foods in there. Moreover, you can have your kids make their own smoothies to get their buy-in to healthy eating while of course building their self-esteem. **You can grab my favorite smoothie recipes here: www.drrotips.com/smoothies**.

Cut Back on Snacks

When your kids graze all day, they may not want to sit down and eat a healthy meal. On top of not really being hungry, they are likely eating food that may not be healthy or filled with nutrients.

Swap out Soda for Seltzer

It seems the memo has been missed—soda is *never* a good idea! Sugar has NO nutritional value. On tap of that, it suppresses the immune system and alters a person's taste buds. Swap it out for seltzer or flavored seltzers.

Use Restaurant Apps

Traveling or going out? Don't stray from healthy eating! Instead, use internet apps to find healthy restaurants. I have been using the Find Me Gluten Free app for too many years to count. Even if you aren't gluten free, the restaurants that list themselves as such have healthier options and know how to cater to restricted eaters.

The Psychology of Nutrition and Teens

We already talked about starting healthy eating habits while your kids are young.

But what if your picky eater is a teenager?

Changing a teen's diet might be incredibly difficult, but it is not impossible. If you reduce the amount of junk food at home in favor of yummy food choices that just happen to be nutritious, he or she *will* eat.

As they go through the process of finding out who they are, teens want control over everything in their lives, including their food. They don't want lectures; they want to eat food that tastes good. So, approaching teens with food choices and empowering them to prepare food for themselves is a great way to get them to eat better.

Kids of all ages love learning about their brain, so teach your teen. I love teaching that age group about what they can do to get their brain working optimally, and which foods power up the different areas. They really seem to enjoy taking an active role in what they can do to get more focused, learn better, and so on.

Starting the conversation is the first step.

Due to fluctuating hormones, teens need extra protein and healthy fats to balance out blood sugar. I like to make my own children aware of the connection between what they ate with how they feel. When we eat nutrient-dense foods and fats, we feel good! Getting teens to connect to that good feeling makes them more likely to eat other nutritious foods.

Make sure to have lots of prepared options in the fridge and freezer for your teen, so he or she can just grab it when s/he wants.

Here are my best tips for getting teens to eat healthier:

- Start with what they love and find a healthier alternative.

- Focus on nutrient-dense foods.

- Think protein!

- Have them meal plan and prep.

- Make them responsible for one meal a week.

- Spice food.

- Make smoothies.

- Have nutritious prepared food accessible.

- Buy less junk.

- Have healthy snacks available.

I know changing your family's diet won't be easy, but it is the quickest way for *all* of you to get some relief. Change can happen, and it all starts with the captain of the ship: you. Just start small and be kind to yourself.

No one is perfect, so simply commit to doing the best you can.

Chapter 7 - Addressing Nutrient Deficiencies to Reverse Mental Health

Pillar 3: Nutrient Deficiencies

The Link Between Nutrients and Mental Health

Genetics and neurotransmitter issues aren't the only reasons a brain gets "stuck." Many mental illnesses arise from dysregulation of the central nervous system (CNS) due to chronic stress states and/or chronic inflammation or result from nutrient deficiencies.

Despite the abundant amount of research linking nutrient deficiency and mental health (Rao, 2008; Gracious et al., 2012; Lakhan & Vieira, 2007; Lim et al., 2016, Sarris et al., 2015; Neugebauer, 2005), we rarely hear about it from medical and mental health providers. The question is, why?

As I mentioned earlier, the answer is a simple lack of training. We already know that neither the standard physician training program nor the graduate mental health training program have one course in nutrition. If those professionals don't have the training, then how can they know enough to share information with parents and patients? I recently saw a thread in a Facebook group for therapists about how therapists should never talk to clients about nutrition, because "We can't advise our clients on things like that." Really?! That kind of thinking is what I have been up against for 30 years—truly, it comes down to a lack of training on, and understanding of, how nutrient deficiencies can lead to mental health issues.

It is getting clearer that *"mental health disorders are associated with low-grade inflammation (e.g., C-reactive protein), oxidative stress, and the elevation of inflammatory cytokines (e.g., TNF-α, IL-1, IL-6)"* (Bested et al., 2013), and that the standard diagnosis of it being *"a biochemical problem"* treatable with medication is inaccurate.

The reality is that, with children getting sicker and sicker physically and mentally, practitioners are failing to look for and provide solutions for families. As a mental health professional, that is what I did, so it is hard for me to understand why pills are continuously pushed without a lot of efficacy or evidence proving they actually work.

We have a serious crisis on our hands. Long before the pandemic, children's mental health issues were on the rise with chronic childhood illnesses such as ADHD, autism, and mental health issues increasing (Delaney & Smith, 2012). And the issues are more severe: *"The number of adolescents who experienced major depressive episodes increased by nearly a third from 2005 to 2014"* (US Department of Health and Human Services, 2019) and *"The suicide rate among people ages 10 to 24 years old climbed 56% between 2007 and 2017"* (CDC, 2019).

The worst of it is that, despite our knowing that early intervention is key, kids aren't getting the help they need to live happy, healthy, and productive lives. *"Typically, 30% of GP consultations concern child behaviour problems, and established behaviour problems can have lasting effects on children's life chances"* (Ryan et al., 2017).

In fact, *"The average delay between onset of mental illness symptoms and treatment is 11 years"* (National Alliance on Mental Illness, 2019).

How can this be when parents are asking (really, begging) their child's physician for help?

The good news is that parents can take a lot of their child's care into their own hands. One way to do so is to address nutrient deficiencies—one of the 8 Pillars of Symptom Reduction and Reversal that we walk you through in this book and in the **Get Unstuck Program**™ (**www. getunstuckprogram.com**). Whether you are addressing the foundational components of changing mental health on your own or with the personal guidance of Yours Truly (yep, I personally coach you in the **Get Unstuck Program**™), you *can* reduce and reverse your child's anxiety, depression, and focus problems. It takes an effort, but the payoff is more than worth it—there is no symptom that won't improve when you consistently apply the eight pillars.

When it comes to looking at nutrient deficiencies, it is ideal to begin by taking your child to a functional or naturopathic physician who can run comprehensive lab work to identify exactly what your child is lacking/missing. That step is critical to getting to the bottom of what is going on (you know … root causes!), and then, in getting your child those exact nutrients.

It is important for parents to understand the connection between nutrient deficiencies and how they impact brain function, and ultimately, your child's behavior. While that may feel overwhelming, look at it this way—it is something you *can* address to improve their issues! Remember, small changes create big waves …

Connor's Story

By age 14, Connor had a long list of school-related and behavioral problems that all came to a head in the ninth grade—the year grades and tests really start to matter. School staff ran out of patience for Connor's *"Homer Simpson ways."* He was impulsive and rarely able to 'connect the dots.' His parents tried every single ADHD medication known to man, which caused him to just about completely stop eating and become *really* cranky!

Luckily, three of the family's friends and their pediatrician recommended they come see me, letting them know that I *"have a way of turning things around."*

I could tell Connor was nutrient deficient just by looking at him; he had shiners under his eyes. I sent him for lab work that revealed very low levels of vitamin D as well as low levels of vitamin B12, essential fatty acid serum levels, and zinc, which all are associated with attention problems. Combining neurofeedback with supplements, Connor began looking better physically as his shiners went away. He also became better at controlling his impulses within a short amount of time. With the addition of executive functioning coaching, he learned how to break habits and new ways to approach tasks.

When we believe the only answer to mental health issues is psychiatric medication, we fail to take a scientific approach—to determine what the body is missing. For Connor, his nervous system just couldn't operate without the essential nutrients he was lacking, and when he got them, he could be more focused and connected. And when he *learned* how to alert and take action differently with executive functioning coaching, it all came together for him, and he got unstuck. Oh, and he never got into trouble in school again for the rest of his educational career!

Supplements for General Mental Health

As a parent, you are right to have concerns about the safety and side effects of psychiatric medications for your child, because there are a lot of them. In fact, there isn't a psychiatric medication out there that doesn't have a toxic effect. It isn't unusual for a child to have medication-induced symptoms ranging from "mild" (like irritability or appetite loss) to more severe (like suicidal thoughts, personality changes, or psychosis). This is especially so with my most fragile and sensitive kids with PANS/PANDAS. Medication reactions are the norm, according to research (Thienemann, Park, Chan, & Frankovich, 2021). I wish I could say these side effects are rare, but I see them every single day at my center. Kids are hurting; families are hurting; and these meds are only throwing fuel on the fire.

That's why so many parents are looking for another way to help their children. Luckily, they don't have to go too far in their Google search to find a host of evidence-based natural solutions. And over the last decade, as mental health issues and the number of psychiatric prescriptions have risen, there has been an increase in research proving the efficacy of natural treatments for mental health issues such as anxiety, depression, OCD, attention, and so on.

Medicinal herbs have been used as a traditional treatment agent for ages in many parts of the world. The increase in many autoimmune and inflammatory disease conditions in the Western world has led to a resurgence in the use of centuries-old herbs to improve health and wellness. Many herbs can provide an alternative treatment for conditions such as pain, anxiety, and depression and can also be used as an adjunctive to conventional medical treatments.

There are nutrients that address specific issues, yes. There are also nutrients and supplements that have general properties that can treat several symptoms at the same time and have a synergistic effect with each other and with your treatment in general.

There are lots of kinds of supplements, and they come in different forms. They are often used in cooking, teas, baths, tinctures, salves, or in capsule form, and each form can be beneficial. The following are some of the most useful in supporting mental health:

Probiotics

We hear so much about a "happy gut" and how important it is for us. And we know that when our gut feels good, so does our body, yet most still don't understand the bi-directional link between our gut and brain. More specifically, many don't realize how having healthy bacteria impacts our brain.

Remember, your intestines have trillions of healthy bacteria. Probiotics contain these healthy strains of bacteria and yeasts that are good for your digestive system and your brain, as those healthy bacteria have a direct impact on the electrical activity of the brain. The microbiome and its bacteria influence the brain through the vagus nerve, and there is a bi-directional influence between the two (Mayer et al., 2014).

Just like stress in the brain can impact your gut, a reduction of healthy gut bacteria can affect the electrical activity in the brain. Ah ha! Now you get it ... our brain and body are connected, and the health of our gut can have a huge impact on our mental health.

Probiotics balance the bacteria in your gut, so your digestive system can work properly, and different types can have specific benefits. For example, there are probiotics designed not just for the gut, but for attention, allergies, metabolism, stress, etc. This of course has a direct effect on children with so many conditions, including autism, ADHD, anxiety, PANS/PANDAS, allergies, and so on.

Research demonstrates the many benefits of probiotics, which are not limited to improving immune function and reducing the chance of common illnesses and conditions (Lammert, 2018; Pärtty, 2018; Kumperscak, 2020; Gilbert, 2013; Rao, 2009; Bested, 2013). Taking probiotics regularly can affect neurotransmitter and brain function, which has a direct impact on mental health (Bested, 2013; Du Toit, 2019). Probiotic supplementation can also improve symptoms of stress, anxiety, and depression by impacting hormone function, and there are numerous studies demonstrating how probiotics improve a variety of mental health issues (Mayer et al., 2014).

Just as adding probiotics can improve gut health, the microbiome is sensitive to disruption from unhealthy bacteria, toxins, and medications (Cussotto et al., 2019), so it is important to take care of our gut by eating healthy, hydrating, and moderating our stress levels.

Saffron

You may be familiar with saffron as an herb used in cooking, but did you know it has also been used in folk and Ayurvedic medicine as a sedative, expectorant, anti-asthma treatment, emmenagogue, adaptogenic agent, and pain-relief solution? Research from Hausenblas et al. (2013) shows that saffron is one of the more effective herbs for reducing depression symptoms. Research from Sarris (2007) has also shown saffron to be *as effective* as the antidepressants imipramine and fluoxetine. Besides being an antidepressant, it calms the central nervous system (CNS) and has anti-anxiety effects. Other studies show a benefit to anxiety, as well (Yalcin et al., 2004). Finally, saffron relaxes the muscles of the digestive tract to reduce spasms, which helps food digestion and enhances appetite (Khorasan & Hosseinzadeh, 2016).

Bacopa

Bacopa is an herb that you may have never heard of, but it has been used for centuries in Ayurvedic traditional medicine and has many pharmacological and therapeutic benefits (Al-Snafi, 2013). It is an adaptogen and antidepressant that is also used for focus and energy. Adaptogens help people lower stress by restoring the biological capacity to adapt and respond to environmental stressors. Bacopa is also considered a nootropic, or a compound, that enhances brain function, especially memory and cognitive processing. It is one of my favorite adaptogen herbs to really "crisp up" one's thinking and can be a useful tool for anyone with focus issues or brain fog. Bacopa may increase the effects of key neurotransmitters, such as serotonin, noradrenaline, dopamine, and acetylcholine, which calm the central nervous system (CNS) and support mood balancing. Research from Bhattacharya and Ghosal (1998) indicates that bacopa is one of the natural anxiety supplements that works for people with post-traumatic stress disorder (PTSD). For those with memory, focus, or learning issues, which can be further impacted by mental health issues, research has found that bacopa improves these conditions (Joseph et al., 2014).

Rhodiola

Rhodiola is an herbal plant that has been a part of traditional medicine systems in parts of Europe, Asia, and Russia for centuries to improve performance and reduce fatigue and depression. It has both adaptogenic properties and ergogenic capacity. Rhodiola supports tyrosine in the body, which assists with focus. It is a mild stimulant and can help with low energy in the afternoon. Research supports its efficacy with stress, anxiety, athletic performance and endurance, mental performance, and fatigue (Cropley, Banks, & Boyle, 2015).

Kava

Kava is a member of the pepper family and native to the islands of the South Pacific. It is known for its anxiolytic, antiepileptic, antidepressant, antipsychotic, and sedative properties. Its calming qualities make it one of the more effective herbs for anxiety that also improves sleep. Short-term use of kava has been noted to be effective for patients with mild to moderate anxiety disorders who are not using alcohol or taking other medicines metabolized by the liver, but who wish to use natural remedies. Research from Malsch and Kieser (2001) supports that kava compares favorably to benzodiazepines, which are used to treat anxiety and can be addictive. Benzodiazepines such as clonazepam, xanax, and prosom may calm someone down or help him sleep, but they are incredibly difficult to titrate down from due to their addictive qualities. Kava is a safe and effective alternative to benzodiazepines. Kava has also been known to improve cognitive abilities, which can be impacted by depression and anxiety (Ooi, Henderson, & Pak, 2018).

Licorice

Licorice, a common herb used in traditional Chinese medicine for centuries, contains beneficial metabolites. Licorice root can be used as an anti-inflammatory, expectorant, demulcent, adaptogen, anti-viral, anti-tumor, and antidepressant. The minerals found in licorice are very stimulating and support adrenal functions, which can be particularly impacted by stress. It also can soothe the stomach, speed the repair of the stomach lining, and restore balance (and remember, research has shown the importance of the brain-gut connection in mental health) (Peterson et al., 2018).

Chamomile

Chamomile, one of the most well-known healing herbs dating back to ancient Egypt, helps to calm the nervous system, reduce inflammation, and bring about a sense of wellness. Many people use it to treat a variety of conditions such as anxiety, fever, pain, inflammation, sleep issues, dental issues, eye problems, and skin problems. It is generally known to be a safe herb and is most famous for helping to induce sleep. While there are many different preparations of chamomile, the most popular form is herbal tea. Even kids can enjoy a cup of chamomile tea in the evening to help ready their body for sleep and calm their minds before bed. Depending on the condition, it can also be used as a tincture, essential oil, or salve.

The healing properties and pharmacological effects of chamomile result from different natural compounds of the dried plant flowers, which contain such healthful compounds as terpenoids and flavonoids. Research from Srivastava et al. (2010) has demonstrated that chamomile is helpful for many ailments such as hay fever, inflammation, anxiety, menstrual disorders, muscle spasms, insomnia, ulcers, wounds, diabetes, gastrointestinal disorders, cancer, cardiovascular support, rheumatic pain, and hemorrhoids. Essential oils of chamomile are used extensively in many cosmetics and in aromatherapy.

Milk Thistle

Our livers are overloaded by everyday toxins in our environment and from the use of psychiatric medication. Therefore, detoxification support has become an essential component of physical and mental health.

Milk thistle, a plant whose fruit and seeds have been used for more than 2,000 years, supports the liver.

One active ingredient in milk thistle is silymarin, which is extracted from the plant's seeds and fruits. Silymarin is a complex mixture of flavonolignans that have antioxidant properties (Valenzuela & Garrido, 1994). Research demonstrates that silymarin stabilizes cellular membranes, regulates permeability, stimulates detoxification pathways and the regeneration of liver tissue, inhibits the growth of certain cancer cell lines, and adjunct to established therapies, helps prevent or reduce chemotherapy as well as radiotherapy-induced toxicity (Valenzuela & Garrido, 1994; Fraschini et al., 2012; Ramasamy & Agarwal, 2008).

Milk thistle is a strong liver detoxifier. Specifically, it supports phase 2 liver detoxification, which is needed to remove toxins from the body (Gopalakrishnan et al., 2013). Recent research indicates that poor detoxification can lead to mental health issues. When toxins build up in the brain or body, they can create or contribute to significant psychiatric symptoms. Children are particularly vulnerable to the neurotoxic effect of substances. Pesticides and lead are two substances that are linked to a range of neurological and cognitive issues (Rauh & Margolis, 2016). Milk thistle is one of the primary natural herbs supporting people in detoxification (Jacobs, 2002) related to liver disease (Achufusi, T & Patel, 2020), substance abuse recovery, chronic medical issues, long-term psychiatric medications use, or in those who have been diagnosed with autism, ADHD, depression, anxiety, or OCD.

Basil

We may think of basil only as a fragrant herb to season our food, but basil has medicinal properties, too. There are a number of types of basil, and they differ in taste and smell. Two of the most common are Sweet Basil (Lamiaceae) and Holy Basil (Tulsi). Basil contains a wide range of essential oils rich in phenolic compounds as well as a vast array of other natural compounds (more than 25) including polyphenols such as flavonoids and anthocyanins (Joshi, 2014). Basil has been used for centuries as a traditional and Ayurvedic medicinal plant for the treatment of headaches, cough, diarrhea, constipation, warts, worms, and kidney malfunctions.

Today, basil is often used as an immune booster, anti-inflammatory herb, and for its antibacterial and anti-aging properties. Animal and human studies support basil having multiple therapeutic actions including adaptogenic, antimicrobial, anti-inflammatory, cardioprotective, and immunomodulatory effects (Jamshidi & Cohen, 2017). Research from Jamshidi and Cohen (2017) demonstrates that basil counters metabolic stress through normalization of blood glucose, blood pressure, and lipid levels. With respect to mental health, basil has positive effects on stress, memory, and cognitive function through its anxiolytic and antidepressant properties (Saxena et al., 2012). Moreover, balancing blood sugar is important for mood regulation and an overall sense of wellbeing. Adding it to your food as little as a few times a week can make a difference in how you feel!

Cinnamon

Cinnamon is not only for baking—it's also used in traditional and modern medicines. It comes from the bark of the cinnamon tree and has been enjoyed as a spice for thousands of years. It was first noted in use for medicinal and fragrant properties in China around 2800 BC, and later in Egyptian and Roman times (Kawatra & Rajagopalan, 2015).

Chemically, each part of the tree has different bioactive constituents, such as cinnamaldehyde, cinnamic acid, and cinnamate, but the cinnamon bark contains procyanidins and catechins, which extracted from cinnamon and berries, possess antioxidant activities (Rao & Gan, 2014).

Cinnamon has many benefits and is an antioxidant, anti-inflammatory, antidiabetic, antimicrobial, anticancer, lipid-lowering, and cardiovascular-disease-lowering compound (Kawatra & Rajagopalan, 2015). The chemical compounds in cinnamon have also been reported to have protective properties against neurological disorders (Anderson et al., 2013). In the case of diabetes, cinnamon helps to balance blood sugar, an imbalance of which can contribute to fatigue, brain fog, and mood issues (Allen et al., 2013). We know that diabetes and depression frequently co-occur, so supporting blood glucose is important. It also helps with digestion, which is frequently poor in those with anxiety, OCD, ADHD, depression, and autism.

Anxiety Supplements

Stress and anxiety are common conditions affecting children and adults. In fact, anxiety disorders affect 40 million adults in the United States age 18 and older, or 18.1% of the population every year, making it one of the most common mental illnesses. About three percent of children in the U.S. have an anxiety disorder with the average age of onset being six years. This can perhaps be at least partially attributed to the cultural shift toward adopting a high-stress lifestyle, along with poor dietary habits, reduced sleep, health issues, and increased genetic mutations—all of which are contributing factors.

It all begins with stress—and we can't underestimate how stressed our kids really are! Research has found that almost 50% of school children report and show signs of stress (Valizadeh, Farnam, & Rahkar, 2012).

I see children as young as three years old showing clear signs of stress. Once, one of my typical teen clients told me that almost every one of her friends was on ADHD or anxiety medications or both. She said they just can't keep up with all the schoolwork and pressure. I even once had a girl so stressed with the pressure to keep up on social media that she paid her younger sibling to post for her when she was too busy with schoolwork and activities. I am sure most of us read that and think *what*?! But the reality is, social media is a big driver in our kids' lives today. Good or bad, it is here to stay, and we need to help kids set healthy boundaries. It isn't the only reason why these kids are struggling, but it is one of them.

On top of our regular lives, stress, anxiety, focus problems, isolation, and depression have only gotten worse during the pandemic. As parents, we were already worried about our kids, but now, we are overwhelmed and don't know where to turn. That is what the eight pillars are for … to guide you through the foundational components to change your child's (and hopefully your family's) mental health.

The following seven supplements for anxiety are backed by research that supports their efficacy. They should be considered for symptom reduction in anyone who has difficulty focusing, anxiety, mood, or behavioral issues, and all the other symptoms that co-occur with these conditions.

Looking for the research-recommended dosage amounts for these supplements for anxiety? Download them at <u>www.drrotips.com/anxietysupplements</u>.

Magnesium

One of the most prominent natural anxiety supplements, magnesium is a cofactor in more than 300 enzyme systems that regulate diverse biochemical and enzymatic reactions within the body (Al Alawi et al., 2018). These include metabolizing food, synthesizing fatty acids and proteins, transmitting nerve impulses for better muscle and blood glucose control, and regulating blood pressure. We need a lot of magnesium to support all the ways it is used in the body, because without it, our brain and body just won't work as well. Taking magnesium as a supplement really is beneficial for so many bodily functions, but it is also a fast-acting and effective stress reliever.

Magnesium is actually so fast-acting that most people report feeling less stressed after just one dose! I worked with one mom who, after noticing how calm her son was within one hour of taking magnesium, started giving it to everyone in the whole family. She swore it just *"dialed down the chaos,"* and everyone was a whole lot nicer.

Many chemical functions that support the central nervous system (CNS) in managing stress require magnesium's assistance. And as we talked about, our CNS is so stress hyperactivated from everyday life that we need to help it regulate and get into that calm parasympathetic state. Magnesium is needed for energy production (mitochondrial function) and the glucose breakdown for energy (glycolysis). Cerebral energy metabolism is often associated with anxiety and social behavior (Hollis et al., 2015). Magnesium binds with ATP, the main source of energy for the cells (oxidative phosphorylation), regulates transmembrane transport, and plays a variety of roles in function and structure of proteins, nucleic acid, and mitochondria for cellular energy. It is also required for the synthesis of DNA, RNA, and glutathione, a powerful antioxidant that supports detoxification and a healthy immune system. Oxidative stress and improper detoxification are associated with increased levels of anxiety (Bouayed et al., 2009; Drigen et al., 2001), so the use of magnesium can go a long way in helping us feel calm.

The majority of Western populations consume less than the recommended amount of magnesium. Many studies have reported that reduced levels of magnesium are associated with a wide range of chronic diseases including, among others, anxiety (Al Alawi, 2018). As one of the primary vitamins for reducing anxiety, research from Boyle et al. (2017) supports its efficacy. It also plays an important role in the hypothalamic-pituitary-adrenocortical (HPA) axis to help manage the body's stress-response system. Again, we want the body to be able to physiologically respond to stressors and get back into that calm, parasympathetic state, and having enough magnesium in our body to support that process is critical.

Ingested magnesium is absorbed through the gut, and absorption levels vary depending on a number of factors, including gut health. Aside from eating magnesium-dense foods like avocados, legumes, or nuts, it can be directly taken in capsule or powder form. Magnesium is considered one of the safest supplements for stress regulation, and dosage can be determinative via bowel tolerance (one should lower the dosage when loose stools are present).

L-Theanine

L-Theanine is an amino acid found in green tea that is widely used in Asian countries. Known for its calming and relaxing properties, many use it as one of the natural remedies for anxiety and depression (Kimura et al., 2007). L-Theanine assists neurocognitive functioning in several ways, supporting both neurotransmitter functioning and brainwave activity. It modulates aspects of brain function in humans by increasing alpha brainwave activity, which calms the brain. L-Theanine also increases levels of the brain neurotransmitters serotonin, dopamine, and gamma-aminobutyric acid (GABA) (an important inhibitory neurotransmitter). L-Theanine produces its anti-anxiety effects by increasing GABA without producing sleepiness or impairing motor behavior common to prescription anti-anxiety drugs. It also reduces anxiety by blocking the excitatory neurotransmitter glutamate. By inhibiting the overstimulating glutamate, the brain learns to calm, and one feels more relaxed. It not only has been shown to reduce stress-related symptoms, but to also improve cognitive functioning (Hidese et al., 2019) as well as decrease anxiety and depression (Lopes Sakamoto et al, 2019).

Studies from Osborne et al. (2015) demonstrate that L-Theanine, when used as a vitamin for anxiety and stress, can specifically reduce the molecular impacts of acute stress, and the resulting excitotoxicity on brain cells, which can result in cognitive decline. Not only are chronic stress states associated with anxiety and depression, but they are also associated with neurodegenerative disorders. It can be directly taken in capsule or powder form. L-Theanine is considered safe; research reveals no negative effects. It is a well-tolerated and effective amino acid for stress, anxiety, and depression.

Using supplements that are safe and effective in reducing excitatory neurotransmitter activity can be a natural solution for anxiety.

GABA

Gamma-aminobutyric acid (GABA) is a neurotransmitter that inhibits nerve transmission in the brain, calming nervous activity. The neurotransmitter GABA blocks the excitatory neurotransmitter glutamate, keeping nerve cells from firing too often and too easily (Boonstra et al., 2015). When there is too much excitatory or inconsistent activity, a person can feel anxious.

People deficient in GABA are prone to neurological issues resulting in over-excitability such as agitation, irritability, and, most importantly, anxiety (Nuss, 2015). Further, disorders such as panic attacks and generalized anxiety disorder are also related to low GABA activity making it one of the more effective natural remedies for panic attacks (Boonstra et al., 2015). Additionally, GABA neurotransmitter activity in the amygdala is important in modulating anxiety-related behavior.

The food substance supplement form of GABA is widely available and has been used since at least the 1950's as an aid to reduce stress and anxiety (Nemeroff, 2002). While there have been some questions about the bioavailability of GABA (or how it is absorbed), a number of studies have reported that GABA does cross the blood-brain barrier in small amounts, meaning it can be absorbed and used in the brain (Al-Sarraf, 2002). The use of GABA has been shown to support anxiety, depression, sleep problems, autism, panic attacks, and agitation (Nuss, 2015; Kalueff & Nutt, 2007; Plante et al., 2012; Fatemi et al., 2009; Zwanzger & Rupprecht, 2005; Battaglia, 2005). It can be directly taken in capsule or powder form.

GABA is one of those go-to supplements for someone who is struggling with anxiety or depression. It can be an effective way to reduce those agitated feelings and spinning thoughts. In fact, I remember when a teen trying GABA along with an anti-inflammatory diet asked, *"Can I use this stuff under my tongue too much? Because damn, I feel good."*

Essential Fatty Acid (EPA)

Omega-3 is the name given to a group of polyunsaturated fatty acids of which docosahexaenoic acid (DHA) and eicosapentaenoic acid (EPA) are essential for brain health. Following consumption, omega-3 fatty acids are incorporated into body tissue cell membranes and have powerful anti-inflammatory functions within the body. Research from Novak et al. (2003) supports that at the cellular level, omega-3 fatty acids from fish oils can directly or indirectly modulate a number of cellular activities associated with inflammation. Inflammation is associated with a number of mental health conditions, including anxiety.

Omega-3 is "essential" because it is not made in the body and must be supplied through consumption of foods such as salmon, tuna, sardines, wild game, and walnuts or as a dietary supplement. The other essential fatty acid is omega-6, which can be found in corn, eggs, poultry, and soybean oil. Omega-6 contains gamma-linolenic acid (GLA), which has powerful anti-inflammatory properties (National Institutes of Health, 2020).

The omega-3 fatty acids EPA and DHA are critical for normal brain function and development. Omega-3 can affect the functionality of the neurotransmitter serotonin, which plays a critical role in both depression and anxiety. Perhaps one of the best vitamins for anxiety and stress, omega-3 helps with the functioning of the prefrontal cortex and the nucleus accumbens, the brain regions involved in motivation and emotional regulation (Healy-Stoffel & Levant, 2018). DHA is a critical structural component of the cerebral cortex, which is the area of the brain responsible for language, memory, generalizing, creativity, judgment, emotion, and attention.

Omega-3 is an essential fatty acid with research-noted positive effects on a number of mental health and brain conditions, including anxiety, depression, and panic disorder (Freeman et al., 2006; Kiecolt-Glaser et al., 2011; Logan, 2004; Su et al., 2015).

Vitamin D

We hear so much about vitamin D because it is much needed to support our immune and hormone functions. And during the pandemic, we need its support for our stress levels and immune system, too.

Vitamin D_3 is made in your skin through a chemical process called "photolysis" that occurs when you expose your skin to ultraviolet B (UVB) rays. In the liver, vitamin D is turned into a chemical called "calcidiol," and this vitamin D prohormone travels through the bloodstream to the kidneys, where it's turned into the active form of the vitamin.

Every tissue in the body has vitamin D receptors, including the brain, heart, muscles, endocrine system, and immune system, which means vitamin D is needed at every level for the body to function. Since vitamin D is involved in so many functions in the brain and body, it has an important role in supporting anxiety (National Institutes of Health, 2020).

Upwards of 70% of Americans are vitamin D deficient, which often leads to significant medical and psychological consequences. Low levels of vitamin D are associated with anxiety and depression (Bičíková et al., 2015). I can say that at least 70 to 80 percent of my clients are either low or deficient in vitamin D, and often, their physicians are aware, but don't advise supplementation. This is a travesty, because of its connection to mental health.

In terms of anxiety and mood, if the brain and endocrine system are not getting enough vitamin D, they can't work properly, and these symptoms can result (Hoogendijk et al, 2008; Wilkins et al., 2006; Altieri et al., 2017). Vitamin D plays a role in magnesium homeostasis, which is necessary for so many biochemicals in the body.

If your child has a mental health issue, it is important to have his or her vitamin D levels checked. For those with clinical conditions, blood levels of vitamin D should be on the high end of average.

Vitamin B

The B vitamins are important nutrients in managing stress and anxiety. They are necessary for maintaining healthy nervous and digestive systems and various metabolic functions, and they also play a vital role in brain health. The B vitamins are often used to reduce fatigue, boost mood, and improve symptoms of anxiety (Lewis et al., 2013). B vitamins come from food sources such as whole grains, rice, meat, eggs, dark leafy vegetables, fruit, and legumes, and can also be taken via a supplement. The body does not store B vitamins well, and the need for them is increased by stress and illness, so supplementation and eating foods with high B levels should be a priority.

There are several types of B vitamins, and each one supports the brain and body in different ways. They all support proper nervous system function, and that has a direct implication for those with anxiety (Lewis et al, 2013). For example, pyridoxine (B6) helps the body manufacture neurotransmitters, such as serotonin, which aids in the body's ability to cope with depression, stress, and anxiety (Merete et al., 2008). The B vitamins include (B1) thiamine, (B2) riboflavin, (B3) niacin, (B5) pantothenate, (B6) pyridoxine, (B9) folate, and (B12) cobalamin. Many individuals take a B complex that contains all of these B vitamins.

A common genetic mutation called methylenetetrahydrofolate reductase (MTHFR) impacts how folate is used in the body and brain (Almeida et al., 2005). It affects upwards of 40 percent of the US population, and is implicated in a variety of physical and mental health conditions including anxiety, depression, autism, ADHD, chronic disease, etc. (Lewis et al., 2015; Pu et al., 2013; Spellicy et al., 2012). This gene mutation can lead to high levels of homocysteine in the blood and low levels of folate and other vitamins. There are two MTHFR mutations—C677T and A1298C—and a person can have one or both impacting the bioavailability of folate. Folate (B-9) is important in the detoxification process and necessary for normal CNS regulation. When CNS dysregulation occurs, conditions such as anxiety and depression can result, which is why testing vitamin B levels and supplementation are necessary.

These deficiencies can also impact how psychiatric medications are metabolized, leading to paradoxical reactions, adverse reactions, or no responsiveness. There is testing readily available that should be done before taking any psychiatric medication to ensure your child isn't harmed by one of the many side effects. As you already know, I believe you can reduce and reverse mental health without psychiatric medications, and I have helped thousands of kids do it. And that's why I'm so glad you're reading this book. If you'd like to learn more, you can work with me in my Get Unstuck Program™ (www.getunstuckprogram.com), too.

Ashwagandha

Ashwagandha is a natural herb from India that has been used for centuries as a body tonic to promote overall wellness, and more specifically, to manage stress and anxiety. It is an adaptogen that helps to balance the body's physiological systems, which can be out of balance when anxiety is present.

From a biochemical perspective, Ashwagandha supports the GABAergic signaling system and the main inhibitory receptors in the CNS, ionotropic GABA receptors, which can be faulty in those with anxiety (Candelario et al., 2015).

It contains several naturally occurring phytochemicals that help regulate the hormone system. In terms of anxiety, the evidence demonstrates that Ashwagandha helps to lower the stress hormone cortisol and blood sugar levels, which have resulted in lower reported levels of stress and anxiety (Chandrasekhar et al., 2012; Auddy et al., 2008). Cortisol is known as a stress hormone because the adrenal glands release it in response to stress, as well as when your blood sugar levels get too low. Ashwagandha boosts the adrenal glands by supporting normal HPA axis function, which helps the hypothalamic, pituitary, and adrenal glands communicate effectively and is critical to the body's and brain's ability to manage stress. Ashwagandha also lowers inflammation, which has been shown to be associated with anxiety (Salim et al., 2012).

OCD Supplements

If there is one condition that is often missed and on the rise, it is obsessive-compulsive disorder (OCD). OCD starts with a worry that morphs into intrusive thoughts, obsessive thinking, or compulsive behaviors.

I am seeing such an uptick in kids with OCD, and that's not limited to my extensive work with kids with PANS/PANDAS. People are stressed and anxious, and kids are no different. When a person is anxious, he or she can choose to cope with it in healthy ways or unhealthy ways, and that is exactly how OCD ignites—it is one of the unhealthy ways to manage anxiety. When one's subconscious brain learns to avoid the uncomfortableness of anxiety by employing obsessive thinking or compulsive behaviors, those behaviors quickly become negatively reinforced or otherwise learned.

Phillip's Story

Phillip was a sweet boy with a history of social anxiety. He often clung to his mom's leg and needed a lot of reassurance from his parents, grandma, and babysitter. Being the sweetheart he was, when Phillip asked worried questions (*"Is it going to thunder? What time will you be home? Will you stay in my room until I fall asleep?"*), his loved ones always comforted and reassured him. Little by little, his anxiety became more heightened, causing him to become more fearful and controlling. Reassurance no longer helped Phillip to calm down, and he was often emotional, had trouble sleeping, and withdrew from others. Then, the compulsive behaviors started.

At first, they were hard to spot. On occasion, things had to be a certain way, or he'd get tearful or angry. But then it started happening more and more. And when his mom, Patty, caught him counting while climbing the stairs and then having to restart because it *"wasn't quite right,"* she knew they were dealing with more than anxiety. Still, she didn't understand it was OCD. It wasn't until she got to me that we put the pieces together that his therapist and physician had missed. OCD can be difficult to identify in children. It takes an experienced clinician to really assess for obsessive thinking and compulsive behavior.

With a combination of supplements, neurofeedback, and exposure and response prevention (ERP) therapy for OCD, Phillip and his parents learned to talk back to his OCD and worries. His parents learned how to encourage Phillip to cope with uncomfortable emotions and not accommodate them, and he went on to completely reverse his OCD! He was even able to break free from social anxiety. Today, Phillip is a happy, well-liked teen.

Looking for the research-recommended dosage amounts for the following supplements

for OCD? Download them at <u>www.drrotips.com/ocdsupplements</u>.

N-Acetylcysteine (NAC)

NAC is an amino acid derivative of cysteine that supports brain function and has antioxidant effects as well as anti-inflammatory properties. NAC helps the body synthesize glutathione, an important antioxidant necessary for detoxification of the liver. Moreover, because of the organic compounds of the sulfhydryl groups, NAC protects the body from different toxins, as it can bind and inactivate toxic heavy metals in drugs like acetaminophen, environmental pollutants, herbicides, mercury, cadmium, lead, microbes, etc. (Mokhtari, 2017). High toxin loads create an inflammatory response in the brain and body and can lead to a variety of mental health issues, including OCD.

NAC modulates the expression of genes that affect the inflammatory process. Inflammation and excess neurotransmitter activity have been implicated in the occurrence of OCD (Lawrence, 2009). Research from Lawrence (2009) supports that NAC is an effective dietary supplement for those with OCD, as NAC reduces inflammation and inhibits the release of excitatory neurotransmitters. It inhibits the expression of pro-inflammatory cytokines and suppresses pro-inflammatory signaling pathway NF-kappa B and regulates the gene for cyclooxygenase-2 (COX-2), which promotes carcinogenesis, thereby preventing inflammation and pain (Lawrence, 2009).

NAC also targets the glutamatergic system. Research from Pittenger et al. (2011) suggests that the excitatory neurotransmitter glutamate is dysregulated in OCD patients, and that this dysregulation may contribute to the behaviors. NAC stimulates inhibitory metabotropic glutamate receptors, which then reduces the synaptic release of glutamate. The restoration of the extracellular glutamate concentration in the nucleus accumbens seems to block the reinstitution of compulsive behaviors (*Psychology Today*, n.d.).

Glycine

Glycine is a naturally occurring amino acid that supports nerve and neurotransmitter functions. It also helps support the detoxification process, assist with cellular energy, and support intestinal and brain health—all important factors in OCD. It is made in small amounts by the human body, but can also be acquired through food and supplements. The highest sources of glycine are found in collagen, gelatin, high-protein meats, and bone broth (Razak et al., 2017).

This amino acid is important for different muscle, cognitive, and metabolic functions (Razak et al., 2017). As you've already learned, strong gut health is important for brain health. Glycine inhibits oxidative stress, which can interfere with intestinal health (Wang et al., 2014). Glycine enables the production of collagen, a protein that is an essential component of muscles, tendon, skin, and bones. It also facilitates the production of creatine, a nutrient stored in and used by the brain for energy. Glycine helps break down and transport nutrients like glycogen and fat to be used by cells for energy, thus supporting the brain, and in the process, reinforcing a strong immune, digestive, and nervous system (Razak et al., 2017).

We know from research that bacteria can be a source of obsessive-compulsive behaviors, which results in a disorder called PANDAS when from a streptococcus infection, or PANS, when from other infectious sources (Perlmutter et al.,1999). Within the detoxification process, glycine is necessary for the synthesis of bile salts, which is needed for the excretion of toxins from the body and inhibiting pathogenic bacterial overgrowth. Glycine has also been shown to reduce inflammation (Stalp et al., 2001), which is a known contributor to many mental health conditions including PANS/PANDAS, anxiety, autism, and depression.

Glycine is involved in the transmission of chemical signals in the brain with both inhibitory and excitatory functions within the CNS. Glycine works with other amino acids, including taurine and gamma-aminobutyric acid (GABA), as an inhibitory neurotransmitter. Also, it binds to the NMDA receptor, which is an excitatory receptor site for glutamate, thus inducing a sedative or inhibitory effect while also being capable of improving mood and cognition (Razak et al., 2017). Moreover, research indicates that it may be effective as one of the supplements for OCD patients (Razak et al., 2017).

Milk Thistle

Milk thistle is an herb that promotes overall well-being, but it is also specifically used for OCD. As described above, the fruit and seeds from this plant have been used for more than 2,000 years to support the liver. The silymarin (extracted from the seeds and fruits) is a complex mixture of flavonolignans that have antioxidant properties, which stabilize cellular membranes and regulate permeability to stimulate detoxification pathways (Valenzuela & Garrido, 1994; Fraschini et al., 2012).

As we learn more about mental health, we know that poor detoxification can lead to mental health issues. When toxins build up in the brain or body, they can create or contribute to significant psychiatric symptoms like OCD. Specifically, it supports phase 2 liver detoxification, which is needed to remove toxins from the body (Gopalakrishnan et al., 2013).

OCD patients use milk thistle to enable detoxification, thereby promoting better mental health. Milk thistle also increases serotonin, which can be especially helpful to those with OCD, as they may have abnormalities in their serotonin (5-HT) production or removal (Yan et al., 2015; Pittenger et al., 2016). In addition, research studies from Sayyah et al. (2009) indicate that milk thistle lowers obsessions and compulsions in as little as four weeks.

L-Theanine

L-Theanine reduces OCD symptoms by inhibiting the overstimulating glutamate. When the brain learns to calm itself, one feels more relaxed, which helps to reduce obsessions and compulsions. It also has been found to support healthy neurotransmitter activity to clinically reduce behaviors associated with OCD (Nathan et al., 2006). It can be directly taken in capsule or powder form and is considered safe—no negative effects have been found in using green tea (source of L-Theanine) as one of the primary herbs for OCD patients.

Inositol

Inositol is a naturally occurring substance. Also called vitamin B8, it actually isn't categorized as a B vitamin. This B vitamin-like substance can be found naturally in plants and animals or can be man-made. Common sources of inositol are fruits like oranges, cantaloupe, and bananas, and wheat germ, brewer's yeast, liver, brown rice, oat flakes, nuts, unrefined molasses, raisins, and vegetables. It is necessary for proper cell formation, nerve transmission, and transportation of fats in the body. Inositol may affect the action of the neurotransmitters serotonin and GABA metabolism, and therefore has a role in many psychiatric disorders (Levine, 1997).

In my opinion, inositol is one of those supplements that isn't used enough for those with OCD. When it works, I have witnessed remarkable transformations. Even though it doesn't work for everyone, it is generally safe and worth trying if your child has OCD.

A Holistic Approach to ADHD Serotonin and Dopamine Deficiencies: Supplements for Attention

When I started graduate school in 1995, I decided right from my first class that I wanted to work with kids with ADHD. I ended up writing my dissertation on the topic, having always loved working and volunteering with kids with ADHD while in my undergraduate program. These kids were smart, verbal, and typically had a great sense of humor. They just couldn't produce work—especially written work. They really challenged everything I learned in school and pushed me toward neuroscience and looking at integrative approaches to mental health, because they weren't getting better with psychostimulants. Even worse, they were often negatively affected by them, exhibiting personality changes, restricted eating, and crabby behaviors … all part of the "norm" when on Ritalin, Concerta, or Adderall.

As I treated more and more children and teens who thought they had ADHD, I began discovering that oftentimes, it wasn't ADHD at all, but some other condition, like concussion, autism, anxiety, depression, OCD, PANS/PANDAS, Lyme, etc., which can all easily present like ADHD. And guess what else? Nutrient deficiencies and poor diet can appear as a rampant case of ADHD, too!

I also found that we could safely and easily treat someone with focus problems with the nutrients they were missing. This was quite revolutionary in the mid 1990's … really, it still is today in 2021, despite the depth of research that demonstrates the connection between nutrient deficiencies and focus problems.

We don't know all the neurological reasons why a person has ADHD, but we know those with it have different brainwave patterning—their neural networks communicate differently. In some cases, there are suspected structural differences, and their neurotransmitter activity is different from a typical brain's.

In regard to neurotransmitter activity, studies from Oades (2008) provide evidence that those with ADHD have altered (lower) levels of dopamine and serotonin function (Cook et al.,1995). Dopamine allows us to regulate our responses and take action to achieve specific rewards as well as focus and direct our attention. Supplementation can impact how our neurotransmitters work.

The following list of supplements and herbs have proven beneficial for ADHD. Looking for the research-recommended dosage amounts for these supplements for ADHD? Download them at www.drrotips.com/adhdsupplements.

Zinc

When compared to their neurotypical peers, children with ADHD are often deficient in specific essential nutrients, including zinc (Greenblatt & Delane, 2017). Zinc, an essential cofactor of more than 100 enzymes used in the body, plays an important role in brain structure and function. As a necessary cofactor for the production of neurotransmitters prostaglandins and melatonin, it indirectly affects the metabolism of dopamine and fatty acids. Since all of these support attention, it's important to make sure children are not deficient in zinc.

Specifically, a lack of zinc may interfere with brain function and result in difficulties with hyperactivity, impulsivity, and socialization (Bilici et al., 2004). Melatonin, which zinc helps the body metabolize, plays an important role in the regulation of dopamine, which also makes it an effective supplement.

Research from Dodig-Curković et al. (2009) demonstrates that ADHD symptoms improve with the use of the dietary supplement zinc sulfate. You can also implement foods high in zinc into your child's diet, including oysters, chicken, beef, pork, tofu, hemp seeds, nuts, lentils, yogurt, oatmeal, and mushrooms.

Magnesium

Magnesium is the nutrient most used by our body as well as my personal favorite supplement. I use it daily and take four forms of it, one of which is a magnesium salt bath. It helps keep my brain and body working in this stressful world we live in.

When it comes to kids with ADHD, research from Starobrat-Hermelin & Kozielec (1997) has found that children are more likely to have a magnesium deficiency than neurotypical children.

One of the most prominent supplements for focus, magnesium is a cofactor in more than 300 enzyme systems that regulate diverse biochemical and enzymatic reactions within the body (Al Alawi et al., 2018). Magnesium assists many chemical functions that support the central nervous system (CNS) in self-regulation and attention. A mineral necessary for sufficient brain energy, it aids in the transmission of communications through the central nervous system, calms the central nervous system, and enables the body to make the neurotransmitter serotonin (Eby 3rd & Eby, 2010).

A magnesium deficiency can lead to neurological disruption that promotes the development of ADHD and a worsening of symptoms (Kozielec & Starobrat-Hermelin, 1997). This deficiency can also cause reduced attention span, hyperactivity, irritability, and difficulty thinking clearly (Gröber et al., 2015). Research from Hegvik et al. (2018) finds a link between a healthy immune system and ADHD. Elevated oxidative stress can therefore lead to progressive neuronal damage and deterioration of normal cerebral functions such as attention (Verlaet et al., 2018).

Aside from eating magnesium-dense foods like avocados, legumes, and nuts, it can be directly taken in capsule or powder form. Magnesium is considered one of the safest supplements for attention and should be taken to bowel tolerance—one should lower the dosage when loose stools are present.

Vitamin D

Scientists have noted that low blood serum levels of vitamin D are associated with ADHD (Sharif et al., 2015). Vitamin D also plays a role in magnesium homeostasis. Since vitamin D is involved in so many functions in the brain and body, it has an important role in supporting attention and impulse control. In terms of neurotransmitter function for those with ADHD, vitamin D supports dopamine levels, norepinephrine levels, and serotonin release. Vitamin D increases the production of acetylcholine, an important neurotransmitter in maintaining focus and concentration. It also facilitates the growth of nerve cells for executive function and memory storage, which can be impaired in those with ADHD (Sharif et al., 2015).

Research from Elshorbagy et al. (2018) has found that vitamin D supplementation for those with ADHD results in improvement in cognitive function at the conceptual level, inattention, opposition, hyperactivity, and impulsivity. Besides regular, short amounts of sun exposure without sun protection, foods such as fish, beef liver, egg yolks, and mushrooms provide small amounts of vitamin D.

Vitamin B

The B vitamins are necessary for maintaining healthy nervous and digestive systems and various metabolic functions. They play a vital role in attention and executive functioning, as well. The B vitamins are often used to reduce fatigue, boost mood, and improve symptoms of attention.

As described above, there are several types of B vitamins ((B1) thiamine, (B2) riboflavin, (B3) niacin, (B5) pantothenate, (B6) pyridoxine, (B9) folate, and (B12) cobalamin), and each one supports the brain and body in different ways. They all support proper nervous system function which has a direct implication for those with ADHD. For example, pyridoxine (B6) helps the body manufacture neurotransmitters such as serotonin, which plays a critical role in attention.

Several studies have demonstrated that the combination of magnesium and vitamin B6 improved behavior, decreased anxiety and aggression, and improved mobility among children with ADHD (Nogovitsina & Levitina, 2006).

As previously discussed, a common genetic mutation called methylenetetrahydrofolate reductase (MTHFR) impacts how folate is used in the body and brain (Almeida et al., 2005). Low vitamin B levels can lead to CNS dysregulation and when this occurs, conditions such as ADHD can result.

Many individuals take a B complex that contains all of the B vitamins, but they also come from food sources such as whole grains, rice, meat, eggs, dark leafy vegetables, fruit, and legumes.

Essential Fatty Acid (EPA)

Omega-3 is the name given to a group of polyunsaturated fatty acids, of which docosahexaenoic acid (DHA) and eicosapentaenoic acid (EPA) are essential for brain health—specifically, attention and impulse control. Following consumption, omega-3 fatty acids are incorporated into body tissue cell membranes and have powerful anti-inflammatory functions within the body. Research from Novak et al. (2003) supports that at the cellular level, omega-3 fatty acids from fish oils can directly or indirectly modulate a number of cellular activities associated with inflammation. Inflammation is associated with ADHD—specifically, problems with focus, attention, and impulse control (Anand et al., 2017).

The omega-3 fatty acids EPA and DHA are critical for normal brain function and development. Omega-3 can affect the functionality of the neurotransmitter serotonin, which plays a critical role in attention. Omega-3 helps with the function of the prefrontal cortex and the nucleus accumbens, which are the brain regions involved in selective attention, attentional switching, and emotional regulation. DHA is a critical structural component of the cerebral cortex, which is the area of the brain responsible for attention (National Institutes of Health, 2020).

Research supports that individuals with ADHD have lower levels of essential fatty acids than controls, and that when given direct supplementation, their ADHD symptoms improve. ADHD-related improvements in hyperactivity, impulsivity, attention, visual learning, word reading, and working/short-term memory were specifically found (Derbyshire, 2017).

According to a study at King's College London, UK, and China Medical University in Taichung, Taiwan (Chang et al., 2019), supplementation with Omega-3s can improve attention and be an effective treatment for Attention-Deficit Hyperactivity Disorder (ADHD). Moreover, consistent with prior research that demonstrated the Omega-3s benefits, this research found that Omega-3s not only have a positive effect on attention, but that they are equally effective to psychostimulant medication (Bloch & Qawasmi, 2011).

Melatonin

For various reasons, kids aren't getting enough sleep, and it is affecting their attention, mood, stress, and cognitive functioning. It is estimated that 15 to 25 percent of children and adolescents have problems getting to sleep or staying asleep (Owens, Adolescent Sleep Working Group, & Committee on Adolescence, 2014). A trend toward overall poor sleep hygiene and, more specifically, increased exposure to electronics prior to sleep may be a factor in the significant frequency of sleep disorders. Extended blue light exposure does impact our nervous system's ability to regulate for sleep.

Proper sleep of an adequate length of time and regulation through the sleep cycles aids in focus and detoxification (Inoué et al., 1995). Research from Xie et al. (2013) supports that a good night's sleep allows the brain to flush out toxins that build up during waking hours. Without proper sleep, toxic molecules involved in neurodegenerative disorders accumulate in the space between brain cells (Malhotra, 2018). Melatonin is a hormone secreted at night by the pineal gland and is needed for the regulation of the sleep-wake cycle (Weiss et al., 2006).

Many children and adults who have ADHD also have sleep problems and disorders, so the use of supplements like melatonin to support sleep can be very helpful (Weiss et al., 2006). Several studies have shown that melatonin also supports the central nervous system (CNS) through its ability to reduce chronic and acute inflammation (Esposito & Cuzzocrea, 2010).

Despite a high incidence of sleep disorders in children and adolescents, research has found that the dietary supplement melatonin can improve the sleep of those with ADHD (Weiss et al., 2006). Long-term research demonstrates that melatonin continues to work over time (Hoebert et al., 2009).

Simply put, without adequate sleep, one can't focus, so good quality sleep is needed for focus.

Herbs for Treating ADHD Naturally

Treating ADHD with diet to supplement vitamin and mineral deficiencies is the first step to overcoming it without medication. I've worked with many kids and families and seen beneficial results.

Herbal remedies can increase focus and cognitive functioning, as well. For example, the combination of the herbs ginkgo and ginseng has been studied for its ability to improve symptoms among patients with ADHD (Lyon et al., 2001).

Luisa's Story

Luisa was a bubbly little girl … until the fourth grade. That's when the demands of having to produce a lot of written work and stay in her seat just about did her in. Her mom, Cari, watched her brother and nephews try ADHD medications with no success, and she didn't want that for Luisa. Instead, she tried herbs that stimulated Luisa's attention.

At first, it was slow progress, but then she noticed Luisa putting her lunch box away without being asked. Then, she seemed to no longer need the millions of reminders about other things, either, and that meant less screaming at each other. Cari then added in some diet upgrades and started working with a parent coach, so that she could cue Luisa differently and make learning easier.

Ginkgo Biloba

Ginkgo biloba is an herb known to improve memory and increase mental sharpness as well as support brain functioning (Silberstein et al., 2011; Rokot et al., 2016). Research has also found it improves inattention (Shakibaei et al., 2015).

The antioxidant activity of ginkgo flavonol glycosides reduces oxidative stress, which contributes to neurodevelopmental disorders such as ADHD by causing membrane damage, changes in protein structure and function, lipid denaturation, and DNA damage (He et al., 2018). In addition, components isolated from ginkgo biloba contain terpene trilactones, which have neuroprotective properties and support the brain activity of those with ADHD (He et al., 2018; Taha et al., 2017).

Ginkgo biloba may be taken as tea, herbal tincture, capsules, or tablets. Although considered generally safe, Ginkgo biloba is contraindicated in seizure disorders. It may interact with, or heighten the effects of, other drugs your child may be taking.

Ginseng

Ginseng is an herb that is also regarded for its ability to increase energy and stimulate brain function and memory-boosting capabilities (Zhao et al., 2009). Ginseng extracts have been found to improve a number of cognitive functions, including attention, sensory-motor function, and auditory reaction time (Ahn et al., 2016).

Ginseng supports the central nervous system in a variety of cognitive processing factors. It has been found that ginsenosides, a ginseng constituent, increased dopamine and norepinephrine concentrations in the cerebral cortex (Itoh et al., 1989). These effects suggest that long-term administration of ginseng extract may result in positive growth in the neurodevelopment of an immature brain. Ginseng components are also researched and noted to have neuroprotective properties (Cho, 2012). These factors contribute to ginseng's ability to support inattention and hyperactive and impulsive behaviors (Ko et al., 2014).

Ginseng may be taken as tea, herbal tincture, capsules, or tablets.

Rhodiola Rosea

As noted previously, Rhodiola Rosea is an adaptogenic herb with neuroprotective properties that supports brain functioning and focus. Adaptogens are known for their capacity to protect organisms from numerous kinds of stressors.

Those with ADHD are deficient in dopamine and norepinephrine. Rhodiola Rosea supports brain function by stimulating the reticular activating system and elevating levels of the neurotransmitters dopamine, serotonin, and norepinephrine. For most, it enhances alertness, which is often lacking in those with ADHD.

Scientists have discovered that Rhodiola Rosea supports many aspects of cognitive processing and attention including learning, cognitive functioning, stress and fatigue, and attention (Petkov et al.,1986; Nicolas et al., 1976; Spasov et al., 2000; U.S. National Library of Medicine., 2019).

What's Next?

Phew! I've gone over a lot of vitamins, supplements, and herbs that can be helpful in reducing the symptoms of some of the most common mental health issues kids face today: stress and anxiety, mood, obsessions and compulsions, sleep problems, and attention and cognitive processing. This big list of supplements may feel overwhelming, but think about this way ... you now know of several research-supported ways to address your child's symptoms!

My recommendation is to start with the basics: vitamin D, magnesium, essential fatty acids, and a good probiotic. These vitamins are so needed in the brain and body. They not only help with mental health, but are important to our immune system, too. Once you get a few weeks of those supplements under your belt, then think about your most pressing symptoms, and add a supplement or herb to the mix.

If you're in crisis or unsure of what to do, I strongly recommend going to a functional physician or naturopathic doctor who can guide you. And always check with your medical provider before adding any dietary supplements, especially if you are on a psychiatric medication.

As complementary and alternative medicine become more accepted by the traditional medical community, natural supplements for mental health issues (including vitamins and herbs for anxiety and stress) will continue to become an increasingly common treatment method for mental health symptoms.

Chapter 8 - Our Genetics DON'T Define Us!

Pillar 4: Genetic Mutations

More Than Genetics: Our Mental Health Crisis

Today, mental health issues are at an all-time high, and one in six Americans is on a psychiatric medication (Martin, Hales, Gu, & Ogden, 2019). With the rates of serious mental health issues growing in children, suicide rates doubling, and emergency room and police interactions skyrocketing due to mental health issues, mental health *is* a global issue.

"About 25% of the world population is affected by some type of psychiatric disease that can alter intellectual ability, behavior, affectivity, and social relations" (Cross-Disorder Group of the Psychiatric Genomics Consortium, 2019). Kids are no different, with 21 percent of children in the United States ages 9 through 17 having a diagnosable mental illness with some degree of impairment (Singh & Chang, 2012). And according to the CDC (2020), ADHD, behavior problems, anxiety, and depression are the most commonly diagnosed mental disorders in children.

- 9.4% of children aged 2-17 years (approximately 6.1 million) have received an ADHD diagnosis.

- 7.4% of children aged 3-17 years (approximately 4.5 million) have a diagnosed behavior problem.

- 7.1% of children aged 3-17 years (approximately 4.4 million) have diagnosed anxiety.

- 3.2% of children aged 3-17 years (approximately 1.9 million) have diagnosed depression.

(Center for Disease Control and Prevention (2020). Data and Statistics on Children's Mental Health)

I wish I could say that this crept up on us, but that's not the case. We have been talking about children's mental health being a national crisis throughout the three decades I have been supporting children and their families! The research about how to help kids and their families has been there that long, too.

More than 20 years ago, one researcher wrote that we must use genetics to understand and treat mental illness. *"Gone is the idea that symptom clusters, course of illness, family history, and treatment response would coalesce in a simple way to yield valid diagnoses"* (Hyman, 2000). Yet despite the host of accessible lab work that has become available to patients and physicians over the last 10-20 years that illuminates the genetic issues actually interfering with one's mental health, we have still somehow managed to turn to medication … and boy, have things gotten worse.

According to the CDC (2020), depression and anxiety in children have increased over time. In 2014, the former director of The National Institutes of Mental Health Tomas Insel noted that the CDC reported a *five-fold* increase in the number of children under 18 on psychostimulants and a *six-fold* increase in the rate of antipsychotic prescriptions for children from 1988-1994 to 2007–2010. Clearly, the mental health of our children isn't improving, and this pandemic is only worsening anxiety and depression for so many.

We need to use scientific research to guide how we treat mental health issues in our most precious commodity—our children. Parents need to understand that just because everyone in your family has anxiety or depression, your child doesn't have to. We can do things to influence our genetics, and more importantly, we can actively unlearn learned behavioral patterns such as negative thinking, worried behaviors, and withdrawn or unsociable behaviors. Yes, you read that right—genetics are only a piece of the puzzle. Surprised? Keep reading …

Genetics and Mental Health

Let's just get this out of the way right now:

Genetics *don't* define us.

You may be thinking, *"What do you mean, Dr. Roseann?!"*

The truth is, genetics are only one part of what makes up our mental health. And believe it or not, we can alter our genetics, and certainly our epigenetics, by changing how we treat our brain and body and the way we live.

There is actually *so much* we can do to bring calm, health, and happiness into our lives without psychiatric medication. Those medications actually often have an opposite-from-desired effect due to their improper use, toxicity, and complete inability to help those with focus problems, anxiety, or depression learn another way to cope, deal with issues, and take action differently.

Now, let's dive into the how and why behind the "genetics-don't-define-us" statement.

Our genes contain the traits that make us who we are as individuals. While over 99% of them are similar to most other people's, the slightest variations in our genetic profiles account for differences in height, the color of our hair, eyes, and skin, and our particular preferences. Variations are what make us beautifully unique, yes. … but they can also create health issues that impair our functioning.

We hear a lot about epigenetics and its link to health, but most people have no idea what it actually is and how it impacts health (and more specifically, mental health).

"Epigenetics refers to [the study of] *alterations in gene expression and in a specific phenotype without involving changes within the DNA sequence"* (Cattaneo et. al., 2006).

While genes are largely inherited, acquired mutations occur, and both inherited and acquired mutations can impact how our brain and body work. Some mutations can be beneficial, while others can lead to physical or mental health issues. There are many common genetic mutations that can result in difficulties with detoxification or issues with hormone or neurotransmitter balance, resulting in a host of health issues, including impairment in brain function and emotional or behavioral imbalance (Duker, 2020; Genetic Alliance, 2009; Peedicayil, 2012). In one large-scale and worldwide study (Cross-Disorder Group of the Psychiatric Genomics Consortium, 2019), 109 genetic variants were associated with eight psychiatric disorders, including autism, ADHD, schizophrenia, bipolar disorder, depression, obsessive-compulsive disorder, and Tourette syndrome.

So, we know that specific genetic variations are associated with a greater likelihood of certain mental health conditions, BUT we also know that it doesn't always lead to them. The question is why? We will get into that more in just a bit, but first, let's talk a little more about genes and methylation—because several of your genes are involved in that vitally important process.

What Is Methylation?

Your body's methylation process is a vital component of optimal health that includes detoxification and affects your body's ability to maintain a clean and healthy internal environment in which key chemical processes can occur. During methylation, certain important nutrients including folate (as methylfolate or 5-mthfr) and vitamin B12 (as methylcobalamin) create SAMe (S-Adenosyl Methionine). SAMe functions as a methyl donor, sharing a methyl group with a variety of chemicals in your body, including DNA, proteins, toxins, hormones, and neurotransmitters, thereby supporting the body to engage in a variety of chemical reactions and effectively manage these chemicals. Dysfunction in any of the genes necessary to this process can result in poor energy production, neurotransmitter or hormonal imbalance, and disruption of proper growth and repair (Duker, 2020; Genetic Alliance, 2009).

Methylation is one of the most crucial pathways the body uses to detoxify. Methylation, which is required for many processes in the body, is a biochemical process involving the transfer of an active methyl group between molecules (Martin & Zhang, 2005). Technically speaking, methylation is the addition of a single carbon and three hydrogen atoms (called a methyl group). If you have a shortage of methyl groups, or your methylation cycle is interrupted in any way, then many bodily processes can become compromised, in which case, a variety of health problems can result (Yang et. al., 2016; Wan et. al., 2018).

Methylation is not one specific reaction that occurs in one location in the body, but many reactions taking place continually in our cells, especially in the liver (Moore, Le, & Fan, 2013).

Why Is Methylfolate and Methylation Important to Health?

This process of methylation is an integral part of many important body processes that are key factors in physical and mental health. The most basic-yet-critical process of methylation is that it converts vitamins (and most prominently folate (B9) and B12) in active forms that the body can use (without it, we can't detoxify properly) (Moore et al., 2013).

And we know that without proper detoxification, toxins build up in the body, which impact physical and mental health (Yang et. al., 2016; Wan et. al., 2018).

Methylfolate is critical to the process of methylation in helping to optimize a huge number of processes in your body, including the production of DNA, metabolism of hormones, and proper detoxification (Martin & Zhang, 2005).

Nicole's Story

Just about every mental health and autoimmune condition you could think of ran in Nicole's family.

The first time we met, Nicole said, "*My mom and brother have anxiety, and so do I. It's just the way it is.*" Sure enough, when I dug into her family's health history, the large majority of her family members suffered from a physical issue or depression and anxiety. I also discovered a lot of trauma had affected how each member managed stress. Nicole often experienced paradoxical (or opposite) reactions to her medications, so coupling that with her family history, I sent her for genetic testing.

Nicole had a single MTHFR mutation—a common alteration that impacts how medication is metabolized and inhibits vitamin absorption. Because of this, she was low in folate and B12, which adversely affected her nervous system's ability to regulate. That caused her nervous system to be in perpetual overdrive—no wonder she was always anxious!

When Nicole took that information to her physician, she was put on a bioavailable form of both nutrients and reported feeling less anxious in the first week. Her family added the supplements to their regime, as well, and worked on their diet and exercise. They also all came in for family therapy to break their behavioral patterns, especially those related to stress.

They had to learn a new way to cope and become resistant, so we worked backwards. First, we taught Nicole and her family to recover from stress, then manage it, and finally, to *view stressors differently*. That's when the magic happens—when you develop a Resiliency Mindset™. You don't see stressors the same way, so they simply don't affect you the same way.

Over time, the whole family got along better, felt healthier, and became less reactive. The tension turned to calm, and words were spoken instead of yelled.

Nicole and her family changed their mental health (without medication!).

Common Genetic Mutations That Impact Mental Health

In a moment, you'll read about the MTHFR gene and mutation. I first heard about it more than a decade ago from one of my autism mamas. Boy, did that discovery open a door for me! It was one of those "big shift" moments in my life, because once I understood what it could do to the brain and body, I realized how many of my clients surely had it. Heck, I had it, and so did my kids and most of my family.

I became even more committed to educating myself and others about detoxification and lifestyle ... and how much we could do to mitigate its effects.

MTHFR

Let's define it:

"The MTHFR gene provides instructions for making an enzyme called methylenetetrahydrofolate reductase" (US Library of Medicine, 2020). This enzyme plays a role in processing amino acids, the building blocks of proteins, and is necessary for other important compounds. Specifically, it breaks down the amino acid homocysteine.

The MTHFR gene is also responsible for converting vitamin B9 (or folate) into that usable form of methylfolate through a process called methylation, which I covered above.

Is MTHFR a Disease?

While MTHFR may be associated with many diseases, in and of itself, it is not a disease. But without proper methylation, you are at risk for a higher rate of physical and mental health issues and conditions (Wan et. al, 2018).

Is MTHFR Associated with Just One Gene, or More?

MTHFR is also the name of the genes that code for the enzyme, methylenetetrahydrofolate reductase. There are a number of these genes, but only two—C677T and A1298C—are well-studied and more widely known (Zintzaras, 2006):

- The **C677T** mutation is responsible for the conversion of homocysteine to methionine. Individuals with this mutation have high levels of homocysteine, which is associated with both heart disease and Alzheimer's (Zintzaras, 2006).

- The **A1298C** mutation is associated with SAMe and does not result in overproduction of homocysteine. Rather, this form of the MTHFR mutation is potentially associated with the inability to convert BH2 to BH4. BH4 is required for serotonin synthesis, dopamine synthesis, and ammonia detoxification (Zintzaras, 2006).

How Does the MTHFR Mutation Happen?

The MTHFR gene that codes for the enzyme, methylenetetrahydrofolate reductase, has the potential to mutate, which can either interfere with the enzyme's ability to function normally or completely inactivate it. And as you already know, genes can mutate due to environmental factors. Alternatively, we can inherit those mutated genes.

Does the MTHFR Mutation Impact Every Individual's Health?

MTHFR mutations are common. While some people are highly affected by them, others are not. It really depends on environmental factors.

We all have varying levels of the enzyme, and it can still work "well enough" to help you detoxify even with the mutation. The real problem is that we are living in a highly toxic environment, which means even if we don't have the mutation, our bodies are struggling to keep up with detoxification demands. Stress also impacts how our genes work, and people across the globe are highly stressed.

On a scale of 1 to 10, the average American reports daily stress of 3.8 or greater in 2019 (APA, 2019). During the pandemic, the average stress level has raised significantly to 5.4 (APA, 2020). And the same survey found that parents are especially feeling stressed due to the unexpected toll of working from home, educating their children, concerns about healthcare, and missing out on major milestones. We are dealing with a lot!

So, our environment and stress levels have a lot to do with gene mutation. And when the gene is mutated, the capacity to convert vitamin B9 into methylfolate is reduced by 40-70 percent, so there often isn't enough enzyme to support detoxification. With MTHFR mutations, the body's demand for the enzyme is often greater than the supply, and that is when toxins and myco-toxins build up in the brain and body and contribute to physical and mental health problems (Wan et. al, 2018).

Remember, toxins have to get out; otherwise, they stay in our organs, including our brain. But don't worry—in this book, we dive into how to get those toxins out—and every parent can do it.

Which Health and Mental Health Conditions Are Linked to MTHFR?

There are dozens of health conditions associated with the MTHFR genetic mutation, including a long list of mental health conditions in addition to those mentioned above. Research has associated MTHFR with 42 clinical disorders (Yang et. al., 2016; Wan et. al., 2018). Research denotes that with MTHFR, there is also an increased risk for many disorders, including vascular and neurodegenerative diseases, autoimmune disorders, birth defects, diabetes, renal disease, osteoporosis, neuropsychiatric disorders, and cancer (Brustolin, Giugliani, & Félix, 2010).

Conditions associated with MTHFR gene mutations include:

- Mental health and behavior disorders (Yang et. al., 2016; Wan et. al., 2018)

- Anxiety (Yang et. al., 2016; Wan et. al., 2018)

- Depression (Yang et. al., 2016; Wan et. al., 2018)

- Autism (Sadeghiyeh et. al., 2019)

- ADD/ADHD (Hazma et. al., 2019)

- Sensory issues or learning difficulties (El-Baz et. al., 2017; Wan et. al., 2018)

- Adrenal issues (Smith et. al., 2014)

- Chronic pain (Smith et. al., 2014)

- Recurrent miscarriage (Sah et. al., 2018)

- Preterm labor (Nan & Li, 2015)

- Pre-eclampsia (Salimi et. al., 2015)

- Cardiovascular diseases, such as blood clots, stroke, and heart attack (Moll & Varga, 2015)

- Pulmonary embolism (Moll & Varga, 2015)

- General chronic health issues (Moll & Varga, 2015)

- Homocysteinemia (abnormally high levels of homocysteine in the blood or urine (Moll & Varga, 2015)

- Migraines (Stuart et. al., 2012)

- Peripheral neuropathy, a neurological condition that damages the nerves (Mottaghi et. al., 2019)

- Microcephaly, a condition present at birth in which the head is smaller than usual (Genetic and Rare Diseases Center, 2020)

- Scoliosis, an abnormal curvature of the spine (Munoz et. al., 2015)

- Tongue and lip ties, cleft palate (Iris et. al., 2003; Lidral & Moreno, 2005)

COMT Mutation

The COMT mutation is lesser known than the MTHFR mutation, but is equally tied to psychiatric disorders (Montag, Jurkiewicz & Reuter, 2012; Taylor, 2018). It is even linked to personality disorders (Montag, Jurkiewicz & Reuter, 2012), which have a higher rate of suicidal ideation and self-harm behaviors. It is a mutation that many of my patients are surprised to hear about, and they often wonder why they hadn't learned about it before. Some of my most treatment-resistant cases of anxiety, depression, and PANS/PANDAS frequently have both the MTHFR and COMT mutation.

COMT is an enzyme that uses methyl groups to remove catechols such as dopamine from the brain. The COMT gene provides instructions for making an enzyme called catechol-O-methyltransferase. Two versions of this enzyme are made from the gene. The first is membrane-bound catechol-O-methyltransferase (MB-COMT), which is mainly produced by nerve cells in the brain. The second form of the enzyme is soluble catechol-O-methyltransferase (S-COMT), which helps control the levels of certain hormones. Other tissues, including the liver, kidneys, and blood produce this shorter form (US National Library of Medicine, 2020).

The COMT gene is responsible for deactivating catecholamines, which are hormones made by your adrenal glands when under stress. The COMT gene's job is to bring your heartbeat down to normal levels and restore balance to your brain and body by breaking down those stress neurotransmitters and hormones (US National Library of Medicine, 2020).

Individuals with COMT mutations (COMT+ or COMT++) have decreased neurotransmitter activity. COMT is important for memory, attention, judgement, motivation, and other executive functions. COMT is also associated with higher levels of stress hormones, including cortisol and HPA axis dysfunction, which leads to difficulties managing stress.

Determining whether COMT is over- or under-functioning influences the proper diet and supplementation needed to support your system. It is also important to know your COMT status in terms of understanding your body's ability to tolerate methylated forms of vitamins in your diet supplementation (Hosák, 2007).

Individuals who are COMT++ are less likely to tolerate supplementation with methyl groups (i.e., SAMe, methyl B12, and so on). On the other hand, individuals who are COMT– typically do well with the supplementation of methyl groups (Montag, Jurkiewicz & Reuter, 2012). This enzyme is especially important to the prefrontal cortex, which organizes and coordinates information from other parts of the brain. This area is the "job manager" of the brain and is responsible for planning, inhibition of behaviors, abstract thinking, emotion, working, and short-term memory. It also affects personality, as the frontal lobes essentially act as the 'braking system' that helps us make decisions and regulate behaviors.

People with a COMT mutation use fewer methyl groups and inactivate dopamine less efficiently, which affects mental health. The COMT mutation is associated with mood disorders, schizophrenia, bipolar disorder, psychosis (Funke, 2005), OCD, addiction, ADHD, and eating disorders (Hosák, 2007). COMT++ individuals have higher dopamine levels, as they do not break down dopamine efficiently, and COMT– individuals have lower dopamine levels (Montag, Jurkiewicz & Reuter, 2012).

My experience is consistent with the research; I have found many highly anxious individuals with treatment-resistant anxiety to have the COMT mutation.

Melinda's Story

I clearly recall Melinda, the poor mother of two anxious kids who went from medication to medication and talk therapist to talk therapist without improvement. She did well with neurofeedback and somatic psychotherapy, but I couldn't get her to at least eighty percent improvement (and she was working hard!).

When I finally convinced her of the importance of genetic and nutrient testing (her GP had told her that it wouldn't help), she learned she was COMT ++.

With dietary and supplement tweaks, Melinda felt calmer than she ever had her whole life! *"I didn't know it was possible to not have that constant anxiety hum,"* she said. And until that constant stress feeling was gone, Melinda hadn't even realized how much it affected her. She of course got her daughters tested, and sure enough, they had it, too. Melinda was relieved to know that her kids would never have to experience what she went through as she struggled to find answers.

MTR Mutation

The MTR mutation can impact our cognitive processing and emotional health because it impacts how we use the B12. B12 is an important nutrient necessary for our central nervous system to work properly, and without it, a host of CNS issues can result, including anxiety and depression (Lewis et al, 2013). The MTR mutation is also associated with intellectual disability (Dutta et. al., 2011).

The MTR gene provides instructions for making an enzyme called methionine synthase, whose job it is to convert the amino acid homocysteine to another amino acid called methionine (US National Library of Medicine, 2020).

The body needs methionine to make proteins and other important compounds and to function properly. Methionine synthase requires methylcobalamin (a form of vitamin B12) and another enzyme called methionine synthase reductase, which is produced from the MTRR gene (US National Library of Medicine, 2020).

The MTR A2756G mutation causes an up-regulation in this gene, which results in an increase in activity of the enzyme, rather than a decrease. That increase can result in the depletion of B12 in susceptible individuals, and B12 is required for a multitude of CNS functions and is incredibly important for cognitive functioning (Dutta et. al., 2011).

MTRR Mutation

The MTRR mutation, which is linked to Down syndrome and schizophrenia (Misiak et. al., 2016), is another genetic mutation that impacts how we use and process the B vitamins. (You're catching on to how important the B vitamins are to our mental health, aren't you? I'm sure you're surprised, too, because you've likely never learned about the science behind it … until now!)

The MTRR gene provides instructions for making an enzyme called methionine synthase reductase. The methionine synthase reductase enzyme works in conjunction with the MTR enzyme to help with the conversion of homocysteine to methionine by regenerating B12. Specifically, it remethylates the cobalamin (B12) to methylcobalamin (a more bioavailable form of B12) and regenerates oxidized methionine synthase (the conversion process), so that conversion of homocysteine to methionine can continue (US National Library of Medicine, 2020).

The MTRR A66G mutation reduces the activity of this enzyme, resulting in even further depletion of B12 in susceptible individuals (US National Library of Medicine, 2020).

CBS Mutation

The CBS genetic mutation is associated with intellectual disability (Dutta et al, 2005), cognitive impairments, and dementia (Ramos et al, 2020).

The CBS gene provides instructions for making an enzyme called cystathionine beta-synthase. This enzyme converts the amino acid homocysteine to cysteine (US National Library of Medicine, 2020).

Individuals with this mutation generate high levels of cysteine. The C699T and the C1080T mutations cause up-regulations in the enzyme's activity. Moreover, high levels of cysteine in the body often lead to the conversion of cysteine to taurine and sulfate, rather than to glutathione, which is the master antioxidant of the body. Individuals with this mutation produce increased levels of sulfur groups, increased ammonia, and decreased glutathione. Glutathione plays a role in many chemical reactions in your body and is needed to combat free radicals that damage the body. Without proper glutathione, detoxification, mitochondrial function, and overall health are affected (Pizzorno, 2014).

SUOX Mutation

Individuals with the SUOX mutation cannot properly process sulfur-containing foods and turn the sulfites into less-toxic sulfates. It is linked to food and environmental allergies, and many people with allergy sensitivities carry the SUOX gene (Ortiz & Barnes, 2015). Schwarz and Belaidi (2013) denote the importance of sulfite oxidase in human health and disease, and the SUOX mutation has been associated with neurological problems such as seizures.

The SUOX gene provides instructions for making an enzyme called sulfite oxidase, which helps break down protein building blocks (amino acids) that contain sulfur when they are no longer needed. Sulfur-containing molecules called sulfites are converted to other molecules called sulfates by adding an oxygen atom in a process called "oxidation." The SUOX pathway requires molybdenum to function properly. This gene is important for detoxification. Individuals with cystathionine beta-synthase (CBS) up regulations need to support the SUOX pathway by supplementing with molybdenum in order to support the detoxification process (US National Library of Medicine, 2020).

Brain-Derived Neurotrophic Factor - BDNF Mutation

BDNF is one of the most-studied neurotrophic factors in the central nervous system because of its importance in the development and maintenance of normal brain function (Cattaneo et. al., 2006). *"Neurotrophic factors are a family of proteins that are responsible for the growth and survival of nerve cells during development, and for the maintenance of adult nerve cells"* (Liou, 2006). BDNF regulates neuronal differentiation, migration, survival, and synaptic plasticity. Expressed in the prefrontal cortex (PFC) and hippocampus, BDNF has been implicated to play a role in the etiology of several psychiatric disorders including depression, anxiety, ADHD, and the biology of learning and memory (Cattaneo et. al., 2006; Friedel, 2005).

It is believed that epigenetic factors such as DNA methylation are contributing factors to the link between BDNF and the development of psychiatric disorders (Cattaneo et. al., 2006). BDNF has been shown to influence synaptic plasticity by modulating hippocampal long-term potentiation. The Val66Met polymorphism is associated with reduced BDNF secretion, depression, and altered stress reactivity. Several studies indicate that physical activity may improve cognition, working memory, and depression in Met allele carriers and may be implemented as therapy, if clinically indicated (Mata, Thompson, & Gotlib, 2010).

D-Amino Acid Oxidase (DAO)

DAO processes histamine and expels histamine from the gut, skin, and brain, whether it derives from allergies or a food source. It ensures a steady maintenance of histamine allowing multiple chemical reactions in the body to occur. Too much histamine over-excites the immune system, resulting in skin rashes, migraine headaches, and allergy-like symptoms. The DAO mutation is associated with psychiatric conditions such as schizophrenia (Yang et. al., 2013), postpartum depression (Maintz et. al., 2008), ADHD, and other mental health and cognitive issues (Vinita et. al., 2017). Changing to a low histamine diet and adding B6, B12, iron, copper, vitamin C, zinc and magnesium can all support DAO in properly modulating histamine.

What Can I Do If I Suspect My Child Has a Genetic Mutation?

First, I recommend getting tested for genetic mutations and the specific nutrients they affect. Working with a functional physician to look at specific mutations and nutrients you might be lacking or missing is very helpful, as there are supplements and treatments that can help. Identifying those unique snippets allows a practitioner to take an individual approach to treatment.

These mutations impact how you detoxify and how the CNS regulates, so environmental changes can go a long way in reducing and reversing mental health. If you recall, Nicole and her family have all struggled with mental health for more than one generation. Nicole may have been the first one to break that cycle, but her whole family benefited from understanding that they all had the MTHFR genetic mutation. They added folate and B12 to their diets, and that began their health journey. Next, they worked on stress management and did some deep psychotherapy to learn new ways to cope and communicate. It wasn't an overnight fix, but they took the time to get unstuck and break free from generational stress! They didn't let genetics, clinical diagnosis, and behaviors stop them. Healing is never easy or convenient, but they shifted all that negative energy into the work that it took get unstuck, and they never looked back. Today, Nicole and her family invest in their health, which means they do a lot of things from the list below.

If there is a known genetic mutation, the following suggestions can be helpful:

- Follow an anti-inflammatory diet.

- Limit exposure to nitrates (Slote, Luu, Georg, & Osier, 2019).

- Add detoxification techniques and therapies into your child's regime.

- Avoid nitrous oxide (with MTHFR).

- Reduce your overall toxic load.

- Avoid X-Rays whenever possible (Slote et. al., 2019).

- Avoid smoking and second-hand smoke (Slote et. al., 2019).

- Follow a healthy lifestyle, including stress management.

- Improve sleep.

How Can I Improve My Child's Detoxification While Addressing the MTHFR Mutation and Other Mutations That Impact the Methylation Process?

While the MTHFR gene mutation inhibits the way the body processes folic acid and other important B vitamins, researchers believe that we can diminish its effects through nutrition, lifestyle, and reducing environmental toxins.

Supplements to Improve Methylation

The most well-known and evidenced supplements, methylated forms of B9 and B12, can counter the effects of the mutation and help support necessary bodily processes for detoxification (Mahmood, 2014; National Institutes of Health, 2020). These supplements are readily available and come in multiple forms that your child can ingest.

Improve Digestion and Gut Health

Improving digestion and overall gut health can help a multitude of problems, including lessening the impact of the MTHFR mutation. Having a healthy gut means you have balanced gut bacteria, which are known to influence our brain chemistry, hormones, sleep cycles, detoxification, blood sugar, and overall physical and mental health. Good gut flora help produce and absorb B vitamins and folate, so taking probiotics is a good idea (see Chapter 6 for information about probiotics).

On the flip side, we know that poor digestion prevents us from absorbing folate, B-12, and other vital nutrients from food. More specifically, gut problems can impair the methylation cycle, which is necessary for detoxification (Arrieta et. al., 2014; National Institutes of Health, 2020).

Focus on Diet, Nutrition, and Hydration

Eat healing and nourishing foods such as bone broth, gelatin, and fermented foods to support the gut and immune system. Focus on whole foods with reduced inflammatory components and eliminate foods such as wheat, those with gluten and dairy, and processed foods to build gut flora and reduce inflammation. It is important to eat the rainbow of colors from fruits and vegetables and rotate your foods. You know I love an anti-inflammatory diet, because it has the science to back it up, and it is power-packed with nutrients to support the brain and body.

Adding in at least two cups of dark, leafy green veggies daily provides you with natural folate, which is necessary for proper methylation. You can add them to a smoothie, toss them into soups and salads, or eat them raw. Getting kids to love their green veggies early in life is important, but it's never too late.

Sulfur is a key component of glutathione, which is our master detoxifier, so eating enough sulfur-containing foods is great for supporting detoxification. Sources include garlic, onions, and cruciferous vegetables like kale, broccoli, cauliflower, cabbage, watercress, and bok choy.

Eating foods that are high in the glutathione precursors—cysteine, glycine, and glutamate—can help boost your glutathione. Sources of these important amino acids include organic omega-3-enriched eggs, safe fish, and organic lean meats.

Adding in curcumin can raise glutathione levels in the liver and support detoxification. It's also a powerful anti-inflammatory food and pain modulator. You can add it to food, tea, or take a curcumin supplement.

It is important to drink a lot of chlorine-filtered water to keep the body hydrated to better remove toxins. We never think about how important hydration is, but it really helps clear toxins while supporting every process in the body.

Reduce Stress and Sleep at Least 7 Hours per Night

We dig into both of these topics in their own chapters later, but reducing stress and getting enough sleep are lifelines for mental health.

We are going through life with stressed, hyperactivated nervous systems, and our children are no different. They are tired, cranky, and unfocused. Calming the CNS is critical for so many bodily functions that directly impact physical and mental health. We can't think, behave, or heal properly with a stress-hyperactivated CNS. A nervous system that is in a constant hyper state can't work properly, either, and that includes detoxification.

Adults should get between seven and 10 hours of sleep nightly. Children need anywhere from nine to 15 hours depending on their age (until age 18). If you're not getting anywhere near that now, don't feel defeated. Instead, commit to working toward it.

Boost Glutathione

Glutathione is often referred to as the "master" antioxidant. It helps with detoxification, because it directly binds heavy metals and helps make them more water-soluble, so they can be eliminated in bile and urine (Meister, 1991). Low levels of glutathione are associated with a long list of clinical and physical issues (Minich & Brown, 2019).

Besides direct supplementation, adding foods high in glutathione and sulfur, taking vitamin C, omegas, and curcumin, drinking green tea, getting enough sleep, and exercising daily are all ways to boost glutathione (Minich & Brown, 2019).

Increase Detoxification Support

Improper methylation interferes with detoxification, so it is critical to add in detoxification support to one's daily regime. Infrared saunas, ion foot baths, Epsom salt (or magnesium) salt baths, dry skin brushing, and increased exercise are all effective tools that promote detoxification. Exercise in particular improves lymphatic drainage and helps to clean the blood of substances that can be harmful to the brain. We will go into all the ways you can detoxify in the next chapter, but it is important to mention here.

Caution: Watch out for Drug Interactions

Having the MTHFR mutation means you have a higher chance of drug interaction due to difficulties with methylation and the subsequent detoxification and CNS issues. There are numerous psychiatric medications that a child with the MTHFR mutation will react to. There is testing available, so children and adults should refrain from taking a psychiatric medication without first undergoing genetic testing to determine which medications are safe to take. It is also best to avoid folic acid blocking drugs such as birth control or Methotrexate, which increase homocysteine, medications such as Nitrous Oxide (most used in dentistry), and antacids, as they block absorption of vitamin B12 and other nutrients.

Can MTHFR Interfere with My Child's Response to Medications?

Yes, the MTHFR mutation can interfere with one's response to various medications, including antidepressants and arthritis and chemotherapy drugs (Schwahn & Rozen, 2000-2013). This mutation can increase the risk of having an adverse reaction to nitrous oxide anesthesia (Nagele et. al., 2008), as previously stated. Therefore, individuals with an MTHFR mutation should speak with their physicians or dentists prior to undergoing any procedure that requires anesthesia.

General Nutrient Recommendations for MTHFR mutations:

- Methylfolate
- Methylcobalamin
- Betaine in the form of TMG
- NAC
- Glutathione
- Pyridoxal-5-phosphate (vitamin B6)
- Riboflavin (vitamin B2)
- Curcumin
- Mixed tocopherols (vitamin E)
- Silymarin (Milk Thistle)
- EPA/DHA
- Phosphatidylcholine
- Nattokinase
- Vitamin C
- Vitamin D3
- Comprehensive multivitamin/multimineral
- Probiotics

Should I Get Tested or Test My Child for MTHFR or Other Mutations?

If you think you have the signs and symptoms of this mutation, then yes, it is a good idea to get tested. I also suggest checking your vitamin B levels since they seem to be most impacted. There are also labs available that look at other important nutrients such as glutathione, essential fatty acids, and so on. This may or may not be covered by insurance.

You can get tested through private genetic websites, but be careful; these databases can be public and used in a variety of ways. If you choose this often-cheaper option, be sure to protect your identity.

We covered a lot of super-technical stuff in this chapter! Hopefully, your takeaway is that there is a science behind how our brain works and our subsequent mental health, and there are A LOT of things we can do to 'hack' into our system to improve it and reduce symptoms. You *can* control stress. You *can* control your diet. You *can* add supplements. You *can* exercise. And you *can* make lifestyle changes.

That is what this book is all about.

Remember, just take one step at a time. Start somewhere, and stay consistent. CHANGE WILL HAPPEN.

It's Gonna Be OK! **And if you'd like even more support, check out my Get Unstuck Program™, because I walk you through it, personally:** www.getunstuckprogram.com.

Either way, you've got this!

Next, we dive into detoxification, so you can gain a more thorough understanding of how to work effectively with your genetic mutations.

Dr. Roseann-Capanna-Hodge

Chapter 9 – Detoxification: A Little-Known Game-Changer in Mental Health

Pillar 5: Detoxification

What Is Detoxification?

"Detoxification" is one of those buzz words you hear a lot about but aren't sure what it really means or how it helps. It has become a popular topic, because so many children and adults have chronic health issues from asthma, eczema, ADHD, etc., and the numbers are increasing. The excessive toxins in our environment are in part responsible for the rise.

In the last chapter, you learned about how genetic mutations interfere with the detoxification process. Now, we dive into what detoxification is and how we can improve it.

Time and time again, I see issues with detoxification coupled with a stressed, hyperactive CNS as major barriers to reversing mental health and with healing in general. If a good detoxification regimen can help my most challenging cases of PANS/PANDAS, Lyme disease, depression, and OCD, it most certainly can aide in reducing symptoms associated with other mental health and cognitive issues.

Detoxification involves the removal of toxins or substances from the body to improve overall health, gut health, and mental/cognitive functioning, and to increase energy and manage weight (National Center for Complementary and Integrative Medicine, 2019). By adding detoxification methods to our daily regime, we can support the body's ability to excrete toxins and improve our overall health.

Changing one's diet is the most powerful method of improving detoxification. Most detoxification regimens involve adding fruits and vegetables, especially dark leafy greens, as well as organic, whole, and unprocessed foods (Hodges & Minich, 2015). It goes without saying, but when detoxifying through diet, it is important to avoid adding additional toxic substances like alcohol, processed foods, sugar, and so on. No one is perfect, but staying the course when you and/or your child is suffering is important.

There are two kinds of detoxification—internal and external—and they both can be very effective in eliminating toxins. Internal detoxification involves eating differently and/or taking supplements, tinctures, juices, etc. to cleanse the internal organs, particularly the liver, which can contain harmful toxins. External detoxification involves using methods to excrete toxins through the skin and sweat glands. There are many ways to support the excretion of toxins through the skin, including sauna, ion foot baths, massage, exercise, etc.

Carly's Story

When I met Carly, she was a teen with Lyme who, despite receiving excellent medical care, couldn't seem to fully recover. She was plagued with anxiety and a constant list of infections that just made life hard. She was too tired to go out with friends, or to even get through the school day. After a couple of colds, she had a major setback, and hadn't been to school for a month.

Carly's mom had caught an episode of a podcast I was on during which I talked about Lyme and PANS/PANDAS, as well as how improper detoxification and chronic stress are often the two biggest barriers to healing. She realized these things were likely what was holding her daughter back.

From her QEEG brain map, I could see that Carly had all the classic signs of someone with chronic inflammation, stress, and poor gut health, which all impacted her mental and physical health.

We put a detoxification plan in place that incorporated homeopathy, diet, exercise, and of course, stress management. This was by no means easy for a teenager, but her alternative was feeling like garbage and missing out on life, so she was in.

Since anxiety was such an issue for Carly, she used PEMF and neurofeedback to help get her nervous system out of its hyperactive state. As her anxiety lessened and her CNS learned to get into a calmer rhythm, she felt better, and her body was better able to excrete and eliminate toxins from both infectious disease and the everyday.

Carly was able to return to school part time, and within a couple of months, she was back to full time! She went on to graduate high school and college. Now, she continues to incorporate detoxification, healthy eating, exercise, and stress management into her daily life. It is a joy to see her thrive and transform her own life!

Why Is Detoxification So Important?

Even though the body *should* be fully capable of ridding itself of toxins without any help, the reality is that we are bombarded with chemicals in the air, water, our food, and environment. There are over 100,000 chemicals in our environment alone, and we simply can't keep up. Our children are born with over 200 chemicals in their system (Goodman, 2009). And research denotes that chemical exposures have an effect on health and mental health (Chin, 2010, and Dunaev et. al, 2008, and Ramos, 2004). Chemical exposure isn't going away, either. In fact, it is increasing, with over 1,000 new chemicals discovered every year (Roundtable on Environmental Health Sciences, 2014).

Plus, as you learned in the last chapter, our kids are dealing with genetic mutations that interfere with detoxification more and more.

Without proper detoxification, these toxins end up in our organs, including our brain, and tax out our body, which of course impacts our mental health.

Detoxification doesn't just get rid of harmful substances. Our body's ability to detoxify also impacts the overall functioning of the immune system. If the body is overworking to get rid of toxins, then it can't take care of its other duties, which include dealing with bacteria and viruses.

The good news is we can do a lot to support our body's ability to detoxify, and I'm covering that below.

What Are the Phases of Detoxification?

It is important to know that there are three phases in the detoxification process. We often think of it as a single process, when in fact each of the three distinct phases are necessary and must work in unison to clear toxins from the cells.

Phase 1: Functionalization

In Phase 1, volatile toxins are converted into small substances. A group of enzymes transform toxins to be more water-soluble for excretion as well as make them easier to bind with other molecules in the next phase (Hodges & Minich, 2015). Antioxidants such as C and E, minimizing toxic exposures, and eating organic food help in the Phase 1 detoxification process. In addition, adding supplements such as N-acetyl cysteine (NAC) to help produce the master antioxidant, glutathione, as well as B vitamins, magnesium, selenium, and zinc is very helpful in this detoxification phase (Schaeffer, 2014).

Phase 2: Conjugation

Phase 2 is called "the conjugation pathway" because it takes the products from Phase 1 and binds them with Phase 2 substances (liver cells add another substance, such as cysteine, glycine, or a sulfur molecule) to make those substances less harmful and more water-soluble for easier excretion. Phase 2 is about reducing the toxicity of the substances to make them easier to get out of the body in Phase 3. This process uses six different pathways to take water-soluble metabolites out of the body through bile, urine, and stool, and requires sulfur, amino acids, molybdenum, vitamin B12, and glutathione (Schaeffer, 2014). Sulfur-containing foods and other nutrients, including flavonoids and bitter herbs to stimulate bile, can help the process (Hodges & Minich, 2015).

Phase 3: Elimination/Excretion

Phase 3 is when waste is removed through the bowels or excreted through the skin, which is our largest organ. In Phase 2, the conjugates have been made water-soluble, and the toxicity of those substances are reduced and ready to be removed from the body. Bile is a critical part of Phase 3, as your liver uses it as a way of getting rid of waste products through its secretion, which leads to the final step of the body cleaning its own liver (Boyer, 2013). Phase 3 requires hydration for the kidneys to do their job properly, as well as proper functioning of the gastro-intestinal tract to promote elimination. Certain foods support the elimination of toxins, so adding those high in fiber, alginate, and chlorella as well as herbs such as cilantro and parsley, sulfur-containing foods, and garlic and onions are easy and flavorful ways to support the body's elimination process (Hodges & Minich, 2015).

What Is the Impact of Genetic Mutations on Detoxification?

In Chapter 7, we covered how critical the methylation process is for the body to detoxify. There are several genetic mutations that impact the methylation process. And without proper detoxification, toxins build up in the body, which impact physical and mental health. Moreover, toxins can alter and change how genes are expressed, which has been linked to many diseases and disorders (U.S. National Library of Medicine, 2020) and many psychiatric conditions (Yang et. al., 2016; Wan et. al., 2018).

Mycotoxins and Gut Health

In recent years, mycotoxins have become an increasing issue interfering with the physical and mental health of my patients.

Mold is a mycotoxin, and we are learning just how much it can cause chronic, difficult-to-pin-down health problems. I have worked with several families who have had to leave their homes after getting sick from mold. In one case, a mom and her toddler daughter both suffered from non-stop sinus infections and skin rashes. The child had severe behaviors, tics, and rage. But after leaving the home, things got better, although they had to follow a strict detoxification protocol to really turn their physical and mental health around.

So what are mycotoxins and where do they come from? They are naturally occurring toxins that form from fungi or molds and grow on crops (World Health Organization, 2018). They are also used in drugs due to their pharmacological properties (Bennett & Klich, 2003). Mycotoxins are stable enough to survive food processing and can be passed from eating the meat of animals who have consumed them. They enter the body primarily through ingestion, but can also enter through inhalation and absorption (Haschek & Voss, 2013).

"Mycotoxins can cause a variety of adverse health effects and pose a serious health threat to both humans and livestock" (World Health Organization, 2018). Mycotoxins can cause immediate, acute illness, as well as long-term adverse effects such as immune deficiency, cancer (World Health Organization, 2018), allergies, and asthma (Ratnaseelan et. al., 2018). Exposure to mold has also been associated with malaise, fatigue, and cognitive impairment (Ratnaseelan et. al., 2018).

The bacteria found in the gastrointestinal tract is part of the microbiome. It plays an important role in regulating the immune system and digestion and has a direct effect on the brain (University of Pittsburgh, 2020). And we know how important our gut health is and how it is tied to our brain health.

Mycotoxins can directly impact the health of the gut, as they cause disturbances, especially in the intestinal epithelial cells (Liew & Mohd-Redzwan, 2018). *"There are types of mycotoxins that can cause gastroenteritis in humans such as Agroclavine, Setoclavine, Chanoclavine, and Elymoclavine"* (Haschek & Voss, 2013).

The Effects of Mycotoxins on the Brain

Should we be worried about the effect of mycotoxins on the developing brain? The answer is, "Of course!" Toxins have a known effect on the developing brain and on health (Lanphear, 2015). Systems in the body are in place to try to protect the brain from toxic exposures, but as previously discussed, the body simply can't keep up with the more than 100,000 known toxins in our environment.

The brain is protected by something called the blood-brain barrier (BBB). The BBB is a semi-permeable border that selectively allows some materials to cross but stops others.

It is a barrier between the brain's blood vessels and the cells and other components that make up brain tissue. The BBB's role is to protect against toxins or pathogens in the blood that could cause injury or infection in the brain and to allow important nutrients to get to the brain. The other and lesser-known role of the BBB is to help maintain CNS homeostasis by keeping a constant level of hormones, nutrients, and water in the brain. *"This precise control of CNS homeostasis allows for proper neuronal function and also protects the neural tissue from toxins and pathogens, and alterations of these barrier properties are an important component of pathology and progression of different neurological diseases"* (Daneman & Prat, 2015).

Thankfully, the BBB is there to protect us, but the BBB isn't impregnable, as there are events and substances that cause it to break down, including physical trauma such as head injury, high blood pressure, neurological disease, certain medications, radiation, infection, inflammation, and developmental formation issues present at birth (Ballabh, Braun & Nedergaard, 2004: Daneman & Prat, 2015). While we can't control everything, we can do what we can to prevent inflammation and avoid medications that open up the BBB.

How Toxins Affect Mental Health

How can two people be affected differently by toxic exposures? Well, it has a lot to do with how our body detoxifies. And today's children have a lot more exposure to toxins, which we know affects the developing brain (Lanphear, 2015) and is correlated to neurological and cognitive issues (Lanphear, Vorhees, & Bellinger, 2005).

Toxins directly impact the brain and how it functions, and the health of our central nervous system determines our mental health. The blood-brain barrier (BBB) helps to maintain CNS homeostasis, which allows for proper neuronal function (Daneman & Prat, 2015). When too many toxins build up inside of the body, the BBB can break down and let in toxins. Free radicals, which can contribute to a host of physical and mental health issues, can also compromise the BBB (Zheng, 2001). When toxins enter the CNS, they can impact neurotransmitter function, including dopamine, glutamate, GABA, and serotonin (Camardiel et. al., 2004), which you are now well aware are important in how we regulate behaviors and emotions. A disruption in either inhibitory or excitatory neurotransmitter functioning can directly affect mental health and lead to clinical conditions such as anxiety, OCD, focus problems, and depression.

Mental Health Symptoms of Toxic Exposure

Toxic exposures impact the central nervous system in its homeostasis (its set point) and neurotransmitter functioning of the brain, so it can produce a host of symptoms. Specific toxins, such as mold and mycotoxins, can affect the CNS, *"directly or through immune cell activation, thus contributing to neurodevelopmental disorders such as autism spectrum disorder"* (Ratnaseelan et. al, 2018).

Symptoms of toxic exposure include:

- Brain fog

- Decrease in attention and focus

- Fatigue

- Anxiety

- Slowed cognitive processing

- Memory difficulties

- Mood issues

- Emotional imbalance

- Neurodevelopmental disorders

(Daneman & Prat, 2015; Ratnaseelan et. al, 2018)

We can't ignore the crossover with mental health issues. Toxic exposures and improper detoxification can exacerbate pre-existing conditions or cause new symptoms to appear. With the high rate of genetic mutations impacting how we clear toxins from our body, adding detoxification protocol to your regime is a logical step to reduce and reverse mental health symptoms.

Are There Side Effects of Detoxification?

Yes, you can have side effects when starting any kind of detoxification program. As toxins release from your organs, they can flood back into your system if you aren't excreting them properly. It is very important to work with a medical provider. It is also best to start off very slowly, especially if you have had a chronic disease for a long time or since birth. There is a belief that experiencing detoxification side effects indicates a *"healing response,"* but I believe it just means you are supporting all the phases of detoxification, especially the excretion process. Moreover, specific organs may need additional support.

Detoxification symptoms can include:

- Fatigue

- Headaches

- Brain fog

- Irritability

- Joint pain

- Issues using the bathroom

- Discharge or mucus

- Rashes

- Worsening of symptoms

*Check with your doctor if any of these detoxification symptoms present when beginning any new protocol.

Detoxification Basics

The daily practice of detoxification can help your body's ability to get rid of toxins, which can have a direct and positive impact on physical and mental health. There are many easy, little things you can do to promote the excretion of toxins.

The ability in which the body can detoxify itself is based on the diet a person follows, the over-all lifestyle he or she lives, the environment in which he/she lives in, the medications taken, and genetics. That said, we can control our diet and lifestyle to improve not only detoxification, but our overall health.

A Good Detoxification Plan Includes:

- Diet

- Homeopathy

- Addition of nutrients

- Incorporating lifestyle strategies

- Sleep

- Stress management

- Exercise

- Hydration

- Reduced toxin exposure

- Reduced processed foods and sugar

- Reduced consumption of alcohol in adults

Using Food to Detox

We have control over what our children eat, even though they may be stinkers about it! Diet is the first line of defense in supporting the body's ability to detoxify, because it is effective (Hodges & Minich, 2015) and the most common physician-recommended means (Allen et. al, 2011). The easiest way to start is by working off this list and committing to adding in one or two foods a day. Pay attention to your or your child's body and behavioral responses. Some-times, the changes are noticeable, while other times, it really takes a pairing with a stress-man-agement therapy such as yoga or neurofeedback.

Foods That Help with Detoxification:

- Allium Vegetables - astaxanthin
- Apiaceous vegetables - caffeic acid
- Black Raspberry - catechins (including EGCG)
- Black Tea - chrysin
- Blueberry - curcumin
- Chamomile tea - daidzein
- Chicory root - ellagic acid
- Citrus - ferulic acid
- Coffee - fish oil
- Cruciferous vegetables - genistein
- Dandelion tea
- Garlic
- Ghee
- Ginger
- Grapefruit
- Green tea
- Honeybush tea
- Peppermint tea
- Pomegranate
- Purple sweet potato
- Rooibos tea
- Rosemary
- Soybean/black soybean
- Turmeric

(Hodges & Minich, 2015; Schaeffer, 2014)

Nutrients Found in Foods That Naturally Help with Detoxification

While I am a big fan of supplements, I also know that food can give us a lot of what we need to support our mental and physical health. Tweaks to our diet to increase nutrition and support detoxification can go a long way. I can't even tell you how many people I've worked with who had depression and thyroid issues and have improved their health with the addition of selenium dense Brazil nuts! Remember, just start with one or two things, to avoid feeling overwhelmed.

- **Vitamin C:** broccoli, Brussels sprouts, cauliflower, leafy greens, peppers, lemons, limes, kiwi

- **Bioflavonoids:** citrus, green peppers, cherries, grapes

- **Carotenes:** sweet potato, carrots, pumpkins

- **Vitamin E:** egg yolks, liver, nuts, seeds, leafy greens

- **CoQ10:** organ and some muscle meats, fatty fish, legumes, spinach, cauliflower, broccoli, oranges, strawberries

- **Thiols:** garlic, onions, cruciferous vegetables

- **Sulfur:** broccoli, cauliflower, cabbage, Brussels sprouts, kale, onions, garlic, leeks, shallots, chives, beans

- **Silymarin:** milk thistle, artichoke, turmeric

- **Manganese:** seafood, nuts, seeds

- **Selenium:** Brazil nuts

- **Zinc:** red meat, shellfish

(Hodges & Minich, 2015; Schaeffer, 2014)

Using Homeopathy to Improve Detoxification

Homeopathy is a safe and natural form of healing based on the belief that the body can heal itself and the use of homeopathy can aid in the process. It is believed that with homeopathy, the blood can be cleaned, and the liver, intestines, kidneys, and skin can be stimulated to promote the release of toxins with very small doses. Homeopathic products come from plants, minerals, or insects and animals. They can come in the form of sugar pellets to be placed under the tongue, ointments, creams, gels, drops, or tablets (National Center for Integrative and Complementary Health, 2018).

With homeopathy for detoxification, there are both organ-specific remedies and combinations that can be useful. Draining one or more of the organs—liver, kidney, gallbladder, lymphatic system, colon, lungs, and the skin—is often a recommended part of a detoxification program for those with chronic disease states because of homeopathy's gentle-but-effective manner.

For my patients with chronic long-term mental health and physical issues such as PANS/PAN-

DAS, Lyme, anxiety, depression, and so on, homeopathy is essential, because there is almost always a detoxification issue with chronic mental health conditions. We need to be gentle when there are layers, like within these conditions. In other words, there is really never one issue, but rather several physical and mental health issues tangled together.

Jacinda's Story

When I met Jacinda, she was a young woman with Lyme, PANS, anxiety, depression, vertigo, and multiple sclerosis. She was only 23, but had spent more than a dozen years dealing with several tick-borne illnesses, and it took at least five years to even get that diagnosis. By the time she got to me, Jacinda had been to almost 30 doctors.

Poor Jacinda was struggling with everything from walking to watching television. She was so super-sensitive to any kind of treatment or medication that she would often destabilize. I knew we had to start with homeopathic organ detoxification, and really, with one drop at a time and the most gradual increase possible. We weren't going to jump into PEMF, biofeedback, or neurofeedback until we got her very slowly and gently detoxifying.

At first, Jacinda and her family were disappointed in my plan, but they trusted me enough to do it the right way—slowly. And slowly, Jacinda started to notice little changes, like her vertigo lessening and feeling a smidge less tired. Then, we added a little biofeedback to help her sync her breath with her heart rate, and we saw some more gains. Over months, we added more and more of the 8 Pillars into her lifestyle little by little until she was stable enough for more powerful treatment, like PEMF and antimicrobials for the infections. With the antimicrobials, Jacinda had setbacks, causing us to adjust and move forward. Those infections had been there a long time, and ticks are one of the most genetically complex bacteria in the world, so it was going to take patience and out-maneuvering.

Today, Jacinda isn't cured of her MS, but she leads a functional life. She is no longer bedridden and completely ruled by her infectious disease. She has learned that she must take meticulous care of her body, and treat it like the temple it is.

Single Homeopathic Remedies for Organ Detoxification

- **Liver:** Berberis vulgaris, Carduus marianus, Chelidonium, Fumaria officinalis, Nux vomica, Taraxacum, sulphur

- **Kidney:** Berberis vulgaris, Juniperus, Kali bich, Solidago, Uva ursi

- **Gallbladder:** Berberis vulgaris, Chelidonium

- **Pancreas:** Hepar compositum, phosphorus

- **Lymphatic:** Aesculus, Camphor, Calcarea Carbonicum, Phytolacca, Pulsatilla

- **Colon:** Hepar sulfur, Hydrastis, Lycopodium, Nux vomica, Ruta graveolens

- **Lungs:** Senega, Balsamum peruvianum, Causticum, Eucalyptus, Lobelia inflata, Spongia, Tussilago

- **Skin:** Berberis aquifolium, Calendula, Lappa major, Saponaria, Sarsaparilla, Vinca minor, Viola tricolour

Using Supplements to Improve Detoxification

As much as I love to change the brain and body through food sources, it isn't always easy with our picky eaters, nor possible with the limitations of our bodies. Since we know that genetic mutations impact the methylation process, which directly impacts the body's ability to detoxify, adding supplements becomes a critical component of improving the mental and physical health of your child. Remember, each of the three phases of detoxification are necessary for proper detoxification, so each needs to be supported (refer back to the section on the three phases of detoxification for foods and supplements that support each phase).

This list of supplements may feel overwhelming, but again, start where you can and with what makes the most sense for your child and family. Having lab work to take the guesswork out of what you may or may not be missing is helpful, but you can start adjusting your diet and adding supplements without it. When adding new supplements, start with one or two at a time, and watch for the effects. If your child is sensitive to supplements and especially to detoxification, allow for at least five days between adding each one.

Supplements for Detoxification

- Multivitamins

- Liposomal Glutathione 400-500 mg 1-2x a day

- Curcumin 500 mg 1-2x a day

- Probiotics

- Alpha Lipoic Acid 350 mg 1 pill 2x a day

- N-Acetyl Cysteine 500 mg 1 pill 3x a day

- 5-MTHF 400 mg and Methylcobalamin 400 mg Combination 1-3 pills 1x a day

- 5-MTHF 1 mg or 5-MTHF 5 mg 1 pill daily

- Glycine

- Taurine (has direct detoxification pathways, supports liver health)

- Green Tea Extract (a potent antioxidant, it increases Phase 2 enzymes—note that it can be stimulating and should only be taken in the morning)

- Herbs such as, rosemary, cilantro, and parsley

- Ellagic Acid (found in grapes, pomegranates, and raspberries, induces Phase 2 detoxification enzymes)

- Sulforaphane or SFN (supports the body's response to oxidative stress and inflammation)

- Glucosinolates

- Schizandra Berry Extract (enhances liver detoxification pathways)

- Fiber/Psyllium Husk (Psyllium is from the plant Plantago ovata and is used for its fiber content)

- Binders such as clay and charcoal are necessary to assist with the excretion process and are often missing in a good detoxification plan. It is important to take binders at least two hours apart from all other supplements and food.

Phase 1 Detoxification:

- Vitamin C

- Vitamin E

- N-acetyl cysteine (NAC)

- Glutathione

- B vitamins

- Magnesium

- Selenium

- Zinc

- Homeopathy

Phase 2 Detoxification:

- Sulfur

- Amino acids

- Molybdenum/vitamin B12

- Glutathione

- Homeopathy

Phase 3 Detoxification:

- High Fiber foods

- Sulfur-containing foods

- Alginate

- Chlorella

- Cilantro

- Parsley

- Garlic

- Onions

- Psyllium Husk

- Charcoal

Lifestyle Considerations for Detoxification

One of the common themes throughout this book is that lifestyle changes can have a big impact on so many aspects of mental health, including detoxification. I know popping a pill may seem easier, but I promise you, doing so will keep moving you down that road of dead ends, at the expense of your child's self-esteem and likability, as well as your family harmony.

Lifestyle changes can include:

- Removing plastics, pesticides, toxic cleaners, and other toxins from your environment.

- Using low chemical cleaners.

- Buying only safe, low-toxin toys and products for your family.

- Eating high-quality foods without added hormones, food dyes, pesticides, or other toxins.

- Adding a daily vegetable/fruit smoothie (add foods from the detoxifying foods list).

- Getting at least seven hours of sleep at night.

- Exercise at least 30 minutes daily (your body will excrete toxins through sweat).

- Hydrate with water daily (at least two quarts).

- Use saunas or hot baths.

- Support the gut and take probiotics.

- Avoid endocrine disruptors which are found in skin products, fragrances, cleaning products, medicines, processed foods, and plastics.

- Practice daily breathing exercises, such as a 4-7-8-second breath.

- Use stress management techniques (see Chapter 5).

- Try meditation and yoga, or any other mindful stress-reducing activities.

- Focus on the positive … mindset is everything.

- Practice mindfulness.

- Dry brush your skin.

- Use detox foot baths.

When you are considering making lifestyle changes, it may feel like you have to climb a mountain to see results. But so many of these changes are easy, and the more you do them, the better you and your kids feel.

Just this week, one of the moms I work with said, *"The whole house is lighter. No one is perfect, but we aren't at each other's throats, and Tony isn't a hot mess anymore. I feel like I can breathe! I am no longer waiting for the other shoe to drop, because I can see these changes are sticking."* And let me tell you, I had to *work* to win this mom over. She was out of hope, and just didn't think anything would help anymore. We had some tough sessions, and I had to push her at times to follow the program when she really didn't want to do more than just dip her toe in the water. But Tony was a traumatized child who was, behaviorally, a tyrant at home. His rages kept the whole family on edge. Even the dog was scared of him!

So eventually, his mom trusted the process just enough to try, and I knew we had nowhere to go but up. That is exactly what happened; gradually, Tony changed, and the whole family was able to begin taking care of themselves, too.

Chapter 10 - The Importance of Sleep

Pillar 6: Sleep

The Science

Sleep. It can be an elusive friend when we have worry, pain, or hormone-related issues. But our body needs it, and so does our brain.

As adults, we think we can do without and live off caffeine, but it doesn't work that way. And it definitely doesn't work that way for a developing brain.

Lack of sleep impacts our kids' behavior. Without proper sleep, they can be cranky, unfocused, and unmotivated. So many times during an intake, I help parents connect the dots between a child or teen's lack of sleep and what is going on with them *behaviorally*.

So, what does sleep actually do for us? While sleep affects many body processes, the powering down of our brain and body is *vital* for both to work at optimal levels. A healthy level of sleep is needed for neuroplasticity—the brain's ability to adapt when learning or to experiences. And since the developing brain is changing all the time, neuroplasticity is so important. When we sleep too little, our learning, memory, and attention become labored and our reflexes slow, which means we can't physically respond quickly.

Knowing how a lack of sleep affects you, you can imagine how it affects kids who have to sit still all day and learn!

One of the most important roles sleep plays in our health is the clearing of toxins from the brain. The brain literally 'empties the garbage pail' when it sleeps. Research has shown that the space between brain cells may increase during sleep, allowing the brain to flush out toxins that build up during waking hours. Therefore, without sleep, waste products build up in the brain cells (Xie et al., 2013). More specifically, the glymphatic system drains waste products from the brain via cerebrospinal fluid that moves through a series of channels that surround blood vessels. This same system removes a toxic protein called beta-amyloid from brain tissue associated with neurodegenerative disorders such as Alzheimer's (Jessen, Munk, Lundgaard, & Nedergaard, 2015). And I can tell you that every single one of my chronic cases of PANS/PANDAS, Lyme, anxiety, and depression 100 percent of the time have sleep problems. It just takes common sense to figure out that there is a connection between sleep and mental health.

Katherine's Story

When Katherine was a teen, her parents knew that sleep deprivation came with the territory. Their daughter stayed up late at night doing her schoolwork and was up before the sun to grab the bus. The thing was, Katherine was *never* a good sleeper. Even as a baby, she would wake up often and never liked to nap, which meant she was also crabby a lot. When Katherine and her parents came to me when she was 16, she was a high-achieving student, but also a sleep-deprived, anxious mess. She was unable to fall asleep easily because her mind was continuously racing, and she wasn't staying asleep, either. It was wearing her down physically and emotionally. She had headaches, thinning hair, constipation, fatigue, and was at times irritable and unfocused.

After a QEEG brain map, it was clear that Katherine's brain was stuck in an anxious state and that she was sleep-deprived. There were also indications that she sustained a birth trauma, which was substantiated by her parents, and that is likely why she never slept. With a combination of neurofeedback to regulate her brain waves and supplements such as magnesium, GABA, B6, Vitamin D, and L-Theanine, Katherine began to get to sleep and stay asleep for the first time in her life. Her anxiety decreased along with her stress-related headaches and gut issues. Her body began to heal, and she felt energized. Processing information became easier, and she felt all-around happier.

What Happens During Sleep?

A lot of good stuff happens during sleep! We move through a cyclical sleep patten as we doze, and each stage is important. A "predictable pattern" of sleep includes the natural cycles of activity in the brain that promote sleep. These cycles of brain activity consist of two basic states: rapid eye movement (REM) sleep and non-REM sleep, between which the body cycles.

The first four stages of sleep are non-REM sleep and last about 90 minutes. The first two are light and shorter in duration. In stage one, your brainwaves and autonomic functions begin to slow as you move from wakefulness to sleep. In stage two, brain waves begin to slow further down as it prepares for deeper sleep in stage three. In that third stage, delta brain waves slow down. Stages three and four are both deep sleep, with no eye movement or muscle activity. Your body becomes less able to respond to outside stimuli, so it moves into an even deeper, more restorative sleep. In stages three and four, the body repairs muscles and tissues, growth hormones are released for tissue growth, and cellular repair takes place. Immune function is boosted, the emptying of waste occurs, and energy builds for when you awaken.

The fifth stage is REM sleep, also referred to as "rapid eye movement" sleep. The first REM cycle lasts about 10 minutes and then lengthens after each 90-minute cycle (you cycle through all stages of non-REM and REM sleep four to five times a night).

REM is also referred to as the "dream state." Your arm and leg muscles become temporarily paralyzed, which prevents you from acting out your dreams. REM is associated with memory consolidation, learning, and problem-solving (yes—you get smarter when you sleep!). Each of the cycles is linked to specific brain waves and neuronal activity.

What Are Circadian Rhythms and Homeostasis?

Our body and brain work from a set point—a constant rhythm of sorts—and that homeostasis can be a healthy or an unhealthy set point. Just like our body likes to be at a certain weight, our sleep cycle and our brain find their own set point. And just as we can do things to positively impact our weight, there is a lot we can do to help our brain and sleep cycle get into a healthy rhythm (or homeostasis).

"Sleep is regulated by a homeostatic and a circadian process" (Deboer, 2018). The sleep-wake cycle, or the circadian rhythm and sleep homeostasis, function together to regulate sleepiness and alertness. The part of the brain that controls circadian rhythm is the hypothalamus, which picks up light and darkness cues to signal sleep and awake states. The circadian rhythm works best with regular sleep habits and provides the body with the signals of feeling alert and drowsy. Your body's biological clock is based on an approximate 24-hour day and controls most circadian rhythms (Deboer, 2018).

It is very easy for our circadian rhythm to get "off track," resulting in slightly shorter or longer rhythms. On the other hand, the homeostatic sleep drive reminds the body to sleep after a certain time and regulates sleep intensity.

Homeostasis and circadian rhythm regulate how we sleep, which is important for physical and mental health. Just like Katherine, when we regulate our sleep, we improve how we think, feel, and act.

Why Is Sleep Important for Mental and Physical Health?

When we don't get enough sleep, there are increased mental and physical health risks. Sleep deprivation has been shown to be associated with mental health issues such as anxiety and depression, cognitive and memory issues, weight gain, hormone function, insulin sensitivity (Steiger, 2002), impaired blood-brain barrier function (He, 2014), increased inflammation (Meier-Ewert et al, 2004), and decreased immune function (Cohen et al., 2009). It has even been shown to be related to premature death (Cappuccio, 2010). Lack of sleep also worsens pre-existing conditions, seizures, high blood pressure, and migraines (Institute of Medicine (US) Committee on Sleep Medicine and Research, 2006).

As I said before, I rarely see someone with ADHD, anxiety, depression, or any chronic issue who sleeps well. Of course there is a connection … at the basic level, we just don't feel right when we don't sleep properly, and the same is true for our children.

Importance of Sleep in Children, Teens, and College Students

30-40% of children in the U.S. have trouble getting to sleep, and 17 % of adolescents have insomnia (Fricke-Oerkermann, 2007). Just a few nights of low sleep levels can impact how one thinks, his or her motor skills, and of course how one *behaves*. There are many factors that can impact a child/teen's ability to fall asleep, including caffeine, too much screen time, stressors, medication side effects, and medical issues.

Most parents already have concerns about our kiddos' screen time, right? Well, an increased amount of screen time throughout the day has been linked to insomnia and symptoms of depression in adolescents (Staiano et al., 2015). Believe it or not, just having a phone near your bed keeps your mind psychologically engaged and in an alert stage, thereby interfering with sleep, as well (Rod et al, 2018).

These variables sometimes have a short-term effect, but what I have seen is that over time, they degrade the quality of sleep and interfere with our homeostasis. For example, during my

"Corona Creative Period," I wrote four books. Boy, did all that excitement (or "good" stress) mess up my sleep cycle! I had to work really hard to repair the effects of that stress on my sleep. The good news is that with consistent and intentional breathwork, magnesium baths, and increased weight-bearing exercise, I was able to restore my sleep.

Sleep issues affect kids even more than adults, as they are constantly learning. *"Research tells us that kids who don't get enough sleep on a consistent basis are more likely to have problems at school and develop more slowly than their peers who are getting enough sleep"* (University of British Columbia, 2018). These children and adolescents are also at increased risk for obesity, diabetes, injuries, poor mental health, attention and behavior problems, and poor academic performance (Wheaton & Croft, 2018). There is also a relationship between not enough sleep and at-risk behaviors such as smoking, drug usage, and sexual activity (McKnight-Eily et al., 2011).

We know all the negative effects of sleep deprivation, including irritability, mood issues, increased stress, forgetfulness, difficulties with learning, and low motivation, because we are living with kids who are sleep deprived! I know when my son was at the height of his Lyme- and PANS-related struggles, he wasn't sleeping, and he was a behavioral hot mess. Restoring his sleep was a HUGE part of his healing journey. It allowed for so many good things to happen. His brain could detoxify, so his health, mood, and behavior improved. And of course, a much-needed and prayed-for calm fell over the house.

Ok, you get it … sleep is darn important, and a lack of sleep leads to a list of physical and mental health issues. On the flip side, kids who regularly get enough sleep have improved attention, behavior, learning, memory, and overall mental and physical health. They do better in school because they can focus, and their memory systems work correctly. They can think, feel, and behave differently (I mean, isn't that what we're trying to help them with?!). Adequate daily sleep is also tied to strong immunity due to lowered inflammation levels and improved detoxification.

Symptoms of Sleep Deprivation in Children

A lack of sleep will show in physical and cognitive symptoms. As you will recognize, many of these symptoms cross over with mental health symptoms in general. There are many sources of mental health issues, and sleep is one that also often exacerbates issues. In Katherine's case, sleep was one of her many issues, but it was key in holding her back from healing.

Physical Symptoms of Sleep Deprivation in Children:

- Difficulty waking in the morning

- Repeatedly falling back asleep after waking

- Chronic fatigue

- Asking to rest or lay down during the day without physical exertion

- Frequent yawning

- Falling asleep or seeming drowsy at school or while doing homework
- Craving carbohydrates or wanting caffeine-based stimulants

Cognitive Symptoms of Sleep Deprivation in Children:

- Memory difficulties
- Slowed processing
- Word-retrieval problems
- Problems learning new information, especially complex concepts
- Difficulty following directions
- Lacking interest, motivation, and attention for everyday tasks

Behavioral Symptoms of Sleep Deprivation in Children:

- Increased moodiness and irritability
- Increased impulsivity
- Increased emotionality or tantrums
- Avoidant behaviors
- Slurred words

Physical Signs of Sleep Deprivation in Children:

- Frequent colds and infection
- Blurred vision
- Dizziness
- Weight gain
- Change in appetite

How Much Sleep Do Children Need?

The amount of sleep children need might be surprising for some parents—most aren't getting enough. With busy schedules, loads of homework, and too much screen time, lifestyle issues are getting in the way of a good night's sleep.

The American Academy of Sleep Medicine (2016) recommends the following amounts of sleep based on age group:

- 4 to 12 months -- 12 to 16 hours

- 1 to 2 years -- 11 to 14 hours

- 3 to 5 years -- 10 to 13 hours

- 6 to 12 years -- 9 to 12 hours

- 13 to 18 years -- 8 to 10 hours

What Is Sleep Hygiene?

Education about good sleep hygiene is an essential part of the cognitive-behavioral therapy used to treat insomnia.

Most kids and adults today don't really prepare for bed. Meaning, we are in a "rev" state until the minute we try to go to sleep.

Uh, even I've been guilty of that … hence four books in four months! Heck, I was so full of excitement, I'd frequently even get up to write from 2:00 to 5:00 am. Yes, it was good stuff, but boy, did my adrenals and sleep pay the price. While that may seem extreme, I am here to tell you that most teens and adults I work with tell me they toss and turn, get up to eat or watch a show, or even work out in the middle of the night due to insomnia. Getting into an abnormal sleep rhythm often happens when we don't have good sleep hygiene.

So, what *is* sleep hygiene? All the things we do to prepare for sleep, such as rituals and behaviors. Good sleep hygiene practices can include everything from setting a sleep schedule to taking a bath to avoiding lights at night.

Sleep hygiene is important for kids because it helps them develop good sleep habits through routine, and kids love routine. A good sleep routine also helps our relationship with our kids and teens, because it means we aren't constantly yelling at them to go to sleep or being awoken by them in the middle of the night. And HELLO, it means we sleep better, too, and gosh we need that!

There are lots of things we can do to improve our sleep hygiene, but the most important one is to set a sleep schedule and routine.

Best Sleep Hygiene Practices:

Set a Sleep Schedule and Routine.

- Wake up and go to sleep within 30 minutes of the same time every day.

Find out How Much Sleep Your Child Needs.

- Children need between eight and 12 hours of sleep depending on their age (see above).

Keep the Bedroom Dark and Cool.

- Having a cool bedroom helps to thermoregulate (or maintain body temperature).

- Keeping it dark helps your brain think it is nighttime.

Limit Screen Time.

- Screen time should end at least 30 minutes before bedtime.

Turn off Lights/ Reduce Blue Light.

- Use blue blocker glasses to reduce the effects of blue lights on your sleep.

Don't Do Work/Schoolwork in Bed.

- Reserve your bed for sleep conditions your brain to sleep.

Stay off Electronics If You Can't Sleep.

- If you are frustrated because you can't sleep, stay away from electronics. It is ok to get up and do something else, though, so you can remain calm before trying again.

Limit Your Daytime Naps.

- Naps of more than 30 minutes can throw off your nighttime sleep.

Meditate.

- Meditation helps to calm your mind and body and prepare you for sleep.

Don't Ingest Sugar or Carbs at Night.

- Avoid stimulating foods that can interfere with sleep patterns.

Eat a Protein-Based Snack, Instead.

- If you need to eat at night, have a protein-based snack. This helps to prevent blood sugar imbalances that can wake you up.

Limit Caffeine and Alcohol.

- Both can throw of your REM sleep and prevent you from getting deep sleep.

Do Weight-Bearing Exercises.

- Working your muscles can cause fatigue, therefore helping you to sleep more soundly.
- Avoid cardio, which can be stimulating.

Take a Magnesium Bath.

- Use magnesium bath salts such as Ancient Minerals. These are a great way to get magnesium *and* calm the body in a hot bath.

When You Wake, Start with Morning Sunshine.

- Get some morning sunshine to help your brain and body set a natural circadian rhythm, upon which our sleep cycle relies.

Eric's Story

Having a sleep routine was a foreign concept to Eric, and his parents had given up trying to get him to sleep. They just couldn't stomach the battle.

Eric had managed to get through high school with less than five hours of sleep each weeknight. He would make up for it by crashing on the weekends between soccer games. When he went to college, he started getting near constant colds and sinus infections. And then, the depression began.

Even though in theory, Eric had enough time to sleep, he was unable to sleep for more than five or six hours at a time. He would lay awake and toss and turn. When he came to me at the end of his freshman year, he was sick and tired of being sick and tired, and willing to do whatever it took to lessen his depression and feel better.

The first thing we did was improve his sleep hygiene. Eric picked a regular time to go to sleep and wake up and cut off all devices one hour before he went to bed. Next, we began some biofeedback and meditation, as well as adding magnesium, B6, vitamin D, and GABA to his regime. Within a week, Eric's quality of sleep improved, so we added weightlifting to his schedule. He cut back on carbs at night and added some extra fat and protein to his diet, too.

As the days passed, Eric began sleeping a little bit more each night. When he made it to about seven-and-a-half hours of sleep, he noticed he wasn't getting sick anymore, and his mood and fatigue lifted. It wasn't easy for Eric to stick to the schedule and cut off his devices before bed, but he felt so good in the long run that it became much less difficult.

Supplements for Sleep

As you already know, if your child isn't sleeping, then regulating emotions, attention, behaviors, and processing becomes even more challenging. Helping your child sleep can be a game-changer for you both.

Taking supplements to get back on a regular sleep cycle can be a very effective way to improve sleep. I personally take several, including magnesium and B6. There are many supplements that impact the sleep cycle at different points. They also serve to calm the nervous system, acting at the neurotransmitter and brainwave level.

Magnesium

As you read above, magnesium is one of the most prominent natural anxiety supplements. It's also a cofactor in more than 300 enzyme systems that regulate diverse biochemical and enzymatic reactions within the body (Alawai, 2018). We need a lot of magnesium; our busy, stressful lives cause us to burn through it. I take four kinds of magnesium *and* a magnesium bath almost every night (remember, I nearly blew out my adrenals with all that "good" stress). Our children have an enormous amount of pressure on them in their academic and social worlds, so they could benefit from magnesium, too.

So how does the body use it? Well, magnesium is required for its assistance with many chemical functions that support the central nervous system (CNS) in managing stress. It plays an important role in the hypothalamic-pituitary-adrenocortical (HPA) axis to help manage the body's stress response system. Our HPA axis has become increasingly stress hyperactivated, and most of the QEEG brain maps I see today reflect that. Moreover, anxiety and stress have long been known to interfere with sleep (Harvey, 2014), and magnesium calms the nervous system (Cuciureanu, 2011).

Magnesium plays a role in a vast amount of the body's daily functions and is directly involved in regulating sleep and our hormone (or endocrine) system. Magnesium not only helps calm and prepare the body for sleep; it also may help reduce leg movements and muscle twitches that are associated with nighttime arousals (Hornyak et. al., 1998). Magnesium, along with zinc, are important in the synthesis of melatonin, and when all three are combined, they help to deepen sleep (Rondanelli, 2011), and we know how important it is to move through all the sleep cycles.

There are different types of magnesium, including:

- **magnesium chloride**
  Promotes sleep, digestion, bone health, and relaxation

- **magnesium sulfate**
  Relaxes muscles and loosens bowels

- **magnesium malate**
  Relaxes muscles

- **magnesium citrate**
  Aides in digestion and alleviates constipation, and acid indigestion

- **magnesium oxide**
  Improves digestion

- **magnesium glycinate**
  Promotes relaxation and alleviates constipation

- **magnesium orotate**
  Supports heart health and repair of tissues and enhances stamina and performance

- **magnesium L-Threonate**
  Promotes relaxation and improves cognitive functioning

(National Institutes of Health, 2020)

Each of these types of magnesium have a specific role. Magnesium has not only been shown to improve sleep and mental health, but also a long list of physical and clinical issues (National Institutes of Health, 2020).

Magnesium dosages vary based on the type of magnesium taken and age of the child. General dosing guidelines are:

- Infants— 75 mg per day

- Children 1 to 3 years of age— 80 mg per day

- Children 4 to 8 years of age—130 mg per day

- Children 9 to 13 years of age—240 mg per day

- Teens 14 to 18 years of age—410 mg per day

- 19 to 30 years of age—400 mg per day

- 31 to 50 years of age—420 mg per day

- 51 plus years of age—420 mg per day

(National Institutes of Health, 2020)

You can also get magnesium from food. The highest concentrations of magnesium are found in almonds, spinach, cashews, peanuts, soy milk, black beans, avocado, brown rice, and yogurt.

When sleep is an issue, adding magnesium to your regime is essential, so select one that meets your needs and load up on magnesium-rich foods. Too much magnesium will loosen the bowels, so lower the dose if that occurs.

Melatonin

Melatonin is a much-misunderstood supplement. Some think taking it too long can be habit-forming or unhealthy, but it isn't. Melatonin is something our body already produces, and having low levels can interfere with one's sleep. Most people can safely take it to help settle and sleep for longer periods of time.

Melatonin, naturally produced by the pineal gland, is a hormone that signals your brain when it's time to sleep and regulates the sleep-wake cycle. Melatonin levels increase at night when it is dark, triggering sleep, and decrease when the sun rises, triggering awakening.

Research from Pandi-Perumal et. al. (2014) denotes that melatonin helps with sleep onset and has been used for an insomnia aide for decades. *"Melatonin has been successfully used to treat insomnia in children with attention-deficit hyperactivity disorder or autism, as well as in other neurodevelopmental disorders in which sleep disturbance is commonly reported"* (Ali et. al., 2020). Melatonin has also been shown to reduce neuroinflammation and depression through the process of autophagy, which is the body's way of cleaning out damaged cells in order to regenerate newer, healthier cells (Ali et. al., 2020).

Melatonin is generally considered safe to take daily, but it is contraindicated with blood-thinning medications (or anticoagulants), immunosuppressants, birth control pills, and some diabetes drugs.

Information from a 2017 study found that, depending on the child's age and weight, between three and nine milligrams were effective in reducing insomnia (van Maanen et. al., 2017).

Melatonin is a good supplement for those who have a hard time settling for sleep; it isn't the right choice for a person who has a hard time *staying* asleep. Like the research reports, I have seen melatonin help the sleep and behavior of children with ASD, ADHD, and behavioral issues.

Vitamin B6

The B vitamins are so important to the functioning of our nervous system, detoxification, and quality sleep. Vitamin B6, or pyridoxine, helps the body manufacture neurotransmitters such as serotonin, a mood-enhancing neurotransmitter used to produce melatonin, which also aids in the body's ability to cope with depression, stress, and anxiety. Research from Lichstein (2007) has found that a vitamin B6 deficiency may be associated with increased psychological distress and resulting sleep disturbance. A deficiency is also associated with insomnia and depression (Zadeh & Begum, 2011).

I recently worked with a young woman, Lauren, with chronic depression. No less than four doctors noted her low levels of B6, but did not advise her to supplement. When I recommended she take 50 mg before bed, Lauren noticed a difference in her sleep and mood *within two weeks*. Taking a functional approach to mental health is so important, and in Lauren's case, doing so created significant improvement in weeks after being stuck for years on an ineffective SSRI and talk-therapy rotation.

The richest food sources of vitamin B6 include chickpeas, tuna, salmon, beef liver and other organ meats, potatoes, starchy vegetables, and non-citrus fruit. Dosage recommendations vary from five milligrams to a maximum of 100 mg (in adults) and no more than 50 mg is recommended in children. High doses of B6 can be toxic, actually contribute to insomnia, and are linked to lucid dreaming. It is contraindicated with several medications, so one should check with a physician before taking.

Vitamin D

Vitamin D is one of the most important nutrients for health because it is involved in many functions in the brain and body. Every tissue in the body has vitamin D receptors, including the brain, heart, muscles, endocrine system, and immune system, which means vitamin D is needed at every level for the body to function.

Just about everyone who walks through my door has low levels of vitamin D, so I recommend supplementing to almost every single parent and client. It is just so important for mental health, and during the pandemic, we need it more than ever for immune health. Since vitamin D is a fat-soluble supplement, it takes time to build in the system, but it can really be a game-changer when it comes to depression, fatigue, and sleep.

Vitamin D plays an important role in supporting sleep, too. A 2018 meta-analysis suggests that vitamin D deficiency is associated with a higher risk of sleep disorders (Gao et al., 2018).

Individuals with vitamin D deficiency have a higher risk of sleepiness and poor sleep quality and duration, as well as an increased risk for sleep disorders.

Vitamin D can be found in a variety of foods like fish, eggs, liver, and fortified foods. Research denotes that low serum 25(OH)D may be a risk factor of unhealthy sleep, so looking at serum levels and supplementing accordingly is where one should start. Recommended maximum vitamin D dosing included 400 to 1,000 IU for infants up to six months old, 1,500 IU for infants aged six months to one year, 2,500 IU for toddlers up to three years, 3,000 IU for children aged four to eight, and 4,000 IU for those nine years and older (Pela, 2012). Too much vitamin D can be harmful, so one should watch dosing. There are many forms that are easy for kids to take, including drops and chewables.

GABA

Gamma-aminobutyric acid (GABA) is a neurotransmitter that inhibits nerve transmission in the brain, calming nervous activity. The neurotransmitter GABA blocks the excitatory neurotransmitter glutamate, keeping nerve cells from firing too often and easily. People deficient in GABA are prone to anxiety and panic attacks (Boonstra, 2015).

GABA helps the body and mind to relax, fall asleep, and sleep more deeply throughout the night. It is long-established that activation of GABA receptors helps to promote sleep (Gottesmann, 2002). It has become an increasingly popular alternative to psychiatric medications for anxiety, depression, and insomnia, because it is so effective at blocking that excitatory neurotransmitter activity without the side effects that medications always carry. And with a developing brain, we should always be concerned about toxicity and side effects from psychiatric medications.

Gabe's Story

When I worked with 10-year-old Gabe, he had OCD and insomnia. We added GABA into his health regime, and he experienced symptom relief almost from day one. It wasn't until we reduced his excitatory neurotransmitter activity that Gabe was able to think clearly enough to take action differently and learn how to talk back to his anxiety and obsessive thoughts. Before GABA and biofeedback, Gabe was too activated to address his worried and intrusive thoughts. With the pairing, he was able to work through his triggers in exposure and response therapy (ERP) for OCD and completely stop his obsessions and compulsions. He was also able to sleep again!

GABA can be found in green, black, and oolong teas, as well as fermented foods. Generally, the dosage recommendation for adults for sleep and anxiety is 100-200 milligrams. Research has found 100 milligrams effective for sleep and ADHD in children (Edden, Crocetti, Zhu, Gilbert, & Mostofsky, 2012).

L-Theanine

L-Theanine is an amino acid found in green tea that is known for its calming and relaxing properties. L-Theanine modulates aspects of brain function in humans by increasing alpha brainwave activity, which calms the brain. L-Theanine also increases levels of the brain neurotransmitters serotonin, dopamine, and gamma-aminobutyric acid (GABA), which are important in mental health. The amino acid L-Theanine produces its anti-anxiety effects by increasing GABA, which cuts that excitatory neurotransmitter activity.

L-Theanine helps promote sleep by lowering stress and anxiety. It calms the CNS down and helps to reduce the stress hyperactive response, so one isn't in a constant fight, flight, or freeze mode. The combination of L-Theanine and GABA has been found to have a positive synergistic effect on sleep quality and duration (Kim et al., 2019).

L-Theanine is found in tea leaves and in small amounts in Bay Bolete mushrooms. Consuming 200–400 milligrams a day may help improve sleep and relaxation for an adult (Lu, 2004), and 400 mg was found to improve ADHD and sleep in boys (Lyon, Kapoor, & Juneja, 2011).

Passionflower

Passionflower (Passiflora incarnata) is an herb that has long been used as a sedative and sleep aid. It is also used to reduce the *"nervous behavior"* of children (Trompetter, 2013). Recent studies have shown that taking passionflower as a supplement or tea is associated with improvements in sleep quality (Kim, 2017).

Animal studies have shown that passionflower significantly increased slow-wave (deep) sleep, reduced rapid eye movement sleep, and helped the rats fall asleep more quickly (Guerrero, 2017). It also reduced the time it took to fall asleep and increased the duration of sleep (Toda, 2017).

Side effects have been rarely reported, but may include rapid heartbeat and irregular heartbeat, nausea, vomiting, drowsiness, and mental slowing.

Trompetter, Krick and Weiss (2013) found passionflower to help children with nervous agitation. Dosing guidelines vary based on the form taken (dried, tea, tincture, or liquid extract) and body weight. The 150lb adult tea dosage is one cup orally two to three times daily and 30 min before bedtime: 2 to 5 g/150 ml water and a dosage for a 50lb child would be 1/3 that of an adult. There are also tincture versions as well (Trompetter, Krick & Weiss, 2013).

5-HTP

5-Hydroxytryptophan (5-HTP) is a compound produced naturally in the body from the amino acid tryptophan. 5-HTP is a precursor to the neurotransmitter serotonin, which regulates mood and sleep-wake cycles. Serotonin is required to make melatonin, which you now know also helps the body regulate its sleep-wake cycles. Because 5-HTP increases serotonin levels, it increases melatonin, which normalizes sleep patterns. 5-HTP may help shorten the time it takes to fall asleep and increase sleep amounts (Hong, 2016). 5-HTP has been shown to reduce night terrors in children (Bruni, 2004) and to reduce stress and anxiety, which aids the body in preparing for sleep.

Potential side effects of 5-HTP include nausea, dizziness, and diarrhea. Children with Down's syndrome or a nerve-muscle disorder are cautioned to not take 5-HTP. Dosing guidelines vary based on the form taken (dried, tea, tincture, or liquid extract) and body weight. The adult dosage is 100–300 mg (for a 150 adult and children are 1/3 the dose for a 50lb child) 30–45 minutes before bed (Hinz, Stein, & Uncini, 2012).

Valerian

Valerian is an herb that increases the levels of gamma-aminobutyric acid (GABA) in the brain, which again, is a neurotransmitter that regulates and calms the nervous system. It also is a potent anxiety reducer. Valerian has long been used to help induce sleep and has been shown to improve the overall quality of sleep (Bent, 2006). It has also been shown to improve impulsiveness (Gromball, Beschorner, Wantzen, Paulsen, & Burkart, 2014).

Potential side effects include migraine and gastrointestinal effects. Dosing guidelines vary based on the form taken (dried, tea, tincture, or liquid extract) and body weight. A 150lb adult dose is one to three times a day of 300 to 600 milligrams, and the dose for a 50lb child is one third of that.

Magnolia Bark

Magnolia bark is known to lower anxiety and depression, reduce stress, and decrease inflammation. It also helps to boost the neurotransmitter GABA that inhibits excitatory activity. Magnolia bark is also an adrenaline inhibitor—too much adrenaline and cortisol can interfere with one's health and sleep (Poivre & Dues, 2017). And yes, just like adults, kids and teens can have adrenal issues when under chronic stress.

Bioactive compounds in magnolia bark impact the sleep cycle by increasing time in both slow-wave sleep and REM sleep. Magnolia bark also acts as a sedative, calming the brain and body for sleep.

Possible side effects include bloating, diarrhea, upset stomach, nausea, and vomiting. Large doses should be avoided. The typical 150lb adult dosage is 200-400 milligrams and 1/3 of that for a 50lb child.

When it comes to regulating a sleep cycle, there may seem to be several directions you can go. Just as I did with Eric, I recommend starting with a sleep schedule and a routine around bedtime. Cutting screen activity at least 30 minutes before bedtime, practicing some deep breathing, and adding in some magnesium (L-Threonate is my favorite) is where you should start. If your child's sleep doesn't improve after two weeks of consistent practice, then consider adding another supplement, some biofeedback, or getting a QEEG brain map to see what else is going on.

Just know that, without proper sleep, your child's behavior won't change.

Chapter 11 - Proven Interventions for Calming the Nervous System

Pillar 7: Brain-Based Interventions

In Chapter 5, we talked about how detrimental stress is to the brain and body. Every time the body is stressed, it mobilizes for battle. It doesn't matter what kind of stress, either—real or imagined, good or bad. Stress is stress. If we don't get that nervous system to calm the heck down, just about every organ in the body, including the brain, can be affected. And a stressed nervous system is the biggest barrier to changing behavior and health. When we are stressed, we get stuck … emotionally, behaviorally, and physically.

Modern medicine continually pushes the medication path. It is considered the highest level of treatment when it should be the *last* treatment. There are so many therapies, such as nutrition, neurofeedback, and psychotherapy that can help children be less stressed and easily frustrated while improving behavioral issues. Yet parents just aren't hearing about them. Why?

There are a lot of reasons, but as I've mentioned, it is mainly a lack of education and training available to mental health and medical providers. Unless providers have had a personal experience or gone out of their way to learn about holistic therapies, they just don't know enough to educate patients about them.

There are other reasons, too, including the strong hold of pharma on our entire mental health system. This is one that we can address! I am doing so by providing CE-based trainings for providers and via **my book, *The Teletherapy Toolkit*™—the first ever about teletherapy activities (you can learn more about it here: www.teletherapytoolkit.com).**

In this chapter, we dive into therapies that can help reduce and reverse stress and clinical symptoms. Each one outlined below is safe, effective, and clinically proven to work for children, teens, and adults.

What Is Neuroplasticity?

Before we talk about natural mental health treatments, it is essential to understand neuroplasticity in order to grasp child development and how parenting can affect the brain.

Neuroplasticity is the brain's ability to reorganize itself by forming new neural connections over time. In other words, it refers to how adaptable and flexible the brain is. The more we learn and experience, the more changes we have in the structure of our brain. And of course, a child's brain is constantly learning and adapting.

Brain plasticity allows children to adapt to environments and experiences as they build connections. Pre-natal (De Asis-Cruz J, Krishnamurthy D, Zhao L, et al., 2020) and environmental factors such as parenting, diet, stress, etc. can have a strong influence on a child's brain development, and ultimately, behavior (Kolb, 2009). A child's brain responds to all its new experiences, and those experiences activate certain neurons, create new connections among them, strengthen existing connections, and prune weaker or unused connections. All our experiences and interventions impact brain development throughout our lifetime (Grigorenko, 2017).

Again, the brain is constantly adapting and being shaped by new experiences, which alters our behaviors and thoughts throughout our lifetime. The greater the neuroplasticity of the brain, the greater capacity a child has for new learning and behavioral flexibility. This is one of the reasons why, even if you haven't found the route yet, change *is* possible. I see it every day!

Natural Therapies That Change the Brain and Behavior

Educating and guiding parents to understand the "why" behind their children's behavior is what I do. The other part of that? Explaining what to do to change behaviors.

Now, let's dive deep into the most effective therapies that change the nervous system and ultimately lead to behavior change.

The Simple Act of Breathing

The act of an intentful, simple breath can do so much to calm the brain and body. From young children to the elderly, anyone can do breathwork. It works quickly, too, helping one to feel calm.

You may recall reading about how breathwork regulates the autonomic nervous system (ANS) and helps put the body into a parasympathetic state, which works to relax and slow down the body's response to stress, in the last chapter. When we learn to take slow, deep, and rhythmic breaths, it functionally resets the autonomic nervous system. As a result, our CNS calms, and our thinking becomes more rational.

Regularly using breathing techniques has been shown to improve mental health symptoms and disorders including PTSD, stress, anxiety, depression, ADHD, and neurodevelopmental disorders (Seppälä et al., 2014; Ma et al., 2017; Newmark, 2017).

There are many different types of breathing than can be beneficial. As you've already read, one of my favorites is the 4-7-8 breathing technique, which helps calm the nervous system by creating a rhythmic breathing pattern. Other rhythmic breathing techniques include star breathing and infinity breathing, which I walk you through on **my YouTube channel, here: www.youtube.com/DrRoseann.**

With a 4-7-8 breath, the exhale is a few counts longer than the inhale. This triggers the vagus nerve to send a signal to the brain to increase the parasympathetic nervous system and decrease the sympathetic nervous system, thereby leading to a calmer state.

Since the 4-7-8 patterned breathing technique calms the body and mind so much, it is best to practice it while seated or lying down. It involves breathing in through the nose for four (4) seconds, holding your breath for seven (7) seconds, and exhaling from your mouth for eight (8) seconds. Repeat the 4-7-8 breath cycle at least three times in a row, two to four times per day.

The key to any breathing technique is to make sure your exhalation is the longest part of the process and to use it frequently. Start out with three rounds, two times a day, and work up to a few times a day. It is the daily practice that teaches your nervous system to get into a healthy rhythm.

Meditation

Meditation can be used to address very specific stressors or issues such as stress, addiction, pain, anxiety, depression, focus, OCD, and so on. Research from Goyal et al. (2014) supports that meditation has long been used to treat stress and stress-related conditions and to promote general health. There have also been dozens of studies that demonstrate the ability of meditation to improve emotional wellbeing (Fang et. al., 2010), mental health disorders including anxiety and depression, and physical pain (Rubia, 2009). While the long-term practice of meditation has also been shown to improve attention, brain connectivity, and the self-regulation of behavior (Brewer et. al., 2011), research from Tang (2007) has demonstrated that it can be improved in as little as five days. Meditation can calm both your mind and body and change the brain (Lazar et. al., 2005).

In as little as a *few days*, you can change your brain waves and decrease your stress! Pretty cool, right?! Another benefit of mediation is that it's free and easy! You can download apps or find meditations on YouTube.

When working on clinical issues with meditation, research from Goyal et al. (2014) supports the criticalness of the trainer's experience and of the participant's dedication to practice, so he or she feels skilled enough to continue using this natural and effective tool.

There are many types of meditation. Some may center on a certain activity, while others can be spiritual or movement-based. Meditation can also involve silence, mindfulness, and/or prayer, or be guided and moderated by someone else.

Progressive relaxation meditation guides you through the process of relaxing each part of your body while calming the inner chatter that often exacerbates the stress and anxiety that feed our worried thoughts. It is a very popular type of meditation in which someone else—live or via technology—guides you in taking a step-by-step approach to breathwork and conscious relaxation of the different areas of your body. Many of these meditations are available through an app such as Calm, Insight Timer, and Headspace.

All types of meditation are effective. Use it daily to see a difference. I always encourage parents to start out with a sleep mediation, because it seems to be the easiest for kids. Keep in mind that while adults might resist the process, kids take to it like fish in water. I recall one mom urgently calling me a few days after we met just to tell me that meditation had improved her son's long-disturbed sleep pattern in less than a week! How lucky am I that I get those kinds of emails and calls every day?! Remember, little waves create big ones.

QEEG, Neurofeedback, Biofeedback, and PEMF

Now, we get to talk about tools I personally use myself every day! My kids use the technology on their own, too, and even my cat, Sweetie Pie, asks for PEMF. For real! She places herself on the mat and rubs it to let us know we should turn it on.

If you've ever used PEMF, this makes sense, because you understand how good it makes you feel.

With the rise of chronic health issues and pain, there has also been an advancement in technology and therapy to support those afflicted. This rise can also be attributed to our health system's tendency to treat symptoms without addressing root causes, as well as an increased need for more integrative therapies that don't carry side effects. Neurofeedback, biofeedback, and PEMF are widely unknown technologies that have a long history of supporting those with health issues.

Anthony's Story

Do you remember the moment you knew your child needed help? Well, I do. It's awful and so painful to think about.

Nancy, mom to Anthony, remembers, too.

Anthony was in the third grade when he came home in tears and said to his mom, *"John called me 'stupid."* His mom's heart sank. How could this soulful, brown-eyed sweetheart think he was stupid?

She knew he was struggling, and now, the other kids were noticing it, too. Nancy thought they had already licked this issue in the first grade, when they had some help with reading at school and were told that everything was *"fine"* … that he would just *"mature and grow out of it."*

That was a load of bologna!! Because guess what? Even though Anthony was a well-behaved, motivated, smart kid, he wasn't reading at grade level and just couldn't keep up.

So, Nancy marched into the school psychologist with his test scores in hand begging for help. And what did that supposedly educated professional and fellow mother tell her to do? *"We know Anthony isn't ADHD, but you should go to the doctor and try a medication for focus."* What?!

Shocked, Nancy replied, *"I didn't know there was a medication for reading problems."* She stormed out, googled "dyslexia," and found me and my center. When she learned I was giving a presentation not far from her home about how to reverse things like ADHD, learning problems, and anxiety, she came to hear what I had to say. After listening to me and other parents who used natural therapies, she was so excited about the possibility of not only reversing her son's issues, but that with neurofeedback, those changes would LAST! She *got* it—there was another way!

Nancy made an appointment with my center the next day, and by the end of the week, Anthony started neurofeedback. It was easy and enjoyable for him: he simply *"watched a movie"* with sensors on his head. Those sensors measured his functioning, and when he produced a healthy combo of brainwaves, which the brain could do after just a few seconds, Anthony received visual and auditory reinforcement.

After just three months of neurofeedback, Anthony improved his reading so much, he landed in the 95th percentile on school reading tests!

His mom didn't really care about that. What she did care about was the light that was back in his eyes and his new confidence. She said her heart was bursting! And for the first time, she could sleep soundly at night, because her baby was smiling again. That was five years ago, and that neurofeedback changed the course of Anthony's life. Now, he is on the honor roll, well-liked by other kids, an athlete, and able to shine as the sweet, capable boy he has always been.

QEEG Brain Map

So many times, a child comes to me with a track record of multiple unsuccessful therapies tried. Most of the time, the biggest problem is an incorrect diagnosis. And that is where a QEEG can be a gamechanger, because only with the right diagnosis can you get the right treatment.

In our mental health system, the standard of care is to really just take an educated guess about the clinical problem at hand. If we aren't using evidence-based tools such as QEEG and functional lab work, we aren't "checking under the hood."

A quantitative EEG (QEEG) is a diagnostic tool that looks at brainwave patterns within different regions of the brain and helps determine the health of the brain. In very simple terms, QEEG is a computer analysis of the EEG data, which is a measurement of the brain's electrical activity. The EEG activity is recorded and statistically analyzed, and the data is compared against a database. It is a visual method of seeing how the brain is functioning both over the brain structures and in the brain's intercommunication via brainwave activity. The patterning of brainwaves gives us clear indicators of clinical conditions such as ADHD, anxiety, OCD, depression, etc. You can even see head injuries such as concussion and birth trauma.

The process of a QEEG brain mapping involves placing a specialized skull cap, fit to the individual, on the head. It has receptacles to hold sensors, which will map each of the nineteen brain sites across all relevant frequencies. The flat, metal sensors called "electrodes" on the scalp track and record brain wave patterns. These electrodes analyze the electrical impulses in the brain and record them with the help of a computer.

An EEG will identify four types of brainwave frequencies: delta (slow), theta (slow), alpha (medium), and beta (fast). Alpha waves are present when a person is taking a moment to reflect or is meditating. Beta waves occur when a person is interacting, talking, or solving a problem. Theta waves are present during drowsiness, daydreaming, restless activity. Delta waves occur when a person is sleeping.

QEEG's give us information about the formation of brainwaves, and with that information, we know that certain brainwave activity in specific regions is associated with specific conditions. Since we know what each of the structures do, we can see which areas have too much or too little activity both over the structure and between structures with a QEEG. Understanding the activity in specific regions helps us make connections between what the brain is doing and behavior.

Research tells us that in terms of diagnostics, QEEG's are more effective than traditional means of assessment for clinical conditions such as ADHD. Snyder et al. (2008) demonstrates that a QEEG brain map is 89% accurate as a diagnostic test of ADHD versus behavioral rating scales which are 47-58% accurate. It has also been used to determine if one has a concussion and verify subsequent cognitive deficits (Ferraracci et. al., 2019), subtypes of insomnia (McCloskey et. al., 2019), and a host of other psychiatric disorders in children (McVoy et. al., 2019).

Behavioral rating scales are not only subjective, but they also only provide a glance into what is impacting the central nervous system (CNS), especially since ADHD in adults is different than in children. Starting with a QEEG brain map is a great way to diagnose the real issues. By objectively looking at the brainwaves, we can see what is impacting the CNS and causing dysregulation, and thereby get a clearer diagnostic picture that leads to better treatment. A QEEG provides a wealth of diagnostic information that is imperative in getting to the root cause.

Neurofeedback

I just love neurofeedback so much for so many reasons! But the biggest one is because it transforms lives.

It you read the story earlier in this book about how I got involved in neurofeedback, then you already know about Alec, and how neurofeedback changed the trajectory of his life. He was the most impulsive child I had ever seen in my life. His behavior wore people out, and when his frazzled mom found neurofeedback out of sheer desperation, I supported her in trying it … and Alec became the child he was supposed to be—focused, communicative, and engaging. This diamond in the rough went on to graduate high school at 16, attend graduate school, and most importantly, be a really happy adult. That is what all us mamas want—for our babies to be happy and self-confident.

- Neurofeedback is a powerful, non-invasive, medication-free treatment for a variety of clinical symptoms and issues. From ADHD to anxiety and PANS/PANDAS, I have successfully used it for dozens of clinical issues. Wondering how it works?

- It involves helping a person learn how to modify his or her own brainwave activity in order to produce a healthy rhythm that helps him or her be focused and calm. We all have the same brainwave frequencies—delta, theta, alpha, and beta—but we don't have the same formation of brainwave activity. Our brain can be over- or underactive in certain regions, and communication networks can be poor or hyper. Those differences affect how the brain works. It is so easy to "see" how the brain is functioning and the exact issues occurring when you pair that knowledge with neurofeedback. You *can* treat the brain!

- Neurofeedback teaches the brain to self-regulate, which calms that CNS and reduces symptoms such as worry, lack of focus, and moodiness. When the CNS is dysregulated, thinking, learning, attention, emotions, and behaviors are, too. Neurofeedback regulates the CNS and brain functioning at that subconscious level, so you or your child can take action *differently, because the brain is regulating.* I hope that's another big "aha" for you!

- Neurofeedback training is grounded in the principle that, by helping the brain self-regulate *over time*, it becomes trained to produce a healthy combination of brainwaves. This results in lasting changes that make you feel calmer, more focused, and in better control of your whole self, no matter your age.

Consider neurofeedback a personal trainer for your brain waves—it really *is* a fitness workout for your brain. You can't just do one workout and build muscle ... that takes time. Changing our brainwaves is exactly the same.

During a therapy session, you reinforce your *subconscious*, which is really in charge, and teach your brain to change its behavior.

How it works:

Neurofeedback may seem mysterious, but it's actually based on a simple process of measurement and reinforcement—or what is known as "operant conditioning."

Neurofeedback teaches your subconscious brain how to shift into a state of concentration more efficiently by learning to produce the brainwaves associated with a calm focus. For kids who are really unfocused or struggle in some way, the good news is that their brain will change regardless ... because we are training the part of the brain that is always running the show— the subconscious.

Neurofeedback is all about helping the CNS find balance. When the CNS is dysregulated, it shows up in our kid's behaviors, emotions, thinking, attention, or social functioning. A variety of behaviors can result, from withdrawal to angry behaviors to focus and learning problems. This reflects that your child's or teen's nervous system hasn't yet found that healthy rhythm.

Our kids are struggling with conscious functioning, like project planning, writing, or sharing their toys. That is the power of neurofeedback; it works at the deeper level, which is why change happens so quickly and effectively. As the brain learns to act in a healthy way that increases focus and motivation while reducing worry, distractibility, and impulse control, you'll quite likely get fewer calls from the teacher, referee fewer sibling brawls, and hear about fewer strained relationships at school.

After a brain assessment that looks at brainwave average (or a traditional QEEG brain map paired with an intake), a protocol is designed. Since many regions of the brain can be trained, and frequencies can be reinforced to increase or decrease depending on the desired outcomes, protocols are selected only by a highly trained and experienced neurofeedback provider. Your provider should be licensed in mental health or medicine, and preferably, certified by the Biofeedback Certification Alliance (BCIA), which ensures that each provider is licensed to practice and meets the training and experience requirements. Neurofeedback is only as good as the provider's ability to assess the issues and determine the protocol that needs to be put into place to addresses the specific issues. That is why people come to me from all over the world ... because I have helped thousands of kids and families.

The next step in the process of neurofeedback involves placing sensors on specific areas of the head that the clinician pre-determined for training in order to get the brain to self-regulate. One receives reinforcement via a computer program that typically uses movies or some other mixed visual and auditory stimuli. Brain functioning is monitored via computers, and the person is shown that live feedback, which helps the subconscious brain to promote or reduce different brainwave frequencies in order to receive reinforcement. The brain, or really the subconscious brain, is rewarded for changing its own activity to produce more appropriate patterns, and that reinforcement begins within just a few seconds of the first session. This new electrical activity is actually produced in the brain, and the brainwave activity is "shaped" toward a more desirable, regulated performance.

These changes result in symptom reduction as the brain learns to self-regulate (get into a healthy rhythm). Progress is typically gradual, but your subconscious is instantly able to get into a healthy rhythm that not only positively impact your brainwaves, but that also pulls a hyper or "stressed out" nervous system out of a sympathetic dominant state and gets it to calm down to the more "Zen" parasympathetic state. Symptoms typically reduce over a series of sessions.

The number of sessions needed depends largely on the clinical issues and flexibility of the brain. Most clinical issues require a commitment of twenty or more sessions with a frequency of two or more times a week to see any significant changes. As noted earlier, symptom reduction is often gradual, but can be improved by the addition of synergistic tools and therapies such as psychotherapy, dietary changes, exercise, and lifestyle changes that emphasize stress reduction.

Unlike medication, neurofeedback side effects are temporary, few, and largely benign. The most common is mental fatigue, which makes sense. After a solid physical workout, you feel a bit fatigued, right? Naturally, if your brain experiences proper exercise, it will be tired, as well. While one can be on psychiatric medications while training, certain medications can cause side effects. However, most side effects are mitigated by a change in protocol.

It is a pleasant, easy, and great therapy for kids as young as three-and-a-half years old not only because they get to watch movies and cartoons, but because it feels good, so they actually enjoy it.

So, now you get it … neurofeedback is a non-invasive, safe, research-proven, effective, and natural therapy for both children and adults, and there is a lot of research to support it. There are thousands of research studies (ISNR, 2020) that have demonstrated the efficacy of neurofeedback over the last five decades. Neurofeedback is a time-tested, proven treatment for ADHD, yielding significant and long-term improvements. As much as 90 percent of people (Xiong, Shi, & Xu, 2005) who undergo neurofeedback for ADHD symptoms show improvement in attention, impulse control, and distractibility. Neurofeedback has also been shown to be an effective treatment for anxiety and depression (Hammond, 2005), OCD (Hammond, 2003), pain (Jensen et. al., 2007), reading comprehension (Orlando & Rivera, 2004), and seizures (Egner & Sterman, 2006), as well as other mental health issues (Simkin, Thatcher & Lubar, 2014).

While there is a variety of different types of neurofeedback your provider can choose from, one is generally not better than the other. It all depends on one's unique bio-individual needs and your neurofeedback provider's experience. One method does not fit all, even if two patients have the same symptoms or conditions. Each of the neurofeedback methods was created to produce neuroplasticity in the brain and regulate the CNS, helping to improve brain health and create wellness, so neurofeedback can improve a variety of issues and conditions.

Wondering if your child is a good candidate for neurofeedback? Download my Will Neurofeedback Help My Child? Checklist at <u>www.drrotips.com/neurofeedbackchecklist</u>.

Biofeedback

Biofeedback, the cousin to neurofeedback, is an evidence-based technology (Kim et. al., 2018) that can help you to reduce stress and enhance your sense of well-being in only a few minutes of practice a day. Biofeedback works at the conscious level as you learn to control your heart rate, breath, body temperature, skin conductance, and or muscle movements, typically in an effort to reduce stress.

The main difference between biofeedback and neurofeedback is that with neurofeedback, you are training your brainwaves at the subconscious level, whereas with biofeedback, you are training bodily functions at the conscious level.

So how does biofeedback work?

One is connected to electrical sensors that measure and provide information (feedback) about the body (bio). This feedback helps one focus on making subtle changes in the body, such as relaxing certain muscles, or changing breath or body temperature, to achieve desired results like reduced pain or stress. Biofeedback gives one the power to use thoughts to control the body, often reducing stress and/or improving a health condition or physical performance. For example, athletes frequently use biofeedback to train muscles to move differently to enhance their athletic performance. In fact, the Italian soccer team used biofeedback and neurofeedback as part of their training to win the world cup in 2006 (Wilson, Pepper, & Moss, 2007).

Heart rate variability training (HRV) is a type of biofeedback device that teaches a person to sync his or her heart rate and breath. Easily incorporated into daily routine, HRV can help calm the nervous system, improve focus, decrease tension, and improve sleep and mood. HRV is so easy, in fact, that my youngest son started using it when he was two years old. I have also had children bring the device to school and use it proactively. In one case, a little boy named Mickey used it at school three times a day. His parents saw an immediate difference in their son's behavior, so they bought three devices for his class, too, so other kids could benefit while removing any stigma from stress management.

PEMF Therapy

PEMF is an acronym for Pulsed Electromagnetic Field therapy. This type of therapy promotes cellular communication, which in turn enhances self-healing and wellness (Funk, Monsees, & Ozkucur, 2009). In recent years, it has become an increasingly popular therapy for autoimmune disease and chronic disease states. I personally have seen many patients struggling with physical and cognitive issues that result from Lyme and tick-borne disease, infectious disease, injury, and/or autoimmune disease use and benefit from therapies such as neurofeedback, biofeedback, and PEMF that reduce the body's stress response and allow the body to do its own healing work instead of expending resources due to chronic stress states. Taming your body's response to stress is critical in reversing mental health and healing in general.

In order to maintain balance and sustain good health, a lot of things have to be working correctly at the same time. All of the body's organs, tissues, and subsystems require precise communications to effectively process instantaneous exchanges, which means that your CNS and organs have to work efficiently. You already know that our high-stress lifestyle is causing our bodies, sleep, and minds to break down. When these critical communication exchanges are disrupted or blocked, the body's cells, tissues, and organs may become compromised, and unhealthy symptoms follow (Funk, Monsees, & Ozkucur, 2009). Those unhealthy symptoms can be physical, cognitive, or emotional in nature.

A central principle of PEMF therapy is the enhancement of this cell-to-cell communication, which is critical for multiple functions within the body. If the cells aren't 'talking,' then the body can't do its job properly. Makes sense! Therefore, intercellular communication is critical to the body's adaptation and regulation processes, which help to maintain overall health and deal with the symptoms and causes of cell deterioration and disease. Every organ in the body has its own bioelectromagnetic field, and every single cell in the body communicates via electromagnetic signals, or fields, at the overall rate of trillions of chemical reactions per second (Pilla, 2006).

PEMF is a way to alter energy fields to enhance cellular functioning. Can you imagine … changing the way your cells are talking? Well, that is what PEMF does. Through controlled and pulsed electromagnetic frequencies (PEMF), it delivers health-enhancing low-frequency energy fields to the cells, which stimulate electrical and chemical processes in the tissues.

With PEMF therapy, the body can more efficiently process the electrical and chemical exchanges associated with those channels and address imbalances or dysfunctions in those areas, leading to improved adaptation and natural healing. PEMF therapy is similar to charging a battery; PEMF stimulates cells and generates very small microcurrents that tend to run along nerve pathways. This leads to an increase in intercellular communication, metabolic processes (in part due to increased circulation), oxygenation, alkalization, ATP production (the form of energy used by cells to perform work such as running enzymes), and optimized cell membrane potential. As a result, cells regenerate, oxidative stress and inflammation are reduced, immune responses are more robust, the feel-good endorphins are boosted, and depleted adrenal and other endocrine gland functions are restored (Pilla, 2006).

Once the cells are working more optimally, the nervous system calms down, diminishing the disruptive signals such as pain, which have become magnified over time. PEMF provides feedback to the body about those bioelectrical signals. The body's nervous system then uses that feedback to reorganize itself and improve its own intercellular communication. With the feedback, the cells better align themselves within the organ system and entire body. The individuals experience feelings of wellness (Pilla, 2006).

What is a PEMF session like? There are different types of devices involved in PEMF, but all work to change the ways the cells are communicating to prompt the body to turn on its own healing mechanisms. A PEMF session typically involves sitting in a chair or lying down. Depending on the equipment available, a mat or sensors are applied. One can sleep, watch a movie, read a book, etc. during a session. It is safe for both children and adults, and I recommend consideration if you are looking to improve wellness.

Side effects after a PEMF session aren't typical, and the majority can be resolved by changing protocols. Detoxification effects or death of bacteria (herxing) are the most common. Detoxification support before or after sessions can also be a helpful tool to assist the body's healing process (please refer back to Chapter 8 for detoxification strategies).

The therapeutic use of pulsed electro-magnetic therapy is now well-established and supported by a growing number of double-blind placebo-controlled studies. There is also an increasing number of modalities now approved by the US FDA and regulatory bodies worldwide for pathologies such as bone repair, pain, inflammation, and chronic repair (Pilla, 2006). BRT devices employ very low-amplitude PEMF signals, which is supported by the literature (Milyaev et al., 2006; Binhi et al., 2007; Machlup, 2007; Muehsam et al., 2009).

At our office, we use a type of PEMF called "Advanced Bio-Regulation Therapy," or BRT, with individuals suffering from stand-alone issues or complex issues. The research supports use with those clinical issues such as inflammation and fibromyalgia (Shupak et. al., 2006), OCD, stress (Usenko, Usenko & Vasendin, 2015), anxiety (Hattapoğlu et. al., 2019), PTSD (Alizadeh et. al., 2019), pain (Nelson, Zvirbulis & Pilla, 2013) and depression (Martiny, 2017). I also work with patients who are experiencing multiple issues simultaneously, such as PANS/PANDAS, tick-borne disease, autism, and depression. It has been a great tool to support detoxification from an overburdened liver due to hormone issues, medications, or infectious disease, too.

PEMF has many therapeutic advantages, and most patients notice the immediate benefit of feeling relaxed.

For so many children experiencing layered physical and mental health issues, PEMF is a good treatment option. Many of the kids I work with have infectious disease and anxiety or depression, and PEMF often brings them immediate relief by supporting the body in going into a calm parasympathetic dominant state. Once the nervous system is regulated, they feel less anxious, and the body can then turn its attention and resources toward healing.

Psychotherapy

When we think of psychotherapy, we think of the traditional "sit-down-and-talk-about-your-problems" model. While talk therapy may have its place in helping a child who is struggling, it should never be *the* go-to therapy for kids.

What?! You may be protesting.

Let's think about this:

Kids show their emotions through their behaviors, and we should always meet kids where they are, right? So why would we try to connect with them through talk? You've already learned about how stress hijacks the brain, and how, when that happens, we aren't really capable of sound, rational thinking. Yet we keep trying talk therapy with kids.

Lightbulb moment? Yes! This is also why all that talk therapy you have tried may have done very little in and of itself. There are thoughts floating around in our kids' subconscious that they just can't access yet.

So, how *do* children who are struggling with regulating their emotions, thinking, and behaviors learn to act differently? Well, neuroscience provides that answer. We need to calm the nervous system down, so your child can think. When we do so with therapies such as neurofeedback, biofeedback, and PEMF, and then, pair it with therapeutic learning through psychotherapy, the magic happens! Children, teens, and even adults can *learn* new behaviors, because their brain is alert and calm enough to consciously take new action.

Of course, new learning doesn't happen overnight. You need time to unlearn habits and adopt different ways to respond. That often requires not just changes from within the individual, but from the family and environment, as well. In therapy, one can learn and safely test out new responses.

Yes, change is always possible. Many factors influence it, including the child's follow-through as well as that of his or her family, the commitment to the eight pillars, neuroplasticity, ongoing stressors, and medical issues. The beauty of the eight pillars is that each one contributes to powerful change, and you can address them one at a time or by combining them to create a synergistic effect.

The bottom line is that YOU are in charge of your child's and family's mental health, and there are so many natural, safe, and powerful tools right at your fingertips.

Chloe's Story

Chloe struggled with anxiety for as long as her parents could remember. She was painfully shy, resistant to change, and couldn't sleep unless her parents put her to bed. By the time she was seven, Chloe had gotten her parents to participate in a lengthy nighttime ritual, and if they didn't, she would tantrum for hours. She also needed a lot of reassurance, asking an ever-increasing number of questions over and over, like, *"Mom, you're not going to die, are you?" "Dad, I am not going to choke, am I?"* When Chloe's teacher mentioned how she was always biting her nails and asking to go to the bathroom, her parents decided to take her to talk with a therapist.

That helped for a bit, but when in-school writing demands increased in the fourth grade, Chloe's anxiety spiked. Off they went to a therapist again. Well, actually, they saw a few different therapists. When one recommended anxiety medication, Chloe's mom decided to try neurofeedback instead, because for all the many family members she knew on meds, not a one was free from anxiety or depression.

When Chloe came in for her QEEG brain map and intake, it became crystal clear that she actually had OCD. In the hands of one of our highly trained OCD therapists, we learned that Chloe struggled with many types of obsessive thoughts. Traditional talk therapy and cognitive behavioral therapy (CBT) wasn't helping; in fact, it was feeding Chloe's anxiety. She wasn't learning how to talk back to her anxiety; she was learning how to avoid it. Plus, her parents were inadvertently contributing to her OCD by accommodating her OCD-driven demands.

A combination of neurofeedback paired with Exposure and Response Prevention (ERP) allowed Chloe to calm her nervous system and manage her own anxiety, obsessions, and compulsions. She learned how to tolerate being uncomfortable and talk back to the anxious feelings and thoughts that plagued her (more on talking back to OCD later). Her mom noted, *"I hadn't realized how much Chloe's anxiety and OCD ruled her life, and ours, until it was gone."*

How Psychotherapy Can Help

To really see how psychotherapy can benefit you or your child, you have to understand that psychotherapy, and all its many forms, is about learning new ways to think, feel, and act.

Psychotherapy is an essential component of reducing and reversing mental health symptoms, and there are many factors that improve treatment outcomes, including the skill and experience of the therapist, client motivation, adherence to treatment recommendations, and psychotherapy at the right time. Without a regulated nervous system, it is pretty hard to absorb what you learn in therapy and then take action. Low motivation often gets blamed for treatment failure, but if we look to neuroscience, we know that stress hyperactivation of the nervous system gets in the way of how we think and act.

The Many Benefits of Psychotherapy:

Get Rid of Old Habits, Gain New Skills

Old habits can find a way to stifle our success and happiness, and we all have unhealthy ways we have habituated from a very young age to manage stressful and anxious feelings. Naturally, the longer habits are around, the harder they are to break, so addressing behavioral habits early is best. However, it doesn't matter if you are 33 or 83; habits can be unlearned with willingness to change, consistency of effort, and loads of practice. Habits don't form overnight, so they aren't going to change overnight. That means effort is required to change habituated behaviors. Your child can't do the work alone, and that is where a therapist who can support your child and your parenting can be so helpful in creating change.

Simultaneously working through the eight pillars gives the brain and body what it needs to regulate, so you are able to make those changes. Always begin with one behavior that is causing the biggest domino effect. Then, consistently apply effort around it.

Support the Nervous System

We know that, when we change the way we react to things, our nervous system doesn't activate as much, and that constant activation makes it hard for our brain to think rationally and exert the effort to change. When in a hyperactivated state, our nervous system responds to stressors in a fight, flight, or freeze manner. When your child is in this state (which I call the "red zone"), he/she isn't thinking straight. Period.

The key is to calm that nervous system and add regular therapy to support behavioral change that will help to reduce activation and gain new skills.

Gain Coping Skills

One of the most important things parents can do for their children is to teach them how to cope with stress. In our fast-paced, intense world, we live with high stress levels and limited downtime. There is little tolerance for the uncomfortableness that comes with stress. Giving kids the tools to self-manage uncomfortable feelings is a gift for today and tomorrow.

Building frustration tolerance is different for every child. Some have a natural stress tolerance and a "sunnier" disposition, whereas others need to develop that skill. Whatever the disposition or skill set, a child can learn healthy coping skills when assisted by counseling. And with therapy, parents can learn how to make slight tweaks in how they communicate to build coping skills.

Make a Mind-Body Connection

One of the most critical ways to manage stress is to make a mind-body connection—and a good therapist will help that process. We all hold stress in our body, and some of us are better at noticing the alerts our body gives us when our brain is stressed. When we learn to recognize that chest tightening, sweating, or increased heart rate, we then need to take a moment and get back in balance, because when we don't address that uncomfortableness, it will creep up in other often-unhealthy ways.

Therapists use "somatic therapy" to help people make the connection. It emphasizes recognizing and tracking sensations throughout the body as well as using breathwork, mindfulness, movement, and sometimes, healing touch.

Gain Self-Regulation

Many behavioral and emotional symptoms result from dysregulation of the central nervous system (CNS), thus impacting how we control our responses, sensations, and thinking. When children or teens get into a pattern of overreacting to situations, people, or stimuli, they find breaking that pattern very hard without direct therapeutic support. Understanding the neurobiological reasons for self-regulation difficulties is very helpful for children and their parents. When a child or teen is able to create those few seconds to respond instead of react, he or she can learn new ways to act without that constant stress activation. Therapists who work with children are trained to not only support the children/teens, but to also teach parents how to manage the behaviors that come with self-regulation issues. A therapist can help children and parents gain the necessary tools to change family dynamics and create healthy behaviors.

Connect with Emotions

Special needs children and teens can have a hard time connecting with their emotions due to constant stress and anxiety. Therapists help kids put words to emotions, so they can connect with their feelings rather than be overwhelmed by stress. For parents, learning how to support their children with emotional language in a positive manner may not come naturally. While neurotypical children may be able to pick up emotional language, special needs children often need to be explicitly taught how to do so. Counseling can help parents and children learn the language tools necessary to discuss emotions in a way that lessens behavioral responses to stress.

Stop Negative Thinking

One of the most damaging things anyone can do to him or herself is get stuck in a pattern of negative thinking. We all have negative thoughts, but when we feel good about ourselves and are positive thinkers, we 'swipe left,' not allowing the negative thoughts to define us. Left unchecked, negative thoughts can become limiting beliefs that define us. When our children think, *"I can't do this,"* or *"I am not good at this,"* guess what? The outcome tends to reinforce those beliefs. When we teach kids in therapy to flip that dialogue to *"I can do that,"* and *"I am good at this,"* the outcome is very different. Do you think athletes go around thinking they won't make the shot? Heck no! They think, *"I've got this."* In therapy, parents can learn how to model positive thinking with their actions and words, and their child can learn the importance of positive thinking.

Improve Self-Esteem and Self-Confidence

So many kids with emotional, social, and behavioral issues are broken down, and that is one of the main reasons I see kids in therapy. They often feel like garbage and think so little of themselves. Hearing the awful statements they make about themselves can just break your heart. Changing their negative inner dialogue is so important, and therapists are often very skilled at helping children challenge faulty assumptions. Only when a child believes in herself can she feel good about herself. Without inner confidence and self-esteem, children and teens are prone to at-risk behaviors and increased severity of mental health issues. Therapy can build confidence, and with self-confidence, the sky is the limit.

Types of Psychotherapy

When most people think of counseling or therapy, the image of a client lying down on a chaise lounge talking to a therapist in a chair comes to mind. That really isn't the standard of care today for adults or children. In psychotherapy, mental health professionals, therapists, and psychologists apply scientifically validated techniques to help people develop healthier, more effective strategies and habits that create behavioral change. It is a process whereby psychological problems are treated through back-and-forth communication as well as the therapeutic relationship development between an individual and trained mental health professional. The rapport between therapist and client is a critical factor that creates a safe space for behavioral change.

The goal of psychotherapy is to help individuals work through their issues in more effective and healthy ways, so clinical symptoms are reduced, and a person can lead a more functional life. Through the psychotherapy process, one learns how to take control of his or her life, change habits, become more adaptive, develop resourcefulness and resilience, and respond to challenging situations with healthy coping skills.

There are many approaches to psychotherapy, including cognitive-behavioral (CBT), narrative therapy, solution-focused therapy, and more, and they all support children and families. They can be quite effective in improving mental health.

For parents, it may be hard to know which might work best for their child.

When selecting a type of therapy, it is important to be clear on your child's specific issues. The most important features of quality therapy for children and teens are the therapist's experience working with kids and your child's specific issues. So many therapists are generalists, which means they don't have expertise in particular issues and types of therapies. In other words, they may have surface training, but not deep training, and you want a provider with deep training. That experience does make a difference in treatment outcomes.

How do you know the difference between a highly trained therapist and a generalist? Simple … you have a conversation with him or her. Trust me, it will become very clear whether s/he has expertise or not. A highly trained therapist will educate you about your child's issues, not the other way around. You can also check out his or her social media posts and blogs. And lastly, a highly trained therapist should belong to professional organizations in his or her specialty area. For example, I am a member of several national organizations related to neurofeedback and biofeedback, as well as Lyme Disease, OCD, and anxiety and depression. Membership to these organizations means a commitment to continual training and a higher level of professional-ism, and most organizations have a vetting process to ensure a minimum level of qualification.

Traditional Psychotherapy/Talk Therapy

Even though traditional talk therapy has been shown to be clinically effective (Bradley et. al., 2005; Weitz et. al., 2018), it should not be the first choice of therapy for a highly distressed or stressed individual or child. Talk therapy relies on rational thinking, so with the absence of a regulated nervous system, talk therapy is not only frequently ineffective (Weisz, McCarty & Valeri, 2006), but it can actually contribute to further activation of the nervous system. Tra-ditional talk therapy can be incredibly helpful in resolving faulty assumptions and negative thinking, and I have found it tremendous for parents who are struggling alongside their child.

Play Therapy and Expressive Arts Therapy

Play and expressive arts therapy are well-established disciplines based upon a number of psy-chological theories. In play therapy, toys are substituted for the child's words while play is used for the child's language. Therapists strategically utilize play therapy to help children express what is troubling them when they do not have the verbal skills to communicate their thoughts and feelings. Play is the language of children, and meeting children where they are at is critical in changing behaviors. Through play and the use of expressive arts, therapists help children learn adaptive behaviors and gain tools for emotional and self-regulation, social skills, and executive functioning skills. Research, both qualitative and quantitative, shows that play and expressive arts therapy are highly effective (Bratton, Ray, Rhine, & Jones, 2005; Leblanc & Ritchie, 2001). The research is also clear that early intervention is critical in mental health, and play therapy is an effective tool for young children to learn new skills to manage feelings, connect to their body sensations, and learn to self-regulate.

Somatic Therapy

The main goal of Peter Levine's Somatic Experiencing™ Therapy, often referred to as "SE," is the recognition and release of physical tension that may remain in the body in the aftermath of a traumatic event. The focus is on teaching individuals to use the tools to settle their fight-or-flight response, or to come out of a freeze response. Developing a window of tolerance for stress, or learning how much stress a person can handle, is a critical part of the process, so one can recognize and connect to his or her own body's alert signals *before* a full activation occurs, and then, employ learned strategies.

SE gives people a sense of empowerment by allowing their bodies and nervous systems to repair ruptures in the threat-response cycle and to experience the act of completing actions that didn't get to happen during a traumatic event, so they can move out of 'stuckness' to 'completeness,' and go forward in life.

After a traumatic event, the body has no idea of when the issue actually happened. Therefore, it gets stuck in an activated state indefinitely, until it is able to release it. That is why connecting to our body's responses is so critical. Children are great at connecting to what their body is telling them, because behaviors are their language. The pioneer in SE, Peter Levine, talks about helping a client to re-associate aspects of experience to regulate the nervous system (Payne, Levine & Crane-Godreau, 2015). When the nervous system is offered options other than flight, fight, or freeze through the use of imagery and sensation, one creates a 'safe space' for feelings, thoughts, and behaviors to change and is able to break through the blocks holding him or her in stress and pain patterns.

An SE therapy session typically involves the patient tracking his or her experience of sensations throughout the body. Depending on the form of somatic techniques used, sessions may include awareness of bodily sensations, breathing techniques, voice work, physical exercise, dance, release movements, and in the case of a highly trained therapist, healing touch. My book, *The Teletherapy Toolkit*™, is infused with somatic therapy techniques, because in my thirty years of working with kids and families, I have learned that reconnecting with one's body is paramount in moving forward when activated by stressors or trauma. Somatic therapy can offer a variety of benefits as it helps reframe and transform current or past negative experiences. It also reduces discomfort, strain, and stress, while developing a heightened ability to concentrate (Hartley, 2004).

*For more information, see **An In-Depth Look at Somatic Therapy** below.

Emotional Freedom Techniques (EFT)

Emotional Freedom Techniques, or EFT (often referred to as "tapping"), is a tool used for physical, emotional, and performance issues. Those with therapeutic issues should learn and practice under the care of a licensed professional.

EFT operates on the premise that no matter what part of your life is in need of improvement, there are unresolved issues preventing that improvement. Any kind of emotional stress can impede the human body's ability to heal itself and the mind's ability to approach problems with clarity. EFT works like emotional acupressure to quickly, gently, and easily release negative emotions and beliefs that are at the root of the problem.

I view EFT as an effective tool to mitigate stress and calm the CNS and have seen it improve a variety of clinical conditions. While I had been using it for many years, it was after the Sandy Hook Tragedy that I really saw how powerful EFT can be for those experiencing trauma. We worked with many survivors and community members who were struggling, and EFT was *such* an effective tool in helping kids and adults to reconnect and calm their mind and body.

So how does EFT work? With its footings in traditional acupuncture, EFT is a form of psychological acupressure that works on the same energy meridians used in traditional acupuncture to treat physical and emotional ailments for over five thousand years. Simple tapping with the fingertips is used to input kinetic energy onto specific meridians on the head and chest while you think about your specific problem and make supportive statements (Clond, 2016; Rancour, 2016).

*For more information, see **An In-Depth Look at EFT/Tapping** below.

Executive Function Training

Executive functioning skills are related to focus, planning, and organization. Controlled by the brain's frontal lobe, there are twelve executive functioning skills that develop throughout childhood and into adulthood. They provide us with the ability to interact in our environments effectively, successfully, and independently. When a person is not strong in a particular skill or skills at a developmentally expected age, it can negatively impact their relationships, school success, career advancement, and overall self-confidence. When someone has weak executive functioning skills, there are many ways to intervene depending on the age. Identifying these weaknesses earlier in life can lead to less resistance and quicker results. During executive function training, these skills are addressed and repeatedly practiced to create mastery, so a child or teen can learn how to *independently* manage their actions. Instead of the, *"Huh"* and *"Wuh"* you hear when you ask your child to do something, EF training helps them to take action differently. As you already know, I love to pair neurofeedback with EF training, so the brain alerts. Then, a child or teen can take action differently.

*For more information, see **An In-Depth Look at Executive Functioning** below.

Exposure and Response Prevention (ERP)

Most often used for obsessive compulsive disorder (OCD), ERP Therapy is a combination of Exposure Therapy and Cognitive-Behavior Therapy (CBT) that exposes a person to his or her OCD trigger, so he learns how to manage his level of discomfort to the point of being able to manage his trigger. A child or person learns to "talk back to OCD," which leads to an ability to control triggers and anxiety. Before ERP begins, deep psychoeducation about how OCD impacts the brain and behavior is essential. One of the key features of ERP Therapy that differs from traditional talk therapy and psychiatric medication (that you have likely already tried with little or no success), is that you understand *why* your thoughts are out of control and then learn how to gain it. Whether for yourself or your child, we use ERP Therapy to help people break free from the constant need for reassurance, questioning, worry, and/or repeated behaviors like hand washing or checking. When families are on board and willing to practice helping their child to cope with stress and worry, ERP unwinds all those habits and negative reinforcements around the behaviors. It really can be a life-changing type of psychotherapy.

*For more information, see **An In-Depth Look at ERP** below.

Eye Movement Desensitization and Reprocessing (EMDR)

Eye Movement Desensitization and Reprocessing, or EMDR, is a powerful psychotherapy technique originated by Francine Shapiro, PhD. It is very successful in helping people who suffer from trauma, anxiety, panic, disturbing memories, post-traumatic stress, and many other emotional problems, including with children (Rodenburg, Benjamin, de Roos, Meijer, & Stams, 2009). Tactile, audio, and visual stimulation are used to activate the opposite sides of the brain to help release emotional experiences that are "trapped" in the nervous system. The overactivation of the brain paired with high levels of emotionality cause neurotransmitters to sort of get "stuck." With EMDR, the goal is to reprocess the trauma and allow the "rational brain" to kick in to free the "emotional brain" of the high levels of emotion tied to the trauma to achieve a more peaceful state.

Hypnosis

Hypnotherapy involves the induction of a trance-like condition that puts people in an enhanced state of awareness as they concentrate entirely on the therapist's voice. In this state, the conscious mind is suppressed, and the subconscious mind can become more open. The therapist may suggest ideas, concepts, and lifestyle adaptations to the patient, the seeds of which become firmly planted for positive change.

Hypnotherapy aims to reprogram patterns of behavior within the mind, helping the patient to overcome irrational fears, phobias, and negative and/or suppressed thoughts. As the body is released from conscious control during the relaxed, trance-like state of hypnosis, breathing becomes slower and deeper, the pulse rate drops, and the metabolic rate falls. Similar changes along nervous pathways and hormonal channels alleviate the awareness of unpleasant symptoms. Hypnosis can help to change the patient's perceptions, open him or her up emotionally to be able to address certain traumas, and free mental obstacles blocking his or her progress. Hypnosis has been used to address mental health issues long before medication, and there are many research studies supporting its efficacy for stress, PTSD, pain, etc. (Bowker & Dorstyn, 2016; Fisch, Brinkhaus, & Teut, 2017; Flammer and Alladin, 2007).

One of the many reasons I love hypnosis is its ease of use with children. When children play, they naturally go into a hypnotic state and are more open to positive suggestions. I recall discussing this very topic with a mom of an easily angered child, Miranda, who said, *"Let's throw loving spinach into the hypnosis, too!"* I laughed so hard, explaining how we always toss that

Dr. Roseann-Capanna-Hodge

one in!

Mindfulness/Meditation

Mindfulness techniques like meditation have become a mainstay of our cultural dialogue because of their many benefits. Meditation encourages and develops concentration, clarity, emotional positivity, and a calmer view of the world around you. Meditation is a cessation of the thought process—in other words, the stopping of the constant chatter related to your thoughts. That allows one to calm and regulate. It is a state of consciousness where the mind is not as activated, as it is free of scattered thoughts and rigid patterns.

That state of mind takes time and practice to achieve, but even children can learn mindfulness techniques and benefit from them. The clinical effects of meditation impact a broad spectrum of physical and psychological symptoms and syndromes in a variety of ways, including reducing anxiety, pain, and depression, enhancing mood and self-esteem, and decreasing stress (Sedlmeier, Eberth, Schwarz, Zimmermann, Haarig, Jaeger, & Kunze, 2012). This daily practice is an amazing tool for encouraging the nervous system to calm down and reduce racing thoughts, which helps the body self-regulate and promotes healing.

An In-Depth Look at Somatic Therapy

What Is Somatic Experiencing™?

Somatic Experiencing™ is a trauma-informed therapy that involves a bottom-up approach to resolving trauma and working with the mind via focusing on body sensations. It is one of my favorite types of psychotherapy, because it is so accessible to both young and older. This therapy also works with memories evoked from body experiences as the person focuses on what is going on with the body. It helps to reset a nervous system that has been holding in stress and trauma by teaching one to connect to body sensations, which in turn stabilizes emotions.

It helps people become more aware of their body state and have more mastery and control over what is going on in their body as they learn how to step back and observe what is happening within instead of having to constantly re-experience stress activation.

SE teaches people to recognize and renegotiate what is going on in the body, so they can settle that uncomfortable feeling on their own. This helps individuals to feel less panicked by better identifying body sensations and their meanings, while using tools gained through therapy to manage stress.

SE can be especially useful for those with compounded chronic stressors—two or more stressors at the same time—which often causes overwhelm.

How Does Somatic Experiencing™ Improve Brain Function?

By connecting to the body's sensations, one can reset his or her nervous system, reaching the activation levels in the sympathetic nervous system and impacting autonomic nervous system functions, which can be influenced by unresolved trauma.

SE is also useful for dealing with chronic stress, because the body will experience fight--flight-freeze reactions similar to those induced by physical trauma, causing one to either be hyper-aroused or to feel low, dissociated, or depressed.

What Can I Do as a Parent to Help My Child Use Somatic Experiencing™?

Core to SE is teaching children to focus on the body's sensations, so they can make a mind-body connection to their stressors, which in turn triggers them to use their tools to self-manage stress. As a parent, you teach and cue your child to pay attention to those body sensations and help him or her work through the uncomfortable sensations. Asking, "Where in your body do you notice it?" is a good place to start.

Jesse's Story

Teenage Jesse was highly affected by the isolation of the pandemic. He was already prone to some level of anxiety, but had learned to manage it with a lot of exercise and the structure of playing year-round sports. So of course, with the cancelation of sports due to the pandemic, Jesse's anxiety began to build. He also started to feel sad and lethargic as the anxiety began overwhelming his body and his thinking. His sleep became disrupted, he had a hard time concentrating, and his stomach hurt most days.

He tried talk therapy, but reported feeling agitated afterward and stopped after a couple of months. As a result, he was hesitant to try more therapy, but agreed to one meeting with me. I started my work with Jesse by illustrating what was happening to his brain and body on a whiteboard. Jesse felt validated and hopeful that there was something he could do to start feeling better.

From there, Jesse learned how to connect with his body sensations, so he could then pay attention to and address the alert signals. He began by interpreting his body sensations and breaking the unkind thought patterns that sent him down Worry Hill. Over time, he learned via psychotherapy that while movement was a great tool for him, he needed to actually slow down, too, so he could connect his sensations to his thoughts to regulate. He needed to understand his over-aroused and under-aroused states, so he could respond without feeling so overwhelmed.

Jesse found that optimal zone—the place where his brain and body could be less reactive and more relaxed in that all-important parasympathetic dominant state. It was there that Jesse was able to be calm, engaged, and alert, instead of feeling so overwhelmed by his emotions and body sensations.

An In-Depth Look at EFT/TAPPING

What Is EFT?

Emotional Freedom Technique (EFT), also known as "tapping," works by combining tapping on different meridian points with cognitive restructuring. This activity allows the brain and body to release stress through the process of regulating the central nervous system (CNS) and releasing negative thoughts and emotions.

Tapping along specific energy points, or meridians, is an integral part of why EFT tapping is so effective. Research indicates that when energy patterns are disrupted due to stressful experiences, the path of energy between neurons can be disrupted. When people release negative emotions with EFT, it may help the energy flow again (Clond, 2016; Rancour, 2016).

Unlike traditional Cognitive Behavioral Therapy (CBT), which works at the conscious level, EFT works at the subconscious level to connect the mind and body in a way that reduces unpleasant, stressful, or traumatic memories, thoughts, emotions, and behaviors. As you are aware, relying on the conscious can be less effective for those in a chronic stress state or who have experienced trauma, as they aren't able to access rational thought when the nervous system is hijacked.

With EFT, you identify what is present, starting with the negative, and then simultaneously tap on meridian points. You clear energy blocks by tapping on stuck emotions and moving information from the subconscious to the conscious, so it can be addressed without activation. EFT is effective because it helps to remove stressors stuck in the brain's emotional center, or the limbic system's amygdala, without causing individuals to relive them or be activated by them. When the nervous system is calmed, EFT allows a person to review an issue without reliving it to the point where the body becomes activated, which would normally induce a flooding of uncomfortable emotions. It can also be done in a much shorter time period than talk therapy.

EFT/tapping may be an emerging therapy, but there is a growing body of literature to support its efficacy and need for further examination (Bach et. al., 2019; Church & House, 2018; Church et. al., 2016; Sebastian & Nelms, 2017).

How Does Tapping Work?

You start with a "set-up statement" to focus on while tapping. Check in with yourself about the intensity of the fear or stressor, typically assigning that intensity a number from one to five. Start at the side of the hand, saying the set-up statement three times. From there, you tap through nine different meridian points.

As you tap through the points, three to five times on each, you repeat your set-up statement. Go through all nine points once or twice, and then, check in with yourself again to determine the level of intensity around the fear/stressor. The goal is to bring the intensity down.

Again, stressful experiences and negative emotions can disrupt the path of energy in neurons, so tapping on the meridian points can release blocked energy and allow proper energy flow to re-open. When you're able to bring the intensity of the emotions down, it becomes easier to talk through emotions and experiences, and positive self-affirmations become more effective. Better yet, individuals who participate in EFT will often come up with their own positive statements to tap on.

EFT often starts with one problem or stressor and leads to the discovery of a limiting belief, which can be eliminated by tapping. Limiting beliefs sound like "I'm not worthy," or "Nothing good ever works out for me." And we know how much those negative thoughts can hold our kids back. By tapping, individuals are able to release these types of negative emotions and more easily regulate and process emotions.

Jordan's Story

Recently, I worked with Jordan, a young man who had tried too many medications and therapists to count for his ADHD and depression (and by the way, the QEEG we did showed that it was really post-concussion syndrome). He was so afraid that our treatment plan wouldn't work, either.

So, I stopped the intake session and had the whole family tap on, "Nothing ever stops my anxiety." On a scale of zero to ten, we were able to reduce Jordan's worry from a ten to a three, and then, we released a whole bunch of emotions around his long health journey. Jordan switched his thinking and dove into neurofeedback and psychotherapy. I can't tell you how happy I was to hear him say, "I have made more progress in the last three weeks than I have in the last five years!" Calming the nervous system and stopping those limiting beliefs can be so powerful.

Which Conditions Does EFT Treat?

EFT is great for many different issues and conditions, including stress, anxiety, PTSD, and really, whenever an individual feels stuck (Clond, 2016).

For children, EFT can be used to combat fears such as that of the dark. It is also helpful in dealing with perfectionism, and can even be used to help with pain, as pain is often somatic and can be caused by emotional upset.

How Can You Help Your Child with EFT?

Sometimes, children don't even need to use a set-up statement. They can start by going through their complaints of the day in their head, no matter how big or small the complaint may be. Then, with the help of parents or a therapist, children start tapping on the pleasant moments of the day. Kids can tap on their own points, but some younger children prefer when parents tap on the points for them. When a younger child is feeling dysregulated, it can be helpful for parents to hold or hug him or her, gently tapping up and down the spine, which is often calming. Children tend to have less limiting beliefs and traumatic experiences than adults, so the effects of this technique are generally noticed pretty quickly. Teaching children these skills early on can help them in both normalizing tapping in later years and in using it as an effective coping mechanism.

How Can You Use EFT at Home?

Once you learn the process of creating a set-up statement, checking-in and identifying intensity, and tapping through it, the tapping can be done anywhere (note that for trauma-related issues, it is often beneficial to tap with a therapist). There are also ways to activate the meridian points discreetly, which can be helpful at school or work. You can touch your fingertips together like a steeple and apply a bit of pressure, or gently hold the gamut point between the ring finger and pinky finger knuckles.

EFT Tapping Points

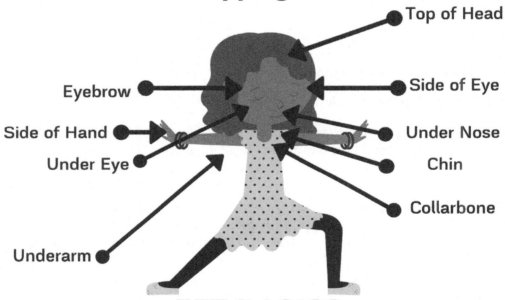

- Top of Head
- Side of Eye
- Eyebrow
- Side of Hand
- Under Nose
- Under Eye
- Chin
- Collarbone
- Underarm

EFT BASICS

- Identify the problem that you are facing.
- Determine what level you are at on a scale of 1 to 10.
- Set up the statement, "Even though, I have X, I love and accept myself."
- Tap the points and complete three full cycles.
- Re-evaluate your level.

www.childrensmentalhealth.com

An In-Depth Look at Exposure and Response Prevention (ERP) Therapy for OCD

Obsessive-compulsive disorder (OCD) is a disorder that often starts in childhood and wreaks havoc on a person's (and his or her family's) life. Children and adults with OCD experience unreasonable thoughts and fears (obsessions) leading to compulsive behaviors and rituals (physical and mental). Individuals with OCD engage in compulsive behaviors and rituals attempting to end the obsessions, decrease distress and anxiety, and/or stop perceived negatives from happening. These OCD-related actions take up a considerable amount of time every day (one hour or more) and interfere with daily functioning (home, school, work, relationships, etc.).

Exposure and Response Prevention Therapy (ERP or ERP Therapy) is a combination of Exposure Therapy and Cognitive-Behavior Therapy (CBT) that exposes a person to his or her trigger, so s/he can learn how to be uncomfortable to the point of ignoring the trigger. It is a well-researched and effective therapy that focuses on breaking the behavioral habituation of obsessions and compulsions through a combination of neuroscience psychoeducation, cognitive restructuring, and safe exposures (Abramowitz, 1996; Ghassemzadeh, 2017; Riise, 2016; Whittal, 2006).

Before ERP begins, deep psychoeducation about how OCD impacts the brain and behavior is essential for both the child or teen and parent. Understanding the neuropsychological mechanisms of anxiety and OCD helps both the child and his family to move forward in therapy, because they then understand the neuroscience of how the habit forms and how to use that science to unlearn obsessions and compulsions; yes, they are learned and negatively reinforced. That pattern of negative reinforcement must be unlearned, and that is what ERP is all about.

With ERP, the person first identifies his or her often-numerous triggers. Next, the therapist exposes the person to the situations that trigger his or her obsessions and compulsions (sometimes starting gradually and other times addressing more moderate triggers). The therapy emphasizes learning how to deal with the uncomfortableness rather than avoiding it, as the latter leads to negative reinforcement of the habit. Patients learn that with exposure, their anxiety increases at first, but then, it decreases. They safely test the limits of their fears with a therapist guiding them through the awareness that their fears aren't rational, and their exposure experiences validate it.

Over time, through psychoeducation and cognitive-behavior therapy, the person's response to triggers changes, leading to a decrease in the frequency of compulsions and the intensity of obsessions. A critical part of ERP is learning how to "talk back to OCD." In this process, a child remembers what he or she has learned about OCD, and that s/he can use science to control it, all while understanding why his or her thoughts are out of control. From there, the child can employ tools to confront the OCD and cope with uncomfortable sensations, thoughts, and feelings without resorting to obsessive thinking or compulsive behaviors.

Children learn that their own negative thinking is feeding the OCD, and that they can take control of their thoughts and break the habits that feed their disorder. Therapeutic exposures repeated over time decrease associated anxiety, because individuals learn that nothing bad happens when they stop performing rituals. They can learn to stop OCD from bullying them!

Cognitive restructuring is part of the process, so children can learn to evaluate perceived threats associated with each obsession, and then, test limits. And, when their anxiety does get too high in a session, a highly trained ERP therapist will support the child or teen through the exposure.

There is work to be done outside of the session, too, as practicing managing exposures transfers from the therapy session to the real world. Review of that practice is part of each session. With children, parents are part of every session, and they learn to support exposures at home, as well as how to get their child or teen to learn how to tolerate the discomfort. Without commitment of the family to practice outside of the session, ERP is often ineffective. Resistance to practice is the number one reason families discontinue this very effective therapy (Ghassemzadeh, 2017). ERP may not always be easy or comfortable for the child or family, but it works in both the short and long term (Hezel & Simpson, 2019). ERP can be done in the traditional weekly format or intensively, and research has found that intensive ERP can be even more effective (Riise et. al., 2016).

Pina's Story

Pina's mom, Joann, was desperate to save her family from her eight-year-old's OCD tyrannical behaviors. After deep psychoeducation about the neuropsychological mechanisms of OCD, Joann signed Pina up for ERP and neurofeedback. She seemed excited, hopeful, and understanding of the work the whole family would need to do to make real changes.

After just two sessions of neurofeedback, the calls and emails started. "When will Pina get better?" After four sessions of ERP, mom began canceling sessions. "Pina doesn't like ERP, and I don't have time to practice it." This required more calls and emails supporting and educating Joann. She kept the neurofeedback, but discontinued ERP, and we agreed to try to calm down Pina's CNS first, because the work was too hard for the family.

When the next brain map showed tremendous improvement, but her behavioral rating scales showed none, I did my best to educate Joann about OCD. I explained, "OCD is the tyrant! Whether you address this now or 15 years from now, ERP is what Pina needs. ERP will be there when you need it. Please seek it out when you are ready." Oh boy, was Joann MAD! A flurry of emails landed in my inbox: "How dare you question my parenting!" Ugh! Joann just didn't get how her daughter's OCD was keeping them all prisoners.

Thankfully, this doesn't happen too often. Therapy isn't magic, and healing isn't a straight trajectory, but when you do the work, it is effective. Although Joann wasn't seeing results in Pina's behavior, the brain map proved we were on the right track—that a shift was needed to address breaking the behavioral patterns or habits she had created around her intrusive thoughts and compulsive behaviors.

The bottom line is that you can choose to spend your time a prisoner to OCD, or you can choose to work through it with ERP. When people choose the latter, so much good happens—mainly, the child can be freed from the prison of his or her worried and intrusive thinking.

When a child and family completes ERP therapy, OCD intrusive thoughts and symptoms often diminish or disappear. Ultimately, the person with OCD learns to tolerate the discomfort and not be so triggered (Hezel & Simpson, 2019). Moreover, as part of the ERP process, he or she also learns strategies to cope with the anxiety, thereby breaking the anxiety cycle. And the results aren't just felt today, but long into the future, too.

An In-Depth Look at Executive Functioning

Executive functioning skills are essential for kids to meet expectations in school and at home on a daily basis. When kids are lacking in executive functioning skills, they struggle with keeping up with both basic and challenging responsibilities and tasks. Despite being bright, your child may not be able to remember to bring his homework to school, put his shoes away, or flush the toilet. This leads to a lot of arguing and frustration at home, because no one understands one another. "How can Alex have a 120 IQ, but not know how to finish his homework?" Well, if you don't have good executive functioning, completing even the simplest of tasks can be hard.

You have expectations of your child (and so does your child's teachers), and he or she has to deal with the constant challenge of living up to them. The problem is, she can't 'see' what she needs to do, because she lacks executive functioning skills. And when the expectations aren't met, these kids have to deal with consequences that don't often help them learn skills. Kids may be labeled as "lazy," "unmotivated," or "careless," as opposed to lacking specific skills. And what does that do for them except increase their shame and frustration? This is where a skilled professional can help, because those skills can be learned with the right interventions.

The Brain and Executive Functioning

Executive functioning skills are controlled by the brain's frontal lobe. These skills are related to focus, planning, and organization. Some people, often those with attention deficit hyperactivity disorder (ADHD), autism spectrum disorder (ASD), anxiety, obsessive compulsive disorder (OCD), depression, or failure to launch have a hard time focusing, managing time, switching focus, and controlling their impulses.

The frontal lobe can affect executive function in multiple ways, including:

- Organization: the ability to gather and order information to process it and organize materials.

- Working memory: a system for temporarily storing and managing the information required to carry out complex cognitive tasks.

- Regulation: being able to take in your environment and control your response to it.

- Inhibition: the ability to stop your own behavior at the appropriate time, including actions and thoughts.

What Are Executive Functions?

There are twelve executive functioning skills which develop throughout childhood and into adulthood. These skills provide us with the ability to interact in our environments effectively, successfully, and independently, and are not fully developed until around 25 years of age. When a person is not strong in a particular skill or skills at a developmentally expected age, it can negatively impact their relationships, school success, and overall self-confidence.

When someone has weak executive functioning skills, there are many ways to intervene depending on the age; identifying these weaknesses earlier can lead to less resistance and quicker results. It is important to understand what executive functioning is, so you can get a better sense as to whether your child is lacking in the 12 foundational components of executive functioning.

The 12 Executive Functions:

- Response Inhibition

- Working Memory

- Emotional Control

- Sustained Attention

- Task Initiation

- Planning/Prioritization

- Organization

- Time Management

- Goal-Directed Persistence

- Flexibility

- Metacognition

- Stress Tolerance

Executive Functioning in the Real World

A child can be very capable of performing tasks, but often fall short with things like doing chores, homework, keeping his or her room clean, being ready on time, or starting and finishing tasks in a specified amount of time. Naturally, you wonder why; is it on purpose? Or is it genetic?

You may feel frustrated and confused, because there have been times when you've witnessed your child willing and able to do things, but unable to *maintain* doing them. Unless you nag him, nada, right? And boy, it's easy to feel like you've simply "had it." (After all, who actually *enjoys* being a nag, besides your Aunt Betty?) You may also wonder why your child can do these tasks sometimes, or why his or her younger siblings can do them better. I mean, they do have the same genetics!

You've probably tried many things to help your child, and you've likely had the same arguments over and over again. With so many therapists, tutors, and meds, and none of them having really helped, parents are often pushed to the brink, and ultimately give up hope.

Here's the good news:

An understanding of what is *really* going on is the first step toward change.

What Happens When You Have Weak Executive Functioning Skills?

A younger child who has weak sustained-attention and task-initiation skills may struggle to complete a chore without a parent's help. A child in middle school who has weak impulse control and flexibility skills may not be able to say "no" to friends or stop playing video games without constant reminders. A child in high school with weak time-management and planning/prioritizing skills may never be on time, fail to start assignments early enough, and/or often miss important details.

If these skills are not identified as weaknesses, but instead labeled as "laziness" or "defiance," the opportunity to improve and strengthen them does not present itself.

If you have tried a bunch of things to improve your child's behavior and nothing has worked, it may be that the help you received wasn't from an executive functioning specialist, or that it wasn't paired with the necessary teaching required to learn NEW behaviors.

Help for Executive Functioning Problems

If you're a parent of a child with executive functioning difficulties, then you've probably realized he or she isn't going to just magically learn how to organize his/her homework or messy room. The good news is that executive functioning skills *can* be taught!

But without new learning, your child or teen will be stuck in the same behavioral patterns, and worse, you'll be stuck nagging him. And no one wants that!

A trained and skilled therapist can identify weaknesses and develop a plan to implement strategies and modifications to strengthen the desired skills.

The first problem that needs to be addressed is how one neurologically orients to the environment around him. A child or teen with EF problems doesn't see the end result, and therefore needs to be directly taught to see the end product *first*, and then, to work backwards. This can be accomplished with executive function coaching.

A checklist isn't going to teach a child to "see" the end product, and frankly, he or she will never connect his/her actions to the end product that way. It will only lead to your child or teen being STUCK with needing constant reminders to do this or that. If YOU have good executive functioning skills yourself, you may be thinking, *"Of course!"* Sometimes, we take the things we do well for granted, and we assume they are things our kids "should just know." Well, some things need to be explicitly taught.

Parents also need to change their language to help reinforce what their child is *learning*, which is why working with a highly trained specialist can really turn things around. This is especially effective when paired with brain-based therapies such as neurofeedback, which gets the brain to regulate and alert differently. Getting the brain into a healthy rhythm through highly effective neurofeedback coupled with new learning through coaching is a great way to get your child/teen to begin taking independent steps that lead to good executive functioning.

Patrick's Story

Patrick is super-smart, yet his parents had to be all over him all the time in order for him to organize himself enough to get his work done—*and turned in*—on time. Patrick liked to 'wing it.' He was used to *"getting by"* just by regurgitating what he heard. And that tactic seemed to work, actually ... until he got to the ninth grade. He just couldn't consistently keep up. By mid-year, his teachers wanted to drop him from his three honors classes.

Understandably, Patrick's parents were worried, and really, they were irritated with their son. *"He is just so smart,"* they would always say. (I had certainly heard that before!)

Simply put, to be in an honors class, you have to do the work. That meant Patrick had to learn how to think in reverse—to start with the end result and work backwards. Fortunately, Patrick understood that he had to use "hacks" to improve his performance, and he embraced his work with our EF specialist. Over time, he got way more consistent, and so did his grades. Patrick still loved to push the limits and procrastinate, but he improved his executive functioning skills so much that he was able to turn his work in on time, and most importantly, *independently*.

Chapter 12 - Rethinking Parenting: Building Resilience

Pillar 8: Parenting

Parenting is a rollercoaster of highs and lows! When our babies are born, our hearts are full of so much love and joy, and we instantly want only the absolute best for them. When our child struggles for any reason, we worry. How can we not, in our fast-paced, high-pressured schools and world? While the growing-up process has never been easy, with modern technology, it is so much more intense. And even though we, as a society, are more knowledgeable than ever about learning and attentional/behavioral issues, the general acceptance of our children with disabilities can sometimes still feel stuck in the dark ages.

What we can do as parents is love our babies unconditionally and teach them as best we can by modeling.

We want our children to be self-confident, independent, and have good self-esteem. That foundation is built with good parenting and resilience. Our children aren't born resilient; they *LEARN* the skills to be resilient. They learn to cope with all the stressors life throws at them by tolerating and dealing with uncomfortable emotions and sensations. Yep, our children have to feel uncomfortable and build their own toolkit to manage stressors … and we must allow them to.

How we parent and discipline our children isn't just about correcting behavior. It is also about teaching them acceptable behaviors and building the skills required to self-regulate their emotions, thoughts, and behaviors. It is about equipping them with what they need to cope with whatever comes at them with confidence and security. When children are resilient, they are able to react to stressors in a healthy way.

So, how do parents build their children's resiliency? By *how* we parent. I love teaching parents about setting "loving limits," which are clear limits with flexibility that accommodate for emotional or behavioral distress. This type of parenting combines positive parenting with flexibility to teach kids how to manage big emotions.

Kids today are stressed and struggling with managing big emotions in a way that I have never seen. Their lack of coping skills is a major factor in the skyrocketing number of mental health issues. Parents come into my clinic every day saying, *"He explodes over the littlest thing."*

While it may be hard for parents who are struggling to help their children manage their behavior, punishment isn't going to stop the anxiety or stress that drives a behavior … but a hug or walking away from each other might do the trick. This isn't to say that you ignore behavior; rather, you focus on the *source* of the behavior and try to teach problem-solving skills without screaming and punishment. Remember, parenting is teaching, and we want our children to build a toolbox of coping skills that will help them be more resilient.

When you focus on teaching and the building of skills, including coping skills, your child can more *independently* manage his or her emotions and behaviors. And that lesson will serve him or her today and tomorrow. Kids who can manage stress and problem-solve are more resilient, and resiliency is associated with greater happiness. Isn't that what we want for our kids?

Margaret's Story

Margaret is a mom of four children who came to me more than twenty years ago saying, *"My fourth child was put on this earth to humble me … because my first three were so easy to parent!"*

Jackson was often cranky and sensory defensive. Despite Margaret's naturally sunny disposition, Jackson made her want to escape to a deserted island. He was tough. And Margaret was a good parent! Jackson just needed to be parented *differently*.

As you have probably already guessed, we put together a comprehensive plan that included occupational therapy for Jackson's sensory issues, lifestyle and dietary changes, and modifications to Margaret's parenting. Jackson needed a lot more routine and structure than Margaret knew how to put into place. He needed predictability and a high level of reinforcement to help him learn.

Over time, Jackson's resistance and temper tantrums became less and less frequent. Margaret could see that he was *learning* a different way to react to stressful situations and experiencing less stress in general. Eventually, Margaret found her own groove and came to appreciate the routine that Jackson craved, because he had become typically pleasant and agreeable. And, at home, balance was restored for all.

7 Steps to Building Resilience in Our Children

So, how do you help your child rely less on you and develop his or her own skills to regulate emotions, thoughts, and behaviors? Well, let me begin with this: no one said parenting is easy!

Building resilience in your child is an evolutionary process. Keep in mind that some kids are just born more resilient—or as I like to say, they are "glass half-full" kinds of kids. Their resiliency develops more naturally, whereas other kids need more reinforcement. The good news is that, when we make the investment in developing coping skills in our kids, they become easier to parent. They are more flexible and adaptable, and less reactive, which translates into a decreased stress level for the whole family. Doesn't that sound lovely?

Here are seven of my best tips for building resilience in children through parenting—below, I go into each more deeply:

- **Role model coping skills and healthy stress responses.**

- **Practice positive and autonomy-supportive parenting.**

- **Connect to emotions to support social-emotional learning and development.**

- **Break ineffective, inherited parenting styles.**

- **Change communication, so everyone is heard.**

- **Understand the cues as to why behavioral issues happen.**

- **Prioritize and practice self-care.**

Tip 1: Role Model Coping Skills and Healthy Stress Responses.

How can parents promote learning? Well, there is actually a lot you can do to teach your child how to cope with uncomfortable emotions, sensations, and experiences. It all starts with role modeling healthy ways to manage stress.

Does that mean we have to be perfect? Uh, no! But it does mean that we can (and should) find the little moments in life that provide us the opportunity to show our kids how to respond to stressors. *That* is how they learn.

We already know that we are our children's first and best teachers. When they are little, they watch what we do and copy us, and we smile. In truth, they are constantly watching and learning from our behavior, including how we manage *all* of life's moments, big and small. That continuous learning through observation carries on throughout their lives.

Parent modeling is largely responsible for how children come to manage their own emotions and stress.

There are plenty of little moments every day to model behaviors: from running late to school to having a disagreement with a family member to forgetting an appointment. Our kids even learn how to parent through observations and experiences—that is how powerful everyday learning is.

And that is why it is imperative that we "put our own oxygen masks on first"—so we can better handle daily annoyances, our kids' behaviors, and unexpected changes to our schedules. When we take care of ourselves, we are physiologically less reactive to things, and that means we are better parents. We have that "space" to slow down a beat to teach our kids how to roll with it. And since a child's brain develops into his or her mid-twenties, we want to take advantage of that neuroplasticity!

Because behaviors can be easily shaped and reinforced, we have so much influence over them. The brain learns through a process called conditioning—changing behavior depending on the reinforcement it receives. Both positive and less-desirable behaviors can easily be conditioned. Think about it: in our daily life, we are constantly being conditioned as behaviors are reinforced, shaped, and refined by our environment and simultaneously influenced by one's thoughts, feelings, and memories.

A few months ago, I got pulled over for speeding with my 10-year-old in the back seat. I knew it was a learning opportunity, and truth be told, that ticket was long overdue! So, before the officer came to my window, I let John Carlo know what was about to happen. I said, *"Hey, it is about time that I got a ticket."* He replied with a laugh, saying, *"Isn't that the truth!"* There were no tears or anger on my part—just a quick acknowledgement, and I got on with my day. In that moment, John Carlo learned that we all make mistakes, and you don't need to "freak out" about them. We ended up chuckling about this incident for weeks … especially when I found the photo he had taken of the officer on my phone!

In the next section, I will show you how positive parenting can help shape behaviors, coping skills, and self-regulation. Remember, when we build a Resiliency Mindset™, kids view, manage, and recover from stressors differently. That means they just don't get activated as easily, and they have the confidence and skill set to cope with stressors *independently*.

Tip 2: Practice Positive and Autonomy-Supportive Parenting.

We want our children to think for themselves and be action takers. Right? Frustration tends to build on both sides when they lack those skills. So how can we build motivation and independent problem-solving and coping skills in our children? Again, by *how* we parent. It isn't anything magical. It comes in the daily interactions we have with our children, and more specifically, in how and what we teach our children.

Through positive reinforcement and promoting autonomous decision-making and exploration, children can develop confidence, motivation, and those all-important coping skills that lend themselves to greater wellness and happiness.

What Is Positive Discipline?

Positive discipline isn't about simply saying nice things to your child. It is a method in which appropriate or "positive" behaviors are acknowledged and reinforced, so desired behaviors occur more frequently. You know that saying, *"You attract more bees with honey"*? Well, that is what positive reinforcement is about. Less desirable or negative behaviors are ignored, while the more desirable behaviors are reinforced to encourage independent thinking and problem-solving. So, you ignore the whining when your son or daughter doesn't get his or her way, and the behavior will come to a stop on its own the majority of the time.

Positive discipline focuses on *solutions* instead of punishment and emphasizes the *learning* of communication and coping skills.

In the beginning, you have to be constantly present to reinforce the prosocial response, so it *does* take patience. It requires a LOT of teaching about solutions and coping skills. But in the long run, this investment more than pays off—kids who receive positive discipline are more independent and better able to self-regulate their own emotions and behaviors. In other words, they are less likely to be emotionally and behaviorally reactive, because they have their own tools and don't need adults to regulate them. Gaining these tools not only helps a child with an immediate problem, but they become powerful assets as the child grows older and has to deal with more complex problems independently.

With positive discipline, you frame your request differently to encourage learning in a more positive manner. For example, instead of saying, *"Johnny, give your sister back her toy,"* you would say, *"Johnny, I like when you ask for your sister's toy. Let's try asking for it."* And when he does ask for it, you verbally reinforce that positive behavior. *"You did a great job giving your sister back her toy and then asking for it back!"* And then, when you catch him independently asking for his sister's toy, you verbally reinforce it again to further encourage that behavior to occur independently. Then, once you see the behavior happening on its own, you stop continually reinforcing it.

The key here is to catch your child being "good" and reinforce that positive behavior, so he can learn that response and display that behavior on his or her own. You also reinforce attempts at the behavior as to encourage the likelihood of the behavior occurring the next time.

When we think of discipline as teaching, it becomes so much easier to parent, because we aren't personalizing or catastrophizing their behavior.

In contrast, with negative discipline, you point out what a child *shouldn't* do without really showing him what he *should*. For example, in negative discipline, you would say, *"Johnny, stop touching your sister!"* You might even give him a punishment for his behavior, which might inadvertently reinforce the behavior you don't want. Johnny might also then blame his sister for his punishment and try to get back at her. We often make the mistake of thinking that just because are kids are bright, they should "just know what to do" … but that isn't the way learning occurs in the greyer areas. It is perfectly normal for children to need more explicit and direct reinforcement, so take the time to show them what to do now, and don't overfocus on what they aren't doing.

What Is Autonomy-Supportive Parenting?

Autonomy-supportive parenting is a style of parenting that promotes and builds autonomy in children through positive parenting and encouraging children to make decisions independently in safe, age-appropriate ways. Parents are supportive and loving as they parent in a way that makes children feel comfortable in their bodies and understand their own feelings. Unconditional love and acceptance are major components of autonomy-supportive parenting, as well as empathy and listening. Children feel heard, and parents don't dominate; rather, they really consider what their child has to say when it comes to making decisions that affect them.

Like positive parenting, children are given structure and limits, but are encouraged to explore and make choices in a supportive way (through positive language) that makes them feel valued and competent. Children are supported enough to make their own decisions without being overly protected or limited, and they feel capable doing so. For example, if your child wants to wear slippers to school, you would discuss the pros and cons of that choice, a*nd then let your child decide.* With autonomy-supportive parenting, there are rules and boundaries, so a parent would supersede if there was a safety concern. For example, if your child wanted to walk to school in his slippers in a foot of snow, that would be a "no"! You would instead discuss with your child why it would be unsafe.

The research demonstrates that children who receive autonomy-supportive parenting are more positive and have better coping skills. They also have better management skills when they are in more controlling situations (Van Petegem et al., 2017). It has also been correlated with increased motivation and emotional development (Froiland, 2015).

Why Should a Parent Choose Positive Discipline and Autonomy-Supportive Parenting?

Positive discipline methods don't just feel good to your child—they feel good to you, too! They reduce the constant nagging and yelling parents often feel they have to do to shape a child's behavior (can I get an "amen"?!). Kids move from obligation to a sense of willingness with autonomy-supportive parenting (Ryan, Deci, Grolnick, & La Guardia, 2006). It also helps a child to shift perspective into that more positive "glass-half-full" mindset and think more independently as he navigates learning at home and at school. He can feel good even when he makes mistakes, because he actually learns from them. Remember, you are using positive language to reinforce behaviors you want your child to repeat. And when we improve our children's confidence and self-esteem, we also improve their empathy and logic. Ultimately, it shows him what he *can* do rather than what he can't, which fosters self-esteem and self-confidence—both of which are so important for mental health and success in all aspects of life.

When practiced regularly, the simple emphasis on focusing on the positive can greatly reduce stress and lead to effective parenting, as it improves communication between parent and child.

When we give our children opportunities to make choices on their own, they learn how to rely on their own problem-solving skills and develop those independent critical-thinking skills. With our love and guidance, we want our children to think for themselves, so they can confidently make choices on their own when we aren't around. Aha! Lightbulb moment.

This type of parenting is not about giving them full control. It is about giving them *enough* control, with limits, so they learn how to do things on their own and be intrinsically motivated to do so.

Who doesn't want to break that "nag" cycle? Well, it starts with giving your child autonomy and opportunities to learn.

While family life may still be over-scheduled and chaotic, building up a practice of positive discipline and providing opportunities for autonomous learning reduces the brain's tendency toward anxious, negative thinking and can increase the brain's capacity to perceive more fully. Remember, when we use neuroscience to guide our interventions, the outcomes are better (Sanders, Kirby, Tellegen & Day, 2014).

How Can Positive Parenting and Autonomy-Supportive Parenting Affect the Brain?

Our brain is constantly changing in response to the stimuli it receives. Because parenting really is teaching, those learned discipline experiences have a huge effect not just on your child's behavior, but on his or her actual brain development. Not only are you creating a more resilient brain, which then contributes to a more regulated central nervous system (CNS), but you are actually building neural networks in your child's brain that help him or her be more focused, calmer, and process more quickly.

Retraining the brain is something that can begin at home as we fight its natural programming to place greater significance on negative events and store them for easy retrieval should a real or perceived threat present itself. This propensity can lead to fear-based thinking and decision making, as well as a greater database of memories of negative experiences. In contrast, the normal flow of life, most positive experiences included, is quickly forgotten or easily overlooked.

In other words, our brain is programmed to be more altered by and reactive to negative experiences. A child whose constitutional makeup is more rigid and negative is impacted even more.

There is also a range of negativity, as well. Some kids are more negative in their thinking, while others are more naturally positive (I've got one of both, so I get it as a parent!). While some children are simply easier to parent than others because of their flexible and easygoing nature, those who aren't can learn to recognize their own negativity bias, which can help make parenting easier. Regardless, disposition is a factor in parenting, as some kids are just more flexible and pick up indirect and direct cues more readily without so much repetition. Remember Jackson's story—he was a much more negative child than her others and challenged her constantly. It wasn't until she implemented a lot of structure and routine that he gained a sense of control around being able to calm and regulate his responses.

Brain research proves parenting skills lead to experiences that shape the way children respond to stress and may contribute to later anxiety (Garland et. al, 2010; McLeod, Wood, Weisz, 2007). Being a good parent is hard for many reasons, but it is especially difficult because it requires you to keep from judging yourself while retraining your brain to think positively. Understanding how the brain's negativity bias works can be especially helpful in reframing parenting actions and verbiage to better support your children. Shifting your inner dialogue and stopping the inner negative chatter is so important, so you can form your vision of success for your child and family.

This will take time, because negativity bias can be especially prevalent in the parenting pressures of today's world. Parents are primed to be on the lookout for potential problems as their children learn to navigate a world that seems to grow more complicated every day with its increasing demands and pressures. The culturally accepted stress and anxiety of daily life also contribute to a propensity toward negativity. That means we are on the lookout for something to go wrong, and we focus on what our kids are doing incorrectly instead of on what they do correctly. Start small, and be intentful in changing your inner and outer dialogue. You will see a shift.

Susan's Story

Susan's parents were Irish Catholic, and she went to parochial school. As she recalls it, *"You just grew up with someone yelling at you or threatening to hit you with a ruler."*

She was a fun, loving, and kind woman, but she really struggled with parenting. She expected near-perfect manners from her kids and found herself constantly yelling at them. She came to me after admittedly *"freaking out because my four-year-old didn't make her bed right."* Yes, you read that right!

But here's the thing: Susan didn't *want* to rule by fear, like her parents did. She just didn't know how to parent differently. When I explained how positive parenting actually wires a child's brain and helps him or her be independent, Susan got it, and was willing to learn a new way. She worked with me in a parenting group learning positive parenting skills, and over time, the yelling stopped and was replaced with laughter. The household felt much lighter.

Susan not only taught herself and her children a different way; she laid the foundation for positive parenting for future generations.

Can Parenting Strategies Really Rewire an Anxious Brain and Build Executive Functioning?

Yes! Neural networks can be altered in a way to promote or enhance mental health. For example, children who display more fearful behaviors are prone to develop anxiety later in life. The good news is that research shows that individuals with anxiety can be reprogrammed to respond to more positive aspects of their environments instead of experiencing a fear response (Huppert, Pasupuleti, Foa & Mathews, 2007; Garland et. al., 2010).

There are definitely things we can say and shouldn't say to a child with anxiety—if you have an anxious child, you know EXACTLY what I mean! Download 5 Things You Never Say to an Anxious Child for my best tips on how to break free from all the bickering and stress here: www.drrotips.com/talktoanxiouskid.

How we parent affects our child's executive functioning, which directly impacts his or her future outcomes. We know that when we parent our children to be more autonomous in the first three years of life, they have better executive functioning skills all the way through high school. In fact, a mother's autonomy support was the biggest determinant of children's future achievement over and above other attributes, including a child's temperament or maternal warmth (Bindman, Pomerantz, E. & Roisman, 2015).

With children, this reprogramming can be done via parenting modifications. Autonomy-supportive parenting lends itself nicely to helping children develop their own problem-solving and coping skills. For some children or adults with a propensity toward negative thinking and fearful or anxious responses, other therapeutic interventions may be necessary. Cognitive behavioral therapy (CBT), dialectical behavior therapy (DBT), neurofeedback, biofeedback, and/or play and art therapy may be needed to retrain an individual's response to his or her environment. The good news is that these research-based therapies are effective and easily accessible.

How Can You Create Your Own Positive Parenting Program at Home?

Simple parenting techniques practiced regularly can help to retrain your child's brain to notice and amplify positive experiences. You just need to invest the time to shift how you parent and be consistent. The first thing parents can do to begin using positive discipline or teaching autonomy is to simply start thinking about the behaviors they want their kids to learn. Positive discipline is all about emphasizing and reinforcing what kids should be doing independently. It's not about punishing (or even acknowledging) the less-desirable behaviors. A simple switch to how you phrase things to emphasize positive experiences as discussed above is generally the best place to start.

Emphasizing positive experiences and actions through discussion and explicit praise can be immensely helpful and have a dramatic effect on everyone. Remember, this can be as simple as pointing out positive experiences as they happen. For example, "Tiger just came up to you and rubbed your leg," or *"George smiled when you helped him out at the bus stop today."* It is likely that your child will not only begin to think more positively, but also respond to positive discipline more readily.

Taking five minutes at the end of every day to notice, reflect on, and write down three good things that happened that day can also have a positive impact. The three things can be about family life in general or more specific to the child. This practice also provides parents an opportunity to reflect on their own positive parenting techniques.

Here are some examples:

"Today, we didn't have to rush to school; everyone got out on time."

"I saw Sarah hold the door for that woman with all the packages, and I felt proud."

"Even though I felt frustrated when John left his saxophone home, I remained patient and did not raise my voice."

These simple steps, when practiced regularly, can greatly reduce stress and lead to effective parenting as well as your child's learning of independent coping skills. While family life may still be over-scheduled and chaotic, building up a practice that reduces the brain's tendency toward anxious, negative thinking can increase the brain's capacity to perceive more fully.

This parenting thing isn't easy, and we weren't trained for it! Positive parenting feels right for a lot of parents because it takes a common-sense approach to teaching and disciplining our kids. At our Ridgefield, CT center, we have seen myriad benefits of positive parenting. In the long run, it benefits the entire family, resulting in everyone feeling less stressed and more supported. And, of course, that leads to even more positives to reflect on!

Are There Other Kinds of Parenting Styles?

I am a huge fan of positive parenting and autonomy-supportive parenting, but there are of course other styles of parenting. Most work well when you consistently use them. Consistency is the key for learning, and that is what discipline is. When you are clear and consistent, your child simply learns better.

Our job as parents is to create self-sufficient, independent beings. That occurs through a lot of teaching and balancing limits with love. When we teach children via loving language and limits, it gives them the security to blossom and grow into who they are meant to be. It also empowers them to learn how to make their own decisions and develop intuition.

There are several styles of parenting, and each one has its pros and cons. Following are the most common.

Authoritarian Parenting

Although the research demonstrates that an authoritarian parenting style is the least effective style, there are some benefits. Children parented in this manner are often more obedient rule-followers. They also tend to have a strong sense of what is right or wrong, which can serve them well as adults. Due to the strictness of this style, these children tend to think about their actions before they do something, which generally means they are less likely to make impulsive choices because they are afraid.

On the flip side, these kids are less independent and often make choices out of fear. Authoritarian parenting and harsh parental control are associated with a higher rate of behavioral problems, externalizing behaviors, and at-risk behaviors (Pinquart, 2017; Thompson, Hollis & Dagger, 2003).

Authoritarian parents focus more on punishment and less on learning through discipline. The downside is that, when parents focus on what a child shouldn't do, they miss the learning opportunity to teach them what they *should*. And when we model and teach positive behaviors and solutions, it builds self-esteem, which is the core of a child's emotional development.

Authoritative Parenting

Authoritative parenting has long been viewed as one of the most effective types of parenting (Smentana, 2017). It focuses on balancing limits with love. Authoritative parents give their child boundaries, but also the freedom to make their own decisions. Authoritative parenting is all about setting up clear limits in advance and then letting children explore independently within those limits. For example, you set your child up with an arts-and-crafts project providing short and clear parameters, and then let him or her work within typical developmental expectations. In my experience, authoritative parenting blends nicely with positive parenting and autonomy support.

Permissive Parenting

Parents who follow permissive parenting take on a role that resembles more of a friend than parent. Permissive parents give their child limited boundaries. The greatest danger of permissive parenting is a resistance to authority and rules. As a child becomes a teenager, his or her acceptance of the rules can become a major hurdle at home and school. Let's face it—the world is full of rules, and some can't be avoided! For example, when an assignment is due at school, there is not a whole lot of flexibility. That can be a challenge for a child/teen raised by a permissive parent who may not set the necessary boundaries for the child to get homework done in a timely manner.

A positive is that children raised by permissive parents tend to be free thinkers who aren't afraid to speak their mind. These aren't the kids who are easily bossed around or lured into activities that don't feel right. They have a strong mind and aren't afraid to be creative or out-of-the-box thinkers.

Free-Range Parenting

Free-range parenting may fall under the umbrella of permissive parenting, but it is different. With permissive parenting, the parent takes on the role of friend and has even less limited boundaries. With free-range parenting, children are raised with limited supervision based on their developmental age and safety needs in order to encourage independence.

Uninvolved Parenting

Yes, this is a thing! Essentially, it is neglectful parenting, as uninvolved parents fail to provide their children with safety and structure. Children may also be exposed to potentially hazardous things or put in dangerous situations while being left to their own devices to figure things out.

Attachment Parenting

Attachment parenting most definitely falls into its own category of parenting styles. Attachment parenting is a style that focuses on nurturing the parent-child relationship, especially in the early developmental period. It incorporates positive, loving care and respect, a lot of nurturing touch, sensitivity, and positive discipline.

One of the biggest criticisms of attachment parenting is the excessive demands on the parents themselves. When you follow an attachment parenting style, you are constantly engaged with your child at a high level, and that takes a lot out of a parent both mentally and physically.

Tip 3: Connect to Emotions to Support Social-Emotional Learning and Development.

One of the most important aspects of parenting is that it lays the foundation of our child's social and emotional development. In a world that tends to overfocus on academics, I can attest to the importance of our children's social and emotional functioning, which has only been highlighted by the pandemic. There is no doubt that kids and families are suffering right now—but they were before the pandemic, too … we are just now connecting the dots.

When a child has a neurodevelopmental disorder, or an issue that interferes with his or her learning, emotions, or behavior, we often can't clearly see or understand our child's behavior. And we certainly don't know what to do about it. We question whether it's just "normal" child development or something else.

Understanding typical social-emotional development will help you decipher why certain behaviors occur.

What Is Social-Emotional Development?

Social-emotional development is a child's ability to experience, express, and manage his or her emotions and behaviors, build positive relationships with parents, caregivers, peers, and others, and explore the environment with curiosity and confidence. One of the key aspects of social-emotional development is the ability to identify and understand one's own feelings, as well as to accurately read and comprehend emotional states in others (National Scientific Council on the Developing Child, 2004).

Children with typical social-emotional development can manage and cope with big emotions, respond to discipline, regulate behavioral responses, put themselves in the shoes of others and have empathy, and establish and maintain relationships. Kids with typical social-emotional development learn from how they are parented and adjust their behavior accordingly with minimal redirection and reteaching.

Why Is Social-Emotional Development Important?

A person's ability to regulate his or her emotions and behaviors, manage frustration, and engage in reciprocal communication and interaction are defining skills in life. These skills help people be good friends, employees, and partners in life. They are what make us resilient and not react to stress in the same way.

With such an overemphasis on academic success, we are losing these important skills that are the foundation of resilience They need to be fostered in young children, as research has established a significant association between stronger social-emotional skills in kindergarten and better life outcomes with regard to education, employment, and at-risk behaviors such as crime and substance use, as well as overall wellness and mental health (Carneiro, Crawford, & Goodman, 2007; Jones, Greenberg, & Crowley, 2015). We know these skills are not only linked to future success, but also that they are quite malleable, particularly in younger children, and therefore worth investing resources into (Jones et al., 2015).

Vanessa's Story

I met Vanessa in one of the play groups I was in with my boys. Whew, her young boys were unruly! They were dolls, too, but because Vanessa didn't really believe in intervening in their play (she was a free-range sort of parent), I was constantly pulling them out of dangerous escapades and showing them what to do. Finally, I had to have a talk with Vanessa.

I explained how her boys were smart, but needed her guidance. They needed her to stay close and be a "parent whisperer." Her response? *"Well, I think kids can figure things out on their own. Besides, this is my time."* Really? A group play date was considered "me" time?! I mean, all the moms were always helping Vanessa's kids while she sat back and hung out.

Of course, this led to a lot of peer issues, and eventually, Vanessa stopped coming to the group. And what a shame that was … those boys were great kids who just needed more supportive parenting.

Learning doesn't just happen. Parents need to be the teacher in all areas, but especially in the all-important area of social-emotional development. If Vanessa had just taken the time to teach her kids (and ok, to actually supervise them!), then they would have learned to self-regulate behaviorally and socially. Instead, without that guidance, they struggled to get along with other kids and became increasingly reactive when things didn't go their way.

How Parents Can Promote Social-Emotional Development

You know strong social and emotional skills are connected to future wellness and happiness, but how do you develop those skills in your kids? For most children, these skills develop in the day-to-day of consistent and loving parenting. However, children are increasingly struggling with less opportunities for social engagement and high stress.

There are many things parents can do if they see their child or teen struggling with social, emotional, or behavioral regulation.

Here are my best tips for building social-emotional skills:

Don't Assume. Thinking your child will somehow pick up social skills or be able to manage stress on his or her own is not a safe bet. Just like anything else in life, we are good at some things naturally, but others, we need help and practice. And with so much in the social-emotional world falling into a grey area, we have to be even more explicit in giving our kids the practice they need. This isn't something a child will learn just by being physically near kids who have those skills. You will need to give your child explicit help with regulating his or her emotions and behaviors.

Practice in Advance. If your child has trouble with x, y, or z, you can begin by previewing the situation with him. Go over (and maybe even role play) what could or couldn't happen. After all, a football team has a practice before the big game; why shouldn't we do the same for a child who struggles behaviorally when he goes to birthday parties or other big events?

Be a "Parent Whisperer." Stay close. Do frequent coaching-type check-ins when playing or interacting with peers. Your child may need more support and structure from you in new situations and with new peers, which is perfectly ok. Be there and guide him or her as needed.

Model Frustration Tolerance. Okay, no one is asking you to be perfect. None of us are! But keep in mind that children learn how to manage stress from watching you. So, try your best to model good skills. Thinking out loud (literally) is a good way for kids to absorb metacognitive strategies they may not have. With consistency, kids will see and learn that even their parents aren't perfect, but they do take the time to problem-solve.

Use Emotional Language. You may be thinking, *"Oh, I do that!"* Great! Kids with developmental lags in the social-emotional area need even more explicit use of emotional language. So, talk about feelings, not just stress or irritations, and tie those emotions to body sensations by asking, *"Where in your body do you feel that anger?"* Your child will become aware of the cues his or her body gives him/her. Then, the next time s/he has that sensation, s/he will be able to identify and address that emotion. Parents should also help their child to connect to his or her own feelings as well as identify the feelings of others. Empathy is such an important skill in life, and one of the greatest predictors of success.

Assign Chores. Yes, you read that right! Having kids and teens do things independently, like chores and cooking, helps to build self-confidence and self-esteem ... which they need to feel good about themselves.

Remember, It Is Never Too Late. As effective as early intervention is, it really is never too late to address social-emotional difficulties. It will just take longer to see results and require a higher level of effort if the child is older. We are lifelong learners, and change is always possible. Find a licensed mental health professional in your area who specializes in social difficulties or behavioral regulation, and get focused on learning new skills.

For more tips on helping your child build social and friendship skills, download 5 Strategies to Help Your Child Make Friends here: www.drrotips.com/makingfriends.

Tip 4: Break Inherited Parenting Styles.

Parenting and Family Behavioral Patterns

When it comes to the things that influence our behaviors, we often don't think about the impact of our family's behavior on how we act today. But the truth is, family behavior patterns often dictate how we navigate through life. We learn how to parent, manage stress, respond to stimuli, and establish thinking patterns from our family (mostly, from our parents).

Family patterns of behavior are often handed down from one generation to the next. For example, how one manages his or her stress and anxiety is often learned from one's parents. If your mother cried over little things and was easily stressed, you are more likely to embody that same kind of behavior. On the flipside, if your grandfather modeled how to not stress over little things, you are more likely to display a higher tolerance for stress.

We have learned a lot about the impact of family behavioral patterns through Family Systems Theory, which draws on systems thinking in its view of the family as an emotional unit, with each part having an interplay. There are generational influences on family and individual behavior and relational patterns that unconsciously replay in all families.

When it comes to parenting, many often find themselves disciplining their children in the same manner in which they were disciplined. Recall Susan, who realized she didn't want to parent in the authoritarian way her parents did. She broke free from the constant yelling she inherited from her mom and switched to positive parenting.

For some, they are passing down the same beneficial parenting they've learned from their parents. For others, though, they may feel stuck repeating the same negative parenting patterns their parents used. Understanding your family's behavior issues (or patterns) is an important step in finding effective ways to deal with every day and difficult family situations.

There are actually different styles of behavioral control that families use when dealing with stressful situations. While each family style of behavioral control is different, there are four basic types: rigid, flexible, laissez-faire, and chaotic (Epstein, Bishop, Ryan, Miller & Keitner, 1993). Based on what is and what is not acceptable within each family system, families develop standards of behavior. Just by regular, day-to-day interaction, these standards are reinforced or extinguished.

If we think about our own families and what we learned when we grew up, I am sure certain family behavior standards jump to mind. For me, I was expected to act with integrity and work hard, and I wasn't allowed to drink beer (they thought it was unladylike).

Depending on family need, behaviors may adapt or change, and more flexible families are better able to change as the demand arises and have healthier communication. In contrast, rigid families not only have more difficulty in adjusting to stressful family situations, but they are more likely to have family conflict as a result of the change. When family behavior patterns are good, then communication is good, and the family tends to be happier (and vice versa). And if all this "togetherness" amongst COVID-19 has taught us anything, it is that family communication is super important in maintaining calmness at home.

If right now you're recognizing that you are continuing a negative cycle of parenting, take heart: even though you may feel limited in your ability to break the cycle, you *can* change. Change is always possible if one wants it. As parents, we are hopefully evolving, mining the gems from our parent's parenting while also adapting to what our children need.

There are several techniques to begin the process of changing dysfunctional parenting patterns and breaking family behavioral patterns that influence parenting.

Mindfulness

If we are to evolve and change, we need to be introspective, mindful, and attentive to our patterns of behavior that influence parenting, as well as to what triggers those behaviors. Consider any moment in which you recognize how you parented just like your mom. Then, you can remember how it felt to you as a kid. When we pay attention to thoughts, sensations, and behaviors, we open our subconscious and gain conscious control, rather than letting our family behavioral patterns limit us.

Ask Yourself, "Is This How I *Want* to Parent?"

Does your parenting feel authentic? If it doesn't, then there's work to be done. That doesn't mean that parenting is all roses and sunshine, but good family communication typically reflects good parenting.

Identify Functional and Dysfunctional Patterns in Your Life.

Just like our children can learn, we can, too. But first, you must determine what is and isn't working. Without attending to the underlying patterns of behavior that create, and therefore drive, our lives and experience, we can end up constantly repeating patterns. Not all family behavioral patterns are bad. Take and use what makes sense to you and adapt to new ways to behave.

Stop Limiting Beliefs and Negative Self-Talk.

We are often our own worst enemies, and how we view ourselves and our negative thinking can limit our capacity for change. One of the first things to do is to identify the negative thoughts that interfere with your behaviors. Next, when you find yourself in that situation, challenge yourself to think differently and change that inner and outer dialogue. With repeated repetition and practice, one learns to break that constant negative inner chatter.

Create a List of Alternative Behaviors.

Start with one alternative behavior and practice. This is often the hardest part, as we can typically see the problem, but feel stuck in taking that first step toward change because we aren't sure where to start or feel that we are climbing a mountain. Start small and know that the problem didn't happen overnight, and it will take time to change it ... so have patience with the process and change will happen.

Learn Coping Strategies.

What we *think* is a stressor is as important as the actual stressor. So if one views a car accident as no big deal, while someone else views her favorite show not being on as the worst thing in the whole world, then the latter is always going to experience a higher level of stress. Having coping skills and a toolkit to pull from when stressors occur is key to managing stress. Remember, it is all about building resilience in our kids and our family.

Recognize Your Triggers.

Recognize when a behavior is a trigger for your "stuff." As wonderful as the notion of having a child is, children aren't perfect, and sometimes, they come with behaviors we don't expect or know how to address. These behaviors can be a real trigger for a parent's own traumas or issues experienced in childhood. The good news is that going to therapy can often be helpful in this area. You can learn to break family behavior patterns and implement new parenting strategies and coping skills.

Family Therapy

When family communication has broken down, family therapy can help. By having a mediator to support communication and new behavioral patterns, families can learn to adapt and be more flexible. Having explicit guidance can put you on the right track and make everyone feel supported enough to make those little changes that create big waves.

Parent Coaching

Working with a therapist who can coach a parent on how to change communications and behaviors can save a lot of time and frustration. In a family system, since there's always an interplay between all the parts, if one part is having difficulty, the rest will, as well. Children who are struggling or special needs can often disrupt the family system, and without explicit coaching, parents aren't sure how to deal with the behavior. Learning the best way to address specific behaviors can be empowering, and when you implement those parenting "hacks" that make parenting about learning instead of punishment, the magic happens!

Recognizing how family behavioral patterns impact parenting is the first step toward positive change. I have worked with many parents over the years, and this book gives you a starting point. In my **Get Unstuck Program**™ (www.getunstuckprorgam.com), I personally coach parents through the eight pillars, one of which is parenting, of course. I definitely see the value of parent coaching and family therapy, because they not only give you the tools, but the guidance to implement them, as well. And you know how powerful parenting is in helping our children become resilient, confident, and happy.

Tip 5: Change Communication, So Everyone Is Heard.

Improving Family Communication

Family communication is a reflection of the health of parenting. When families communicate effectively and feel "heard," all members are happier. Makes sense, right? Ultimately, communication is the basis of all relationships. When we invest in good communication with others, relationships are easier—we know what to expect from people, and we feel safe.

Of course, children learn their communication skills through us. When we show them how to communicate and listen, we provide them the tools they need for healthy relationships in all areas of their lives—friendships, family, love, work, and school. It all starts with teaching them about listening and using kind, emotion-centered language.

Clear limits, use of emotion-centered language, and a good family community are key to cultivating the behaviors of children and teens and for their social-emotional development.

Here are my best tips for family communication:

Make Time for Communication.

Make sure you're eating together or having family meetings. If you don't practice regularly talking with your kids about the everyday stuff, they will never come to you with the big stuff.

Listen.

Being mindful of what your children and teens are saying and what their body language is telling you is *so* important in the communication process. Don't make assumptions, and make an effort to really hear your kid out.

Have Clear Expectations.

A lack of clear expectations is one of the biggest obstacles to effective communication. It is normal to get frustrated when you have mismatched expectations, which can happen so easily if they aren't openly discussed. Especially when emotions are high, we don't always recall information accurately, so being clear is critical.

Speak to Kids at Their Developmental Level.

If your child is young, don't blabber on and on, because it will go right over his or her head. Keep your language clear and concise, and always be clear on your expectations. Use visuals whenever appropriate, and check in with your child or teen as to what s/he "heard" in the conversation. Remember, teens have specific developmental needs for autonomy—to be viewed as competent and have social connection—so keep that in mind when communicating with them. Be prepared to really lean in and listen, and be sure you aren't treating your teen like a baby.

Use Positive Language.

You've already learned how powerful positive language and parenting can be, right? Remember, a simple switch from a negatively framed statement to one positively framed can really create dynamic change in a child or teen. Consider *"I like how you apologized to your sister"* versus *"Why don't you ever apologize?"* The latter criticizes, but the former reinforces what you actually want your child to do. When we point out what a child is doing wrong, we aren't teaching him what he *should* do. Remember, discipline is about teaching, not punishment.

Empower with Choices.

When we give children and teens the power to make choices, it reduces stress and anxiety and builds confidence and self-esteem We want to empower our children to think and act on their own. How else to start teaching those skills than to give them choices? Start easy. One idea is to ask your child to come up with a list of chores she can do to earn media time.

Have Fun and Play Together.

So many good things happen when families have fun! Connection, social-emotional learning, learning in general, and communication are just a few. Children and teens connect through activities, so making time for fun activities is so critical not just for communication, but for connection.

Tip 6: Understand the Cues as to Why Behavioral Issues Happen.

Our children communicate their needs via their behavior. Therefore, when we start thinking about their behavior as a cue for us to dig deeper, parenting becomes more purposeful. Kids always *show* us how they feel, because they lack the communication skills to connect their body sensations to their emotions. As I have talked about previously, they are very capable of learning how to make that connection based on our parenting. When they do, they become more resilient to stress. That doesn't mean your child's behavior will be perfect. But it will improve.

The question most parents have is, *"How do I manage those difficult behaviors when they do come up?"*

How to Manage Difficult Behaviors

When kids are young, they have temper tantrums, which is a normal and common part of child development. Still, parents often struggle with how to manage them. All the parenting books and classes discuss the "terrible twos" and how to handle toddler tantrums, but as children approach five to six, throwing tantrums may trigger worry. While parents become anxious that they are a cause for deeper concern, they are typically part of normal child development. Sometimes, however, when they occur with intensity, frequency, and duration, they *are* a sign of a problem that needs to be addressed. Behaviors should never be ignored, but always supported.

Mark's Story

Mark and his brother *always* threw tantrums. The problem, though, was that Mark was eight years old. It was exhausting for everyone, including Mark. His mom, Catherine, had tried various strategies and came to me worn-out and worried. Mark was really struggling—other kids were starting to avoid him; in fact, he really only had friends because of his other older brother, Kevin.

When we set out to discover what was behind Mark's behaviors, I saw that Mark was a highly sensory kid who was anxious and often negative. If things didn't go his way, the whole family would hear about it. Catherine often gave in to Mark just to avoid a blowout. She was truly at a loss.

It became quickly apparent that Mark was worse when he was hungry, tired, or things were unpredictable. We started with a "sensory diet," adding protein every three hours and extra fat to keep his blood sugar stable. We increased his physical activity, as well.

At the same time, we created a visual schedule for Mark and let him know that two times a day, he would have to make a switch during certain windows of time. This would build tolerance to change, but simultaneously allow him control over it.

Catherine did her part by reinforcing the heck out of every desired behavior or attempt toward it. And with the combination of calming his nervous system and explicit positive reinforcement, Mark's tantrums decreased in frequency and duration! They went from two to three a day to two to three a week, and eventually, to two to three a month. At that point, Catherine knew that his tantrums came with anticipatory anxiety—he would get nervous around exciting events. We worked on that, too, and his behavioral reactions to exciting events lessened. It was still something that had to be managed for years, but the point is, *it became manageable.* Mark felt good about himself for maybe the first time in his young life, and family balance was restored.

What Is a Temper Tantrum?

Temper tantrums are unpleasant, disruptive behaviors or emotional outbursts that children exhibit when frustrated. Children have temper tantrums in response to unmet needs or desires, or when they feel a lack of control. Hunger, exhaustion, discomfort, sensory needs, or wanting something they can't have all trigger tantrums. A tantrum can be a method of getting what they want OR of simply getting a reaction. The behaviors can range from whining and crying to screaming, kicking, hitting, being stubborn, resisting tasks, and/or holding one's breath.

What Is a Meltdown?

A meltdown is a type of tantrum during which a child is totally overloaded, resulting in a complete loss of behavioral control. The child is often totally unaware of his or her environment and lacks safety awareness. She might kick, hit, punch, break things, hurt herself, or harm others. Imagine a child rolling on the ground and screaming at Disney World, totally unaware of the world around her. She typically needs an adult to support her through the meltdown, and it doesn't end quickly.

What Is the Difference Between a Tantrum and Meltdown?

Whether you call it a tantrum or a meltdown, they both refer to scenarios in which a child has an uncontrollable outburst of anger or frustration. All children have them at some point, although they are most common between ages one and four and reduce in frequency as a child develops better communication and coping skills.

The word "tantrum" is commonly used to describe milder outbursts during which a child still retains some measure of control over his or her behavior. Typically, denying something the child wants causes frustration, and the child uses the behavior to get what he wants. Tantrums often end as suddenly as they start and can occur frequently or unfrequently. It isn't unusual for a child to have as many as one or two a week.

A "meltdown," however, indicates a loss of all behavioral control. It usually only stops after pure physical exhaustion. Unlike a tantrum, the child will need time to wind down. While meltdowns can occur for unknown reasons, they typically result from overload. Various types of overload include sensory, informational, and emotional. While a tantrum is about manipulation, a child having a meltdown has no intentions; instead, the meltdown takes control.

Why Do Some Kids Have Outbursts, Tantrums, and Meltdowns and Others Don't?

Self-regulation and resiliency. Outbursts are often an expression of frustration at the lack of control children have over their lives and are more common with strong-willed children. They lack the language to express themselves, so it manifests in their behavior. A child might tantrum when he doesn't get his usual snack at the grocery store because he doesn't understand you are in a rush.

Ultimately, some kids are inherently better at managing and modulating sensory input, frustrations, and emotions than others. Some children can more easily put words to their emotions and react to stimuli in a healthier way because they have coping skills. And some children have biological or neurological issues that make it harder for them to self-regulate, such as ADHD, autism, anxiety, mood issues, OCD, PANS/PANDAS, etc.

Whatever the trigger, most mental health professionals agree that children who have frequent emotional outbursts are lacking certain skills that would help them better handle situations that cause anger, frustration, or anxiety. Problems with impulse control, problem-solving, delaying gratification, negotiating, communicating wishes and needs to adults, knowing what's appropriate or expected in a given situation, and self-soothing are all skills that can be directly supported and learned.

Tantrums 101

Parents ask a lot of questions about tantrums. I've found that simply equipping them with the right information can alleviate a lot of their worry while empowering them to manage them.

How Long Should a Tantrum Last?

Most tantrums typically last a few minutes or less. Even a highly regulated child will have a tantrum here or there. Some children tantrum for less than a minute a few times a week while others might tantrum for five to 10 minutes a couple times a month. Both are normal.

Frequent tantrums lasting more than 25 to 30 minutes are atypical and associated with behavioral issues.

How to Stop a Temper Tantrum

Identifying and proactively managing the triggers to a tantrum are the primary steps to stopping a tantrum from happening in the first place. Knowing your child and recognizing that he has certain behavioral and sensory triggers makes it easier to set up an environment or task in advance.

Identify the Cause of the Tantrum.

Identifying the real reason behind your child's behavior is critical in teaching him to communicate differently and self-regulate. Let him know the schedule and your behavior expectations in advance, and offer choices whenever you can. I often recommend the use of social stories, which is a way to teach appropriate behaviors through the use of visual stories. In the case of a child with transition difficulties, for example, you create a story that displays the problem and appropriate solutions and ways to communicate and review it daily until the tantrums subside. (Note: There are apps for creating personalized social stories.)

Find Ways to Comfort Your Child.

When you aren't able to prevent a tantrum, you need a bag of tricks! Think about what works for your child: a hug, removing her from the situation, a weighted blanket, leaving the room, turning on music, giving her a homeopathic remedy, or whatever it is that helps your child decompress and self-regulate. If she is prone to tantrums, then make sure that you always have access to your toolkit.

Jeremy's Story

I once worked with a dad, Jeremy, who didn't think his wife should comfort their daughter Emilia during temper tantrums, because that meant she was *"condoning"* the behavior.

But once Jeremy understood the "why" behind Emilia's emotional outbursts (anxiety), he felt ashamed. I assured him that it was what he did next that mattered—hugging her was what she needed most.

We created a plan to help Emilia that included breathwork, play therapy, and parent coaching, and her outbursts began to dissipate. She learned to communicate what was bothering her instead of reacting first, as well as new ways to cope and talk back to her anxiety.

Meltdowns 101

Are There Different Types of Meltdowns?

One hundred percent. Whether your child has a developmental lag in self-regulation, a clinical issue, or is displaying developmentally normal meltdowns, there are many sources. Meltdowns often have an emotional regulation or sensory processing component to them. This is especially the case for children that are slow to recover from a meltdown or are experiencing meltdowns outside of the typical developmental window. Parents struggle with how to support their child during a meltdown, so they are important to discuss in-depth.

What Is an Emotional Meltdown?

An emotional meltdown occurs when frustration, anxiety, stress, upset, or depression build up over time.

For children, a single traumatic event can trigger the meltdown, but sometimes, it can come from an inability to manage emotions due to biological or neurological issues. Very bright children can also be more prone to emotional meltdowns, as they cognitively understand more than they "should," yet only have "normal" emotional intelligence to process the information.

Children who experience emotional meltdowns may be irritable, cry, scream, or be snappy. Some children overreact to simple requests, are sensitive to stimuli, display a high level of behaviors, or withdraw easily. Helping them put words to emotions and manage stress is critical in reducing meltdowns.

Meltdowns 101

Are There Different Types of Meltdowns?

One hundred percent. Whether your child has a developmental lag in self-regulation, a clinical issue, or is displaying developmentally normal meltdowns, there are many sources. Meltdowns often have an emotional regulation or sensory processing component to them. This is especially the case for children that are slow to recover from a meltdown or are experiencing meltdowns outside of the typical developmental window. Parents struggle with how to support their child during a meltdown, so they are important to discuss in-depth.

What Is an Emotional Meltdown?

An emotional meltdown occurs when frustration, anxiety, stress, upset, or depression build up over time.

For children, a single traumatic event can trigger the meltdown, but sometimes, it can come from an inability to manage emotions due to biological or neurological issues. Very bright children can also be more prone to emotional meltdowns, as they cognitively understand more than they "should," yet only have "normal" emotional intelligence to process the information.

Children who experience emotional meltdowns may be irritable, cry, scream, or be snappy. Some children overreact to simple requests, are sensitive to stimuli, display a high level of behaviors, or withdraw easily. Helping them put words to emotions and manage stress is critical in reducing meltdowns.

What Is a Sensory Meltdown?

Neurology causes a sensory meltdown, making it different from a tantrum. A sensory meltdown happens when there's too much sensory information to process. The neurodiverse brain is wired differently, which causes a child to interpret his senses more uniquely than neurotypical children.

A child with sensory processing issues can be under- or over-responsive to stimuli, leading her to be extremely uncomfortable or even in pain. A child with sensory processing disorder doesn't choose to get overwhelmed, but she often is. Her body's fight-or-flight response kicks in, leading to agitation and/or discomfort, which causes a sensory meltdown.

I have worked with so many kids with an underlying clinical issue like ADHD, autism, anxiety, or PANS/PANDAS who struggle with sensory issues. When a sensory meltdown hits, they are tough for kids to recover from. Being proactive and meeting a child's sensory needs is critical in preventing those meltdowns.

What Can I Do to Prevent a Tantrum or Meltdown?

Being proactive is key to preventing a tantrum or meltdown. We need to put our detective hats on and think about when, why, and where those behavioral outbursts are likely to happen, and get proactive strategies in place to avoid them.

Remember, offering a child choices is very helpful in empowering him or her to problem-solve on his/her own. It also promotes self-regulation.

Teach coping skills. Once anxiety increases, problem-solving decreases. Teaching kids that they have options and control over their lives as well as those all-important coping skills will help them now and in the future.

Bringing balance into children's lives with good nutrition, following a sleep schedule, and practicing stress management daily (e.g., regular downtime, sensory activities, music, coloring, exercise, meditation, deep breathing, etc.) can go a long way in giving them the tools they need to manage stress in their life.

For more tips on how to deal with your child's behavior, download 5 Parenting Tips for Dealing with Snarky and Cranky Children at www.drrotips.com/snarkykids.

Proactive Support for Behavior and Social Learning

More than any other prevention strategy, planning in advance for changes in routine can reduce meltdowns and tantrums. As the parent, you can set your child or teen up for success by letting him or her know the schedule in advance and giving time warnings whenever possible. While last-minute special events may seem like a fun idea, sticking to the game plan helps sensitive and difficult kids succeed, because surprises can be stressful to them. Lack of sleep and unhealthy eating can cause behavioral flares, too, so making sure your child has eaten protein before he or she has to do a task or go to an event can help cut back on outbursts.

We know that kids with underlying clinical issues such as ADHD, anxiety, autism, OCD, mood disorders, PANS/PANDAS, etc. are more likely to have issues regulating their behaviors. As you know, being proactive and ready is half the battle. So, following are some of my favorite techniques and tools to help kids who aren't regulating at home, school, and/or socially.

Set Social Expectations

If your child has difficulty engaging with or getting along with peers, he or she likely needs direct help. The first step to social success is asking your child what he or she thinks the expectations are. This allows you to process together what it "looks like" and gives children an opportunity to visualize expectations. Also, this process addresses concerns before the event or activity. Sometimes, a little preemptive communication and planning can go a long way in reducing potential conflict.

Use Sensory Tools and Techniques

Using sensory tools and techniques before an event can be incredibly helpful in supporting a child's behaviors. There are so many tools available today that can get the sensory system to calm and regulate, so your child's or teen's brain is more available for learning in all areas.

Sensory Seat Cushion

Many kids with clinical issues have trouble staying seated for long periods of time (and sometimes, for any length of time!). A sensory seat cushion is an amazing tool, as it gives kids the sensory input they crave, so they can focus, reduce hyperactivity, and concentrate better. It can be used while doing any seatwork or even at the dinner table. Using it for about 20 minutes and then taking a break is the best way to optimize focus.

Weighted Blanket

A sensory blanket works by providing a constant level of gentle compression, which calms one's vestibular system. For a child with ADHD, autism, mood regulation issues, or anxiety, self-regulation of the brain and body is problematic. A weighted blanket provides the necessary stimulation to be focused, emotionally regulated, and calm. It is a wonderful tool to help with transitions, like when children get off the bus, or even to help them sleep.

Sensory Putty

While most adults think that fidget items are distractors, for a child with focus problems, a fidget toy can really help him or her focus. Sensory putty is an inexpensive and easy one that gives kids the movement they crave, but in a more "acceptable" way that also helps them stay focused and get work done.

Essential Oils

Essential oils have been used for centuries to treat a variety of conditions. Through clinical research, essential oils such as peppermint, spearmint, lemon, orange, and rosemary have been shown to improve focus. You can inhale them, diffuse them, or apply them topically. Kids love the scent that comes from these brain-stimulating blends.

Mini Trampoline

One of my all-time favorite types of exercise for kids with sensory issues is jumping on a mini trampoline. Pop on a song and have kids jump when they get home from school. It gets out energy, improves circulation and detoxification, moves oxygen to the brain, gives them proprioceptive feedback, and creates alertness.

Kinetic Sand

Playing with kinetic sand is a wonderful way to calm the nervous system, mind, and body. Through the soothing play that comes from the soft-sensory experience of playing with sand, kids with ADHD, anxiety, or stress can often regulate and calm with this technique that builds mindfulness.

Doodle and Coloring Books

Even though teachers used to yell, **"Don't doodle!"** now, many realize how it can help someone be more focused and calm. Researchers believe that doodling allows one to keep his or her mind engaged, so s/he can focus better.

Brainwave-Changing Music

Play music with embedded brainwave-changing technology while a child is playing or doing homework. Musician Jeffery Thompson has created a series of different CD's that can support focus, relaxation, and sleep.

Bookmarks with Windows

Kids with ADHD often know how to read, but struggle with staying focused while reading. Using a simple and inexpensive bookmark that has a highlighted window is an easy way to keep kids focused on what they are reading while eliminating distractions. The highlighting over the words helps to keep the brain's visual system engaged and alert.

When all else fails and a tantrum happens, the best parenting tip I have is to try your best to be calm and understanding. Communicate and support your child throughout the process, keeping in mind that she is learning to navigate her emotions and behavior. Ultimately, don't sweat it. It happens to all of us. Trust me, my kids have had many a tantrum—I even had one myself once, right in the middle of a big box store immediately following my kid's tantrum! Like I said, it happens to all of us, and no one is perfect!

Process and Reinforce Alternatives

Not every kid is capable of communicating his distress. Parents can help the child process the emotions after the tantrum ends by talking about what happened and reinforcing alternatives. Instead of shaming and blaming, parents should try positive parenting skills by focusing on communication and behavioral tools. Typical kids who are learning how to manage emotions and behaviors need support. Children with neurological issues need even more patience and support. Remember, learning a new behavior takes some time, so be consistent and try to remain calm.

Learn and Adapt

Addressing child behavior problems early is critical in helping children to self-regulate, which can have an immediate and lifelong positive impact on behavioral, social, and emotional regulation. Good parenting isn't stopping the behaviors through draconic child discipline methods; it's getting the parenting help that allows you to support your child to learn better skills. Teaching him or her ways to cope and self-manage stress early in life prevents later maladaptive habits that can be tough to break and interfere with cognitive, behavioral, emotional, and social functioning. Addressing issues also preserves and repairs self-esteem and reduces family stress.

Top Questions Parents Ask About Tantrums

You see that your child's siblings or peers are better able to regulate their behavior, and now you are worried. You're not alone! Keep reading for the top questions parents ask me.

Why Is My Child Having More Outbursts at Home Than at School?

School can increase anxiety, stress, and sensory issues in children. After holding it together all day, home becomes the safe place to let frustrations out. Even kids with good self-regulation can get very overwhelmed by being at daycare or school.

It is much more common for children to express challenging behaviors at home then at school. No, they aren't being manipulative; between the structure, routine, and implicit and explicit social reinforcement to "behave" at school, kids are better able to keep it together.

Speaking with your child's teacher can be helpful in figuring out if there are any concerns or issues at school. Parents should become concerned when the behaviors occur frequently and don't decrease with intervention. Seek professional support when you feel overwhelmed or ineffective.

What Can I Do When My Child's Outburst Is Uncontrollable?

Sometimes, even when you have your parenting "A Game" on, your child still throws a tantrum or has an outburst of some sort. Comforting him or letting him safely cry it out is all you can do. Safety is your first priority. Then, focus on calming strategies. Talking too much or yelling isn't going to help. When a child is experiencing a tantrum or meltdown (or is otherwise "in the red,") he is "unreachable"—in other words, certainly not capable of reasoning of any kind.

Why Does My Child Get Aggressive?

Aggression is often a reflection of a child's difficulty dealing with her anxiety or frustration and an inability to verbalize her feelings as others do. Aggression in and of itself is a normal part of child development.

A defiant younger child who engages in verbal aggression is also a normal part of toddler development. Physical aggression can be normal for children up to the age of about six. Most children outgrow these behaviors when guided to communicate better. Really, what child hasn't ever hit her sibling or pushed a kid at the playground?

These kinds of behaviors are a reflection of her inability to regulate or manage her own feelings in the moment. Like all less-than-desirable behaviors, aggression is only an issue when it occurs frequently. A pattern of aggressive behaviors reflects poor impulse control, as well as poor emotional and behavioral regulation.

This same pattern of aggression can also reflect a more significant mental health or behavioral issue. Addressing these behaviors early and getting parenting support can really turn behaviors around.

How Can I Better Support My Teenager?

As I've mentioned, teens are striving to find their way. It is natural for there to be conflict, but it certainly can be greater when a child has a clinical issue that interferes with how they take in information and/or communicate. They need patience and connection from us.

Showing interest in their interests is critical! Is your teen really into anime? Fortnite? Tik Tok? It may not be your thing, but find out why it's theirs. You will learn a lot about your teen's current interests and values, and you might be able to find ways to connect them with your own while developing a deeper bond. Teens are reluctant to share their inner world, but this can act as a window inside.

If you'd like more information about how to talk with teens, download 10 Things Not to Say to a Moody Teenager at www.drrotips.com/moodyteens.

When Should I Worry?

You should worry that your child's tantrum or meltdown isn't normal when they occur with frequent high intensity, are lengthy (more than 25 minutes), and/or if your child is self-injurious.

Tantrums or meltdowns that frequently last a very long time are not only a possible sign of a deeper issue, but they reflect a significant lack of self-regulation. Problems calming oneself after a tantrum is another red flag of a potential behavioral issue. Excessively long tantrums and problems recovering afterward reflect a lack of self-regulation that needs to be addressed.

Certainly, if your child is older, or if outbursts are a new behavior, it warrants concern. A sudden onset of a behavioral issue isn't normal. It could be a sign of a safety issue, traumatic event, a situational stressor, or a medical problem such as PANS/PANDAS.

It is not uncommon at all for children to try to kick their parents during a tantrum, but if it happens the majority of the time, then it may signal a problem.

If these behaviors are present, I suggest a consultation with a licensed mental health provider.

How Can Seeking Professional Support Help My Child's Behavior?

At minimum, kids who haven't outgrown tantrums and behavioral explosions have lagging skills in emotional regulation that warrant support. When strategies that worked for your other kids or advice from solid parenting books haven't helped, you need to seek professional help. No one ever regrets getting help; they only regret when they don't.

A psychologist or therapist offers parenting advice that helps identify behavioral triggers and provides support in how to manage them. Addressing behaviors early is so critical in helping children self-regulate, which can have an immediate and lifelong positive impact on behavioral, social, and emotional regulation. It gives you that lifeline that you need! Teaching them ways to cope and self-manage their stress early in life prevents later maladaptive habits that can be tough to break and interfere with cognitive, behavioral, emotional, and social functioning. And boy, do they disrupt family life. Addressing issues also preserves or repairs that life-defining self-esteem and reduces family stress.

The good news is that most children outgrow tantrums. When tantrums are difficult to manage, are intense, or lengthy, then coaching and counseling can be a valuable shortcut in getting the best parental guidance to support your child's behavioral, social, and emotional needs. All parents want their kids to be healthy and happy, and teaching them how to manage stress and frustration is a vehicle for that.

Tip 7: Prioritize and Practice Parent Self-Care.

Final Thoughts on Parenting That I Wish Someone Had Shared with Me:

As a special needs mom, I have been on the same journey as you. Even I have made mistakes. No one is perfect.

Prepare for a Marathon—Not a Sprint.

Parenting is hard, but can be even more challenging when your child has a behavioral, social, or emotional issue that makes him or her less responsive to standard parenting techniques. When your child can't put on the brakes or process information in the same way as a typical child, he just can't learn in the same way or at the same rate. So, that means a lot of repetition and reminders, which can really strain the relationship between parent and child. Frustration builds all around, which can really leave a mama (or papa!) worn out.

So, how does a parent discipline or teach a child who can't easily attend or learn? There isn't a one-size-fits-all parenting method, but when we focus on learning and use neuroscience to guide how we parent and treat our child's issues, the outcomes are better for everyone.

Know that you need to treat this journey like a marathon, not a sprint.

Taking care of yourself is just as important as taking care of your kids. The road is long, and the journey can be hard and lonely, especially if your child is behavioral or highly emotional. I know I learned that in year seven of my own Lyme and PANS parenting journey, and it is something I wish someone had told me earlier, because the of the long road to healing Lyme.

With that in mind, focus on the following:

Daily Self-Care. If you don't have your stuff together, then you won't be able to handle the stress of parenting. When we take care of ourselves, we have the patience to manage when our kids aren't listening, handle their snarky remarks, and deal with the messy trail they leave behind them. Meditation, yoga, walking, journaling, and/or biofeedback are great tools that help you calm your brain and body, so you can be the best parent possible.

Find Your Tribe. One of the best things a parent can do is to connect with other parents. Parenting today comes with increasing challenges, so you need a "mama tribe" to check in with. Whether you need to get the *real* story about what happened on that group text, or cry to your bestie about the parent-teacher conference you just left, connecting with other moms is key.

Get Help When You Need It.

Seeking help from a licensed mental health professional can give you the tools to help you manage your child's behavior and change the dynamics of your family as well as your relationship with your child.

Parenting Is Powerful.

Don't underestimate the power of your parenting and how much it can teach your child. There is so much you can do to guide your child toward self-regulation and independent behavior. It takes time, effort, and shifting your actions from things that don't work to things that do. There is always a way to reduce and reverse mental health, and you can lead the way for your child.

Chapter 13: What's Next?

Ok, we went over A LOT of good stuff!

Right now, you might feel overwhelmed and unsure where to even start. I get it, because I am a special needs mom, too!

That is why I created this awesome free resource for you—the Mental Health Symptom Reversal Quickstart Guide. You can download it at <u>www.drrotips.com/quickstart</u>.

As we wrap up, I'd love to remind you of the five key takeaways I've shared in this book:

1. YOU are the CEO of your family's health. Changing your child's and family's mental health is something you ABSOLUTELY can do without medication or by taking a whack-a-mole approach to mental health.

2. You CAN reduce and reverse mental health symptoms with PROVEN holistic therapies and feel good about their being safe, natural, and backed by research supporting their efficacy.

3. Making those all-important lifestyle changes such as improved nutrition, sleep, exercise, and stress reduction can make a huge difference in your child's attention, behavior, and regulation.

4. No healing can occur when the nervous system is activated by stress, and that is why we need to use evidence-based therapies that calm the CNS—so the brain and body can work effectively to help your child think, pay attention, and regulate mood and behaviors.

5. Small changes accumulate and create significant change. Start by making one small change, or adding in one type of therapy or technique, and do it *consistently* … and it will have a HUGE positive ripple effect.

And remember, if you ever need step-by-step support, I'm here for you!

My colleague, Dr. Cleopatra Kamperveen, Fertility Specialist, Scientist, and USC professor read this book and said, *"At the end, I didn't want it to be over, with all the good stories, tips, techniques, and research shared."*

That inspired me to create the **Get Unstuck Program**™ for parents who are loving and supporting a child or teen with ADHD, anxiety, learning issues, OCD, PANS/PANDAS, mood or behavioral issues, failure to launch, concussion, or any issue impacting his or her behavior, attention, learning, emotions, or social functioning.

It's for those who want to go deeper into the concepts in this book while receiving my personal guidance. It combines self-guided videos, downloads, and a workbook with weekly calls with me and my team alongside a small group of parents who are on the same journey as you. From my own special needs mom journey, I know firsthand how lonely and overwhelming it can be. Creating this program was equally about guiding parents to help reduce and reverse their child's mental health symptoms as it was about creating a safe space for a small group of special needs parents. We need each other as much as the knowledge, because the road is long and too difficult to traverse alone. Together, we will learn, connect, and laugh, all while creating powerful change for our children and families.

As my bazillion pages of citations below illustrate, natural therapies are effective tools that change mental health. Follow the research, and start adding these powerful natural therapies and techniques to your child's life today. Then, you'll get to watch his or her attention, behavior, and learning improve!

You're excited to begin, right? I hope you're breathing a sigh of relief now that you have action steps to take to create the change you seek!

If you're wondering which technique or tip to implement, remember to just start wherever you are. Some families I work with dive in and combine a bunch of strategies together to create synergy optimization, whereas others start with just one technique or therapy. That is absolutely ok! Just get STARTED!

That is what is important. A magic wand or pill isn't going to miraculously fix your child's behavior, anxiety, ADHD, OCD, or PANS/PANDAS. Change comes from calming down that nervous system and pairing it with new learning—for your child and your family. It will take some work, yes. BUT YOU CAN MAKE IT HAPPEN!

I want your biggest take away to be that ….

Little Waves Create BIG Waves.

You just need to start somewhere, and this book is filled with easy-action resources to do so. Whether you start with changes in how you parent, the food your family eats, or adding a supplement, the KEY is to be consistent about it. Learning takes time, and kids need a lot of reinforcement (which is why you often scratch your head wondering, "Why can't s/he remember that?").

Remember, when our kids are stressed or have attentional or processing issues, they need extra reinforcement (and no, yelling isn't it!), because they don't learn the same way. They *can* learn, though. They just need more consistency from us.

It truly is remarkable how little changes can create noticeable behavioral changes. It brings to mind one more story I'd like to share with you:

Austin's Story

I once worked with a boy named Austin whose mom said that a simple change in how she cued him when he was stressed completely changed the dynamic of their relationship. You see, Austin was a ten-year-old who was super-anxious from the moment he entered school. He moved a lot, and often got in trouble at school despite being very bright. As the demands to finish his work grew, so did Austin's anxiety and dependence on his mom to help him from (as his mom described it), *"freaking out."* Every morning was a nightmare for Donna as she tried to get Austin out the door without tears and yelling.

After participating in my **Get Unstuck Program**™ (www.getunstuckprorgam.com), she learned how to focus on teaching Austin coping skills instead of accommodating or inadvertently feeding into his worries. Instead of saying, *"Let me give you a hug to make you feel better,"* she flipped to, *"Wow, you got through school yesterday. What helped you through it?"* Donna learned that she had to get Austin to recognize how he was coping, or even trying to cope, so that he could build resilience within himself. No looking for a life preserver, because HE WAS HIS OWN LIFE PRESERVER. *Aha,* you say! Well, it was a lot of little moments like those that changed Austin's mental health, and his family's, too.

Whether you are doing the work on your own with this book as your resource, watching the replay of my **Get Unstuck Parenting Summit (www.getunstucksummit.com)**, and/or joining my **Get Unstuck Program**™ (www.getunstuckprorgam.com), you've got this! Every parent has the tools to be the CEO of his or her child's and family's mental health, and when you consistently use the eight pillars to guide you in reducing and reversing mental health, you will see that *IT'S GONNA BE OK!*

I am so grateful that I am on this healing journey with you, and I can't wait to hear about all the ways the natural therapies I've shared within these pages help your child and family. Make sure to share your successes on my Facebook and Instagram accounts, so together, we can help even more families.

With love and light,

Dr. Roseann

Dr. Roseann-Capanna-Hodge

Citations

Abramowitz, J. S. (1996). Variants of exposure and response prevention in the treatment of obsessive-compulsive disorder: A meta-analysis. Behavior Therapy, 27(4), 583-600. https://doi.org/10.1016/S0005-7894(96)80045-1

Achufusi, T & Patel, RK. [Updated 2020 Oct 7]. Milk Thistle. In: StatPearls [Internet]. Treasure Island (FL): StatPearls Publishing; 2020 Jan-. Available from: https://www.ncbi.nlm.nih.gov/books/NBK541075/

Ahn, J., Ahn, H. S., Cheong, J. H., & Dela Peña, I. (2016). Natural Product-Derived Treatments for Attention-Deficit/Hyperactivity Disorder: Safety, Efficacy, and Therapeutic Potential of Combination Therapy. Neural Plasticity, 2016, 1320423. https://doi.org/10.1155/2016/1320423

Al Alawi, A. M., Majoni, S. W., & Falhammar, H. (2018). Magnesium and Human Health: Perspectives and Research Directions. International Journal of Endocrinology, 2018, 9041694. https://doi.org/10.1155/2018/9041694

Ali, T., Rahman, S. U., Hao, Q., Li, W., Liu, Z., Ali Shah, F., Murtaza, I., Zhang, Z., Yang, X., Liu, G., & Li, S. (2020). Melatonin prevents neuroinflammation and relieves depression by attenuating autophagy impairment through FOXO3a regulation. Journal of Pineal Research, 10.1111/jpi.12667. Advance online publication. https://doi.org/10.1111/jpi.12667

Alizadeh, M. A., Abrari, K., Lashkar Blouki, T., Ghorbanian, M. T., & Jadidi, M. (2019). Pulsed electromagnetic field attenuated PTSD-induced failure of conditioned fear extinction. Iranian Journal of Basic Medical Sciences, 22(6), 650–659. https://doi.org/10.22038/ijbms.2019.32576.7\

Allen, J., Montalto, M., Lovejoy, J., & Weber, W. (2011). Detoxification in naturopathic medicine: a survey. Journal of Alternative and Complementary Medicine (New York, N.Y.), 17(12), 1175–1180. https://doi.org/10.1089/acm.2010.0572

Allen, R. W., Schwartzman, E., Baker, W. L., Coleman, C. I., & Phung, O. J. (2013). Cinnamon use in type 2 diabetes: an updated systematic review and meta-analysis. Annals of family medicine, 11(5), 452–459. https://doi.org/10.1370/afm.1517

Alliance, G. (2009, July 8). GENETICS 101. Understanding Genetics: A New York, Mid-Atlantic Guide for Patients and Health Professionals. https://www.ncbi.nlm.nih.gov/books/NBK115568/

Almeida, O. P., Flicker, L., Lautenschlager, N. T., Leedman, P., Vasikaran, S., & Bockxmeer, F. M. (2005). Contribution of the MTHFR gene to the causal pathway for depression, anxiety and cognitive impairment in later life. Neurobiology of Aging, 26(2), 251-257. https://doi.org/10.1016/j.neurobiolaging.2004.03.007

Al-Sarraf, H. (2002). Transport of 14C-gamma-aminobutyric acid into brain, cerebrospinal fluid and choroid plexus in neonatal and adult rats. Brain research. Developmental Brain Research, 139(2), 121–129. https://doi.org/10.1016/s0165-3806(02)00537-0

Al-Snafi, A. E. (2013). The pharmacology of bacopa monniera. International Journal of Pharma Sciences and Research, 4(12), 154-159. http://www.ijpsr.info/docs/IJPSR13-04-12-005.pdf

Altieri, B., Muscogiuri, G., Barrea, L., Mathieu, C., Vallone, C. V., Mascitelli, L., Bizzaro, G., Altieri, V. M., Tirabassi, G., Balercia, G., Savastano, S., Bizzaro, N., Ronchi, C. L., Colao, A., Pontecorvi, A., & Della Casa, S. (2017). Does vitamin D play a role in autoimmune endocrine disorders? A proof of concept. Reviews in Endocrine & Metabolic Disorders, 18(3), 335–346. https://doi.org/10.1007/s11154-016-9405-9

American Academy of Pediatrics (2012). Evidence-based Child and Adolescent Psychosocial Interventions.

American academy of sleep medicine (2016). Recharge with sleep: Pediatric sleep recommendations promoting optimal health. https://aasm.org/recharge-with-sleep-pediatric-sleep-recommendations-promoting-optimal-health/

American Psychological Association (2019). Stress in America: Stress and Current Events. Stress in America™ Survey.

American Psychological Association (2020). Stress in America: Stress and Current Events. Stress in America™ Survey.

Anand, D., Colpo, G. D., Zeni, G., Zeni, C. P., & Teixeira, A. L. (2017). Attention-Deficit/Hyperactivity Disorder and inflammation: What does current knowledge tell us? A systematic review. Frontiers In Psychiatry, 8, 228. https://doi.org/10.3389/fpsyt.2017.00228

Anderson, R. A., Qin, B., Canini, F., Poulet, L., & Roussel, A. M. (2013). Cinnamon counteracts the negative effects of a high fat/high fructose diet on behavior, brain insulin signaling and Alzheimer-associated changes. PloS One, 8(12), e83243. https://doi.org/10.1371/journal.pone.0083243

Antoni, M. H., & Dhabhar, F. S. (2019). The impact of psychosocial stress and stress management on immune responses in patients with cancer. Cancer, 125(9), 1417–1431. https://doi.org/10.1002/cncr.31943

Arrieta, M. C., Stiemsma, L. T., Amenyogbe, N., Brown, E. M., & Finlay, B. (2014). The intestinal microbiome in early life: health and disease. Frontiers in Immunology, 5, 427. https://doi.org/10.3389/fimmu.2014.00427

Auddy, B., Hazra, J., Mitra, A., Abedon, B., & Ghosal, S. (2008). A standardized withania somnifera extract significantly reduces stress-related parameters in chronically stressed humans: A double-blind, randomized, placebo-controlled study. Jana, 11(1), 50-56. https://blog.priceplow.com/wp-content/uploads/2014/08/withania_review.pdf

Bach, D., Groesbeck, G., Stapleton, P., Sims, R., Blickheuser, K., & Church, D. (2019). Clinical EFT (Emotional Freedom Techniques) improves multiple physiological markers of health. Journal of Evidence-Based Integrative Medicine, 24, 2515690X18823691. https://doi.org/10.1177/2515690X18823691

Ballabh, P., Braun, A., & Nedergaard, M. (2004). The blood-brain barrier: an overview: structure, regulation, and clinical implications. Neurobiology of disease, 16(1), 1–13. https://doi.org/10.1016/j.nbd.2003.12.016

Battaglia, J. (2005). Pharmacological management of acute agitation. Drugs 65, 1207–1222. https://doi.org/10.2165/00003495-200565090-00003

Bent, S., Padula, A., Moore, D., Patterson, M., & Mehling, W. (2006). Valerian for sleep: a systematic review and meta-analysis. The American Journal of Medicine, 119(12), 1005–1012. https://doi.org/10.1016/j.amjmed.2006.02.026

Berland, C. (2014). Chronic stress can damage brain structure and connectivity. Psychology Today. https://www.psychologytoday.com/us/blog/the-athletes-way/201402/chronic-stress-can-damage-brain-structure-and-connectivity

Bested, A.C., Logan, A.C. & Selhub, E.M. (2013). Intestinal microbiota, probiotics and mental health: from Metchnikoff to modern advances: Part II – contemporary contextual research. Gut Pathog 5, 3. https://doi.org/10.1186/1757-4749-5-3

Bhattacharya, S. K., & Ghosal, S. (1998). Anxiolytic activity of a standardized extract of Bacopa monniera: an experimental study. Phytomedicine : International Journal of Phytotherapy and Phytopharmacology, 5(2), 77–82. https://doi.org/10.1016/S0944-7113(98)80001-9

Bičíková, M., Dušková, M., Vítků, J., Kalvachová, B., Řípová, D., Mohr, P., & Stárka, L. (2015). Vitamin D in anxiety and affective disorders. Physiological Research, 64(Suppl 2), S101–S103. https://doi.org/10.33549/physiolres.933082

Bilici, M., Yildirim, F., Kandil, S., Bekaroğlu, M., Yildirmiş, S., Değer, O., Ulgen, M., Yildiran, A., & Aksu, H. (2004). Double-blind, placebo-controlled study of zinc sulfate in the treatment of attention deficit hyperactivity disorder. Progress in Neuro-Psychopharmacology & Biological Psychiatry, 28(1), 181–190. https://doi.org/10.1016/j.pnpbp.2003.09.034

Bindman, S. W., Pomerantz, E. M., & Roisman, G. I. (2015). Do children's executive functions account for associations between early autonomy-supportive parenting and achievement through high school? Journal of Educational Psychology, 107(3), 756–770. https://doi.org/10.1037/edu0000017

Bloch, M. H., & Qawasmi, A. (2011). Omega-3 fatty acid supplementation for the treatment of children with attention-deficit/hyperactivity disorder symptomatology: systematic review and meta-analysis. Journal of the American Academy of Child and Adolescent Psychiatry, 50(10), 991–1000. https://doi.org/10.1016/j.jaac.2011.06.008

Boonstra, E., de Kleijn, R., Colzato, L. S., Alkemade, A., Forstmann, B. U., & Nieuwenhuis, S. (2015). Neurotransmitters as food supplements: the effects of GABA on brain and behavior. Frontiers in Psychology, 6, 1520. https://doi.org/10.3389/fpsyg.2015.01520

Bouayed, J., Rammal, H., & Soulimani, R. (2009). Oxidative stress and anxiety: relationship and cellular pathways. Oxidative Medicine and Cellular Longevity, 2(2), 63–67. https://doi.org/10.4161/oxim.2.2.7944

Bowker, E., & Dorstyn, D. (2016). Hypnotherapy for disability-related pain: A meta-analysis. Journal of health psychology, 21(4), 526–539. https://doi.org/10.1177/1359105314530452

Boyer, J. L. (2013). Bile formation and secretion. Comprehensive Physiology, 3(3), 1035–1078. https://doi.org/10.1002/cphy.c120027

Boyle, N. B., Lawton, C., & Dye, L. (2017). The effects of magnesium supplementation on subjective anxiety and stress -A systematic review. Nutrients, 9(5), 429. https://doi.org/10.3390/nu9050429

Bradley, R., Greene, J., Russ, E., Dutra, L., & Westen, D. (2005). A multidimensional meta-analysis of psychotherapy for PTSD. American Journal of Psychiatry, 162(2), 214-227. https://ajp.psychiatryonline.org/doi/full/10.1176/appi.ajp.162.2.214

Brandsma, E., Kloosterhuis, N. J., Koster, M., Dekker, D. C., Gijbels, M. J., van der Velden, S., Ríos-Morales, M., van Faassen, M., Loreti, M. G., de Bruin, A., Fu, J., Kuipers, F., Bakker, B. M., Westerterp, M., de Winther, M., Hofker, M. H., van de Sluis, B., & Koonen, M. (2019). A proinflammatory gut microbiota increases systemic inflammation and accelerates atherosclerosis. Circulation Research, 124(1), 94-100. https://doi.org/10.1161/CIRCRESAHA.118.31323

Bratton, S. C., Ray, D., Rhine, T., & Jones, L. (2005). The efficacy of play therapy with children: A meta-analytic review of treatment outcomes. Professional Psychology: Research and Practice, 36(4), 376–390. https://doi.org/10.1037/0735-7028.36.4.376

Brewer, J. A., Worhunsky, P. D., Gray, J. R., Tang, Y. Y., Weber, J., & Kober, H. (2011). Meditation experience is associated with differences in default mode network activity and connectivity. Proceedings of the National Academy of Sciences of the United States of America, 108(50), 20254–20259. https://doi.org/10.1073/pnas.1112029108

Browning, L. M., & Jebb, S. A. (2006). Nutritional influences on inflammation and type 2 diabetes risk. Diabetes Technology & Therapeutics, 8(1), 45–54. https://doi.org/10.1089/dia.2006.8.45

Bruni, O., Ferri, R., Miano, S., & Verrillo, E. (2004). L -5-Hydroxytryptophan treatment of sleep terrors in children. European Journal of Pediatrics, 163(7), 402–407. https://doi.org/10.1007/s00431-004-1444-7

Brustolin, S., Giugliani, R., & Félix, T. M. (2010). Genetics of homocysteine metabolism and associated disorders. Brazilian Journal of Medical and Biological Research, 43(1), 1-7. https://www.ncbi.nlm.nih.gov/pmc/articles/PMC3078648/pdf/nihms-259545.pdf

Calder, P. C. (2010). Omega-3 fatty acids and inflammatory processes. Nutrients, 2(3), 355–374. https://doi.org/10.3390/nu2030355

Camfield, D. A., Stough, C., Farrimond, J., & Scholey, A. B. (2014). Acute effects of tea constituents L-theanine, caffeine, and epigallocatechin gallate on cognitive function and mood: a systematic review and meta-analysis. Nutrition Reviews, 72(8), 507–522. https://doi.org/10.1111/nure.12120

Candelario, M., Cuellar, E., Reyes-Ruiz, J. M., Darabedian, N., Feimeng, Z., Miledi, R., Russo-Neustadt, A., & Limon, A. (2015). Direct evidence for GABAergic activity of Withania somnifera on mammalian ionotropic GABAA and GABAρ receptors. Journal of Ethnopharmacology, 171, 264–272. https://doi.org/10.1016/j.jep.2015.05.058

Cannell, J. J., Grant, W. B., & Holick, M. F. (2015). Vitamin D and inflammation. Dermato-Endocrinology, 6(1), e983401. https://doi.org/10.4161/19381980.2014.983401

Cappuccio, F. P., D'Elia, L., Strazzullo, P., & Miller, M. A. (2010). Sleep duration and all-cause mortality: a systematic review and meta-analysis of prospective studies. Sleep, 33(5), 585–592. https://doi.org/10.1093/sleep/33.5.585

Carneiro, P., Crawford, C., & Goodman, A. (2007). The impact of early cognitive and non-cognitive skills on later outcomes. Centre for the Economics of Education.

Carr, C. P., Martins, C. M., Stingel, A. M., Lemgruber, V. B., & Juruena, M. F. (2013). The role of early life stress in adult psychiatric disorders: A systematic review according to childhood trauma subtypes. The Journal of Nervous and Mental Disease, 201(12), 1007-1020. https://doi.org/10.1097/NMD.0000000000000049

Case Western Reserve University. (2017, October 23). Protein regulates vitamin A metabolic pathways, prevents inflammation. ScienceDaily. www.sciencedaily.com/releases/2017/10/171023131929.htm

Cattaneo, A., Cattane, N., Begni, V., Pariante, C. M., & Riva, M. A. (2016). The human BDNF gene: peripheral gene expression and protein levels as biomarkers for psychiatric disorders. Translational Psychiatry, 6, e958. https://doi.org/10.1038/tp.2016.214

Center for Disease Control and Prevention (2020). Data and Statistics on Children's Mental Health. https://www.cdc.gov/childrensmentalhealth/data.html

Center for Disease Control and Prevention (2019). Death rates due to suicide and homicide amoung persons aged 10-24: United States, 200-2017. US Department of Health and Human Services: NCHS Data Brief, Number 352, October. https://www.cdc.gov/nchs/data/databriefs/db352-h.pdf

Cueli, M., Rodríguez, C., Cabaleiro, P., García, T., & González-Castro, P. (2019). Differential

Efficacy of Neurofeedback in Children with ADHD Presentations. Journal of clinical medicine, 8(2), 204. https://doi.org/10.3390/jcm8020204

Chacko, S. A., Sul, J., Song, Y., Li, X., LeBlanc, J., You, Y., Butch, A., & Liu, S. (2011). Magnesium supplementation, metabolic and inflammatory markers, and global genomic and proteomic profiling: a randomized, double-blind, controlled, crossover trial in overweight individuals. The American Journal of Clinical Nutrition, 93(2), 463–473. https://doi.org/10.3945/ajcn.110.002949

Chainani-Wu, N. (2003). Safety and anti-inflammatory activity of curcumin: a component of tumeric (Curcuma longa). Journal of Alternative and Complementary Medicine (New York, N.Y.), 9(1), 161–168. https://doi.org/10.1089/107555303321223035

Chandrasekhar, K., Kapoor, J., & Anishetty, S. (2012). A prospective, randomized double-blind, placebo-controlled study of safety and efficacy of a high-concentration full-spectrum extract of ashwagandha root in reducing stress and anxiety in adults. Indian Journal of Psychological Medicine, 34(3), 255–262. https://doi.org/10.4103/0253-7176.106022

Chang, J. P., Su, K., Mondelli, V., Satyanarayanan, S. K., Yang, H. T., Chiang, Y. J., Chen, H. T., & Pariante, C. M. (2019). High-dose eicosapentaenoic acid (EPA) improves attention and vigilance in children and adolescents with attention deficit hyperactivity disorder (ADHD) and low endogenous EPA levels. Transl Psychiatry 9, 303. https://doi.org/10.1038/s41398-019-0633-0

Chatterjee, P., Chandra, S., Dey, P., & Bhattacharya, S. (2012). Evaluation of anti-inflammatory effects of green tea and black tea: A comparative in vitro study. Journal of Advanced Pharmaceutical Technology & Research, 3(2), 136–138. https://doi.org/10.4103/2231-4040.9729

Chiang, E., Smith, D.E., Selhub, J. et al. Inflammation causes tissue-specific depletion of vitamin B6. Arthritis Res Ther 7, R1254 (2005). https://doi.org/10.1186/ar1821

Chin, N. P. (2010). Environmental toxins: physical, social, and emotional. Breastfeeding Medicine : The Official Journal of the Academy of Breastfeeding Medicine, 5(5), 223–224. https://doi.org/10.1089/bfm.2010.0050

Cho, I. H. (2012). Effects of panax ginseng in neurodegenerative diseases. Journal of Ginseng Research, 36(4), 342–353. https://doi.org/10.5142/jgr.2012.36.4.34

Church, D., Sparks, T., & Clond, M. (2016). EFT (Emotional Freedom Techniques) and resiliency in veterans at risk for PTSD: A randomized controlled trial. Explore (New York, N.Y.), 12(5), 355–365. https://doi.org/10.1016/j.explore.2016.06.012

Church, D., & House, D. (2018). Borrowing benefits: Group treatment with clinical emotional freedom techniques is associated with simultaneous reductions in posttraumatic stress disorder, anxiety, and depression symptoms. Journal of Evidence-Based Integrative Medicine, 23, 2156587218756510. https://doi.org/10.1177/2156587218756510

Clond, M., (2016). Emotional Freedom Techniques for Anxiety: A Systematic Review With Meta-analysis. Journal of Nervous and Mental Disease, 204(5), 388-395. doi:10.1097/NMD.0000000000000483

Cohen, S., Doyle, W. J., Alper, C. M., Janicki-Deverts, D., & Turner, R. B. (2009). Sleep habits and susceptibility to the common cold. Archives of Internal Medicine, 169(1), 62–67. https://doi.org/10.1001/archinternmed.2008.505

Cook, E. H., Stein, M. A., Krasowski, M. D., Cox, N. J., Olkon, D. M., Kieffer, J. E., & Leventhal, B. L. (1995). Association of attention-deficit disorder and the dopamine transporter gene. Am. J. Hum. Genet. 56, 993-998. https://www.ncbi.nlm.nih.gov/pmc/articles/PMC1801209/pdf/ajhg00030-0178.pdf

Cropley, M., Banks, A., and Boyle, J. (2015) The Effects of Rhodiola rosea L. Extract on Anxiety, Stress, Cognition and Other Mood Symptoms. Phytother. Res., 29: 1934– 1939. doi: 10.1002/ptr.5486.

Cross-Disorder Group of the Psychiatric Genomics Consortium. (2019). Genomic relationships, novel loci, and pleiotropic mechanisms across eight psychiatric disorders. Cell, 179(7), 1469–1482. https://doi.org/10.1016/j.cell.2019.11.020

Cuciureanu, M.D., & Vink, R. (2011). Magnesium and stress. In R. Vink & M. Nechifor (Eds.) Magnesium in the Central Nervous System [Internet]. University of Adelaide Press. https://www.ncbi.nlm.nih.gov/books/NBK507250/

Cussotto, S., Clarke, G., Dinan, T. G., & Cryan, J. F. (2019). Psychotropics and the Microbiome: a Chamber of Secrets…. Psychopharmacology, 236(5), 1411–1432. https://doi.org/10.1007/s00213-019-5185-8

Dahlsgaard, K. K. & Bodie, J. (2019). The (Extremely) picky eaters clinic: A pilot trial of a seven-session group behavioral intervention for parents of children with avoidant/restrictive food intake disorder. Cognitive and Behavioral Practice, 26(3), 492-505. DOI: 10.1016/j.cbpra.2018.11.001

Daneman, R., & Prat, A. (2015). The blood-brain barrier. Cold Spring Harbor Perspectives In Biology, 7(1), a020412. https://doi.org/10.1101/cshperspect.a020412

Danese, A., & J Lewis, S. (2017). Psychoneuroimmunology of early-life stress: The hidden wounds of childhood trauma?. Neuropsychopharmacology : Official Publication of the American College of Neuropsychopharmacology, 42(1), 99–114. https://doi.org/10.1038/npp.2016.198

De Asis-Cruz J, Krishnamurthy D, Zhao L, et al. (2020). Association of prenatal maternal anxiety with fetal regional brain connectivity. JAMA Network Open; 3(12):e2022349.

Deboer, T. (2018). Sleep homeostasis and the circadian clock: Do the circadian pacemaker and the sleep homeostat influence each other's functioning? Neurobiology of Sleep and Circadian Rhythms, 5, 68-77. https://doi.org/10.1016/j.nbscr.2018.02.003.

Delaney, L., & Smith, J. P. (2012). Childhood health: trends and consequences over the life course. The Future of Children, 22(1), 43–63. https://doi.org/10.1353/foc.2012.0003

Derbyshire, E. (2017). Do Omega-3/6 Fatty Acids Have a Therapeutic Role in Children and Young People with ADHD?. Journal of Lipids, 2017, 6285218. https://doi.org/10.1155/2017/6285218

Dibaba, D. T., Xun, P., & He, K. (2014). Dietary magnesium intake is inversely associated with serum C-reactive protein levels: meta-analysis and systematic review. European Journal of Clinical Nutrition, 68(4), 510–516. https://doi.org/10.1038/ejcn.2014.7

Dodig-Curković, K., Dovhanj, J., Curković, M., Dodig-Radić, J., & Degmecić, D. (2009). Uloga cinka u lijecenju hiperaktivnog poremećaja u djece [The role of zinc in the treatment of hyperactivity disorder in children]. Acta Medica Croatica : Casopis Hrvatske Akademije Medicinskih Znanosti, 63(4), 307–313. https://pubmed.ncbi.nlm.nih.gov/20034331/

Drigen, R., Gutterer, J. M., Hirrlinger, J. (2001). Glutathione metabolism in brain. European Journal of Biochemistry, 267(16), 4912-4916. https://doi.org/10.1046/j.1432-1327.2000.01597.x

Du Toit, A (2019). The gut microbiome and mental health. Nat Rev Microbiol 17, 196. https://doi.org/10.1038/s41579-019-0163-z

Duker, A. L. (2020). The basics on genes and genetic disorders (for teens). KidsHealth. https://kidshealth.org/en/teens/genes-genetic-disorders.html

Dunaev, V. I., Baev, V. M., Frolova, E. G., Shageev, R. M., & Koloskov, S. V. (2008). The structure of a risk to health upon exposure to a complex of chemical factors of the environment. Gigiena i sanitariia, (6), 67–71.

Dutta, S., Shaw, J., Chatterjee, A., Sarkar, K., Usha, R., Chatterjee, A., Sinha, S., & Mukhopadhyay, K. (2011). Importance of gene variants and co-factors of folate metabolic pathway in the etiology of idiopathic intellectual disability. Nutritional Neuroscience,14(5), 202-209. DOI: 10.1179/1476830511Y.0000000016

Dutta, S., Sinha, S., Chattopadhyay, A., Gangopadhyay, P. K., Mukhopadhyay, J., Singh, M., & Mukhopadhyay, K. (2005). Cystathionine beta-synthase T833C/844INS68 polymorphism: a family-based study on mentally retarded children. Behavioral and brain functions : BBF, 1, 25. https://doi.org/10.1186/1744-9081-1-25

Easter, J., McClure, E. B., Monk, C. S., Dhanani, M., Hodgdon, H., Leibenluft, E., Charney, D. S., Pine, D. S., & Ernst, M. (2005). Emotion recognition deficits in pediatric anxiety disorders: implications for amygdala research. Journal of child and adolescent psychopharmacology, 15(4), 563–570.

Eby 3rd, G. A., & Eby, K. L. (2010). Magnesium for treatment-resistant depression: a review and hypothesis. Medical Hypotheses, 74(4), 649–660. https://doi.org/10.1016/j.

mehy.2009.10.051

Egner, T., & Sterman, M. B. (2006). Neurofeedback treatment of epilepsy: from basic rationale to practical application. Expert Review of Neurotherapeutics, 6(2), 247–257. https://doi.org/10.1586/14737175.6.2.247

El-Baz, F., El-Aal, M. A., Kamal, T. M., Sadek, A. A., & Othman, A. A. (2017). Study of the C677T and 1298AC polymorphic genotypes of MTHFR Gene in autism spectrum disorder. Electronic Physician, 9(9), 5287–5293. https://doi.org/10.19082/5287

Edden, R. A., Crocetti, D., Zhu, H., Gilbert, D. L., & Mostofsky, S. H. (2012). Reduced GABA concentration in attention-deficit/hyperactivity disorder. Archives of general psychiatry, 69(7), 750–753. https://doi.org/10.1001/archgenpsychiatry.2011.2280

Ellulu, M. S., Rahmat, A., Patimah, I., Khaza'ai, H., & Abed, Y. (2015). Effect of vitamin C on inflammation and metabolic markers in hypertensive and/or diabetic obese adults: a randomized controlled trial. Drug Design, Development and Therapy, 9, 3405–3412. https://doi.org/10.2147/DDDT.S83144

Elshorbagy, H. H., Barseem, N. F., Abdelghani, W. E., Suliman, H., Al-Shokary, A. H., Abdulsamea, S. E., Elsadek, A. E., Abdel Maksoud, Y. H., & Nour El Din, D. (2018). Impact of vitamin D supplementation on attention-deficit hyperactivity disorder in children. The Annals of Pharmacotherapy, 52(7), 623–631. https://doi.org/10.1177/1060028018759471

Esposito, E., & Cuzzocrea, S. (2010). Antiinflammatory activity of melatonin in central nervous system. Current Neuropharmacology, 8(3), 228–242. https://doi.org/10.2174/157015910792246155

Epstein, N. B. Bishop, D., Ryan, C., Miller, & Keitner, G., (1993). The McMaster Model View of Healthy Family Functioning. In Froma Walsh (Eds.), Normal Family Processes (pp. 138-160). The Guilford Press: New York/London

Etkin, A., & Wager, T. D. (2007). Functional neuroimaging of anxiety: a meta-analysis of emotional processing in PTSD, social anxiety disorder, and specific phobia. The American journal of psychiatry, 164(10), 1476–1488. https://doi.org/10.1176/appi.ajp.2007.07030504

Fang, C. Y., Reibel, D. K., Longacre, M. L., Rosenzweig, S., Campbell, D. E., & Douglas, S. D. (2010). Enhanced psychosocial well-being following participation in a mindfulness-based stress reduction program is associated with increased natural killer cell activity. Journal of Alternative and Complementary Medicine (New York, N.Y.), 16(5), 531–538. https://doi.org/10.1089/acm.2009.0018Fatemi, S. H., Reutiman, T. J., Folsom, T. D., & Thuras, P. D. (2009). GABA(A) receptor downregulation in brains of subjects with autism. Journal of Autism and Developmental Disorders, 39(2), 223–230. https://doi.org/10.1007/s10803-008-0646-7

Ferraracci, J., Anzalone, C., Bridges, R. M., Moore, R. D., & Decker, S. L. (2019). QEEG correlates of cognitive processing speed in children and adolescents with traumatic brain injuries. Applied Neuropsychology: Child. DOI: 10.1080/21622965.2019.1675523

Fisch, S., Brinkhaus, B., & Teut, M. (2017). Hypnosis in patients with perceived stress - a systematic review. BMC complementary and alternative medicine, 17(1), 323. https://doi.org/10.1186/s12906-017-1806-0Flammer, E., & Alladin, A. (2007). The efficacy of hypnotherapy in the treatment of psychosomatic disorders: meta-analytical evidence. The International journal of clinical and experimental hypnosis, 55(3), 251–274. https://doi.org/10.1080/00207140701338696

Folsom, A. R., Desvarieux, M., Nieto, F. J., Boland, L. L., Ballantyne, C. M., & Chambless, L. E. (2003). B vitamin status and inflammatory markers. Atherosclerosis, 169(1), 169–174. https://doi.org/10.1016/s0021-9150(03)00161-8

Ford, J. D., & Kidd, P. (1998). Early childhood trauma and disorders of extreme stress as predictors of treatment outcome with chronic posttraumatic stress disorder. Journal of Traumatic Stress, 11(4), 743–761. https://doi.org/10.1023/A:1024497400891

Fraschini, F., Demartini, G. & Esposti, D. (2012). Pharmacology of silymarin. Clin. Drug Investig. 22, 51–65. https://doi.org/10.2165/00044011-200222010-00007

Freeman, M. P., Hibbeln, J. R., Wisner, K. L., Davis, J. M., Mischoulon, D., Peet, M., Keck, P. E., Marangell, L. B., Richardson, A. J., Lake, J., & Stoll, A. L. (2006). Omega-3 fatty acids: Evidence basis for treatment and future research in psychiatry. J Clin Psychiatry, 67, 1954-1967. http://www.mattitolonen.fi/files/pdf/APA_2006.pdf

Fricke-Oerkermann, L., Plück, J., Schredl, M., Heinz, K., Mitschke, A., Wiater, A., & Lehmkuhl, G. (2007). Prevalence and course of sleep problems in childhood. Sleep, 30(10), 1371–1377. https://doi.org/10.1093/sleep/30.10.1371

Friedel, S., Horro, F. F., Wermter, A. K., Geller, F., Dempfle, A., Reichwald, K., Smidt, J., Brönner, G., Konrad, K., Herpertz-Dahlmann, B., Warnke, A., Hemminger, U., Linder, M., Kiefl, H., Goldschmidt, H. P., Siegfried, W., Remschmidt, H., Hinney, A., & Hebebrand, J. (2005). Mutation screen of the brain derived neurotrophic factor gene (BDNF): identification of several genetic variants and association studies in patients with obesity, eating disorders, and attention-deficit/hyperactivity disorder. American Journal of Medical Genetics. Part B, Neuropsychiatric Genetics : The Official Publication of the International Society of Psychiatric Genetics, 132B(1), 96–99. https://doi.org/10.1002/ajmg.b.30090

Froiland, J. M. (2015). Parents' weekly descriptions of autonomy supportive communication: Promoting children's motivation to learn and positive emotions. Journal of Child and Family Studies, 24(1), 117–126. https://doi.org/10.1007/s10826-013-9819-x

Funk R., Monsees, T., Ozkucur, N. (2009). Electromagnetic effects - From cell biology to medicine. Prog Histochem Cytochem. 43(4):177-264.

Funke, B., Malhotra, A. K., Finn, C. T., Plocik, A. M., Lake, S. L., Lencz, T., DeRosse, P., Kane,

J. M., & Kucherlapati, R. (2005). COMT genetic variation confers risk for psychotic and affective disorders: a case control study. Behavioral and Brain Functions : BBF, 1, 19. https://doi.org/10.1186/1744-9081-1-19

Gao, Q., Kou, T., Zhuang, B., Ren, Y., Dong, X., & Wang, Q. (2018). The association between vitamin D deficiency and sleep disorders: A systematic review and meta-analysis. Nutrients, 10(10), 1395. https://doi.org/10.3390/nu10101395

Garland, E. L., Fredrickson, B., Kring, A. M., Johnson, D. P., Meyer, P. S., & Penn, D. L. (2010). Upward spirals of positive emotions counter downward spirals of negativity: insights from the broaden-and-build theory and affective neuroscience on the treatment of emotion dysfunctions and deficits in psychopathology. Clinical Psychology Review, 30(7), 849–864. https://doi.org/10.1016/j.cpr.2010.03.002

Ghassemzadeh, H. (2017). Mechanisms of response prevention and the use of exposure as therapy for obsessive-compulsive disorder. International Journal of Psychiatry. https://www.researchgate.net/publication/316790525_Mechanisms_of_Response_Prevention_and_the_Use_of_Exposure_as_Therapy_for_Obsessive-Compulsive_Disorder

Gilbert, J. A., Krajmalnik-Brown, R., Porazinska, D. L., Weiss, S. J., & Knight, R. (2013). Toward effective probiotics for autism and other neurodevelopmental disorders. Cell, 155(7), 1446–1448. https://doi.org/10.1016/j.cell.2013.11.035

Godos, J., Currenti, W., Angelino, D., Mena, P., Castellano, S., Caraci, F., Galvano, F., Del Rio, D., Ferri, R., & Grosso, G. (2020). Diet and Mental Health: Review of the Recent Updates on Molecular Mechanisms. Antioxidants (Basel, Switzerland), 9(4), 346. https://doi.org/10.3390/antiox9040346

Goldin, P. R., & Gross, J. J. (2010). Effects of mindfulness-based stress reduction (MBSR) on emotion regulation in social anxiety disorder. Emotion, 10(1), 83–91. https://doi.org/10.1037/a0018441

Gomez-Pinilla, F., & Nguyen, T. T. (2012). Natural mood foods: the actions of polyphenols against psychiatric and cognitive disorders. Nutritional Neuroscience, 15(3), 127–133. https://doi.org/10.1179/1476830511Y.0000000035

Goodman, S. (2009, December 2). Tests Find More Than 200 Chemicals in Newborn Umbilical Cord Blood. Scientific American. https://www.scientificamerican.com/article/newborn-babies-chemicals-exposure-bpa/

Gopalakrishnan, R., Sundaram, J., Sattu, K., Pandi, A., & Thiruvengadam, D. (2013). Dietary supplementation of silymarin is associated with decreased cell proliferation, increased apoptosis, and activation of detoxification system in hepatocellular carcinoma. Molecular and Cellular Biochemistry 377, 163–176. https://doi.org/10.1007/s11010-013-1582-1

Gottesmann, C. (2002). GABA mechanisms and sleep. Neuroscience, 111(2), 231-239. doi:10.1016/s0306-4522(02)00034-9

Goyal, M., Singh, S., Sibinga, E. M., Gould, N. F., Rowland-Seymour, A., Sharma, R., Berger, Z., Sleicher, D., Maron, D. D., Shihab, H. M., Ranasinghe, P. D., Linn, S., Saha, S., Bass, E. B., & Haythornthwaite, J. A. (2014). Meditation programs for psychological stress and well-being: a systematic review and meta-analysis. JAMA Internal Medicine, 174(3), 357–368. https://doi.org/10.1001/jamainternmed.2013.13018

Gracious, B.L., Finucane, T.L., Friedman-Campbell, M. et al. Vitamin D deficiency and psychotic features in mentally ill adolescents: A cross-sectional study. BMC Psychiatry 12, 38 (2012). https://doi.org/10.1186/1471-244X-12-38

Greenblatt, J. M., & Delane, D. D. (2017). Micronutrient deficiencies in ADHD: A global research consensus. International Society for Orthomolecular Medicine, 32(6). https://isom.ca/article/micronutrient-deficiencies-adhd-global-research-consensus/

Grigorenko EL. Brain Development: The Effect of Interventions on Children and Adolescents. In: Bundy DAP, Silva Nd, Horton S, et al., editors. Child and Adolescent Health and Development. 3rd edition. Washington (DC): The International Bank for Reconstruction and Development / The World Bank; 2017 Nov 20. Chapter 10. Available from: https://www.ncbi.nlm.nih.gov/books/NBK525261/ doi: 10.1596/978-1-4648-0423-6_ch10

Gröber, U., Schmidt, J., & Kisters, K. (2015). Magnesium in Prevention and Therapy. Nutrients, 7(9), 8199–8226. https://doi.org/10.3390/nu7095388

Gromball, J., Beschorner, F., Wantzen, C., Paulsen, U., & Burkart, M. (2014). Hyperactivity, concentration difficulties and impulsiveness improve during seven weeks' treatment with valerian root and lemon balm extracts in primary school children. Phytomedicine : international journal of phytotherapy and phytopharmacology, 21(8-9), 1098–1103. https://doi.org/10.1016/j.phymed.2014.04.004

Guerrero, F. A., & Medina, G. M. (2017). Effect of a medicinal plant (Passiflora incarnata L) on sleep. Sleep Science (Sao Paulo, Brazil), 10(3), 96–100. https://doi.org/10.5935/1984-0063.20170018

Guilleminault, L., Williams, E. J., Scott, H. A., Berthon, B. S., Jensen, M., & Wood, L. G. (2017). Diet and asthma: Is it time to adapt our message?. Nutrients, 9(11), 1227. https://doi.org/10.3390/nu9111227

Hammen, C., Kim, E. Y., Eberhart, N. K., & Brennan, P. A. (2009). Chronic and acute stress and the prediction of major depression in women. Depression and Anxiety, 26(8), 718–723. https://doi.org/10.1002/da.20571

Hammond, C. (2003) QEEG-Guided neurofeedback in the treatment of obsessive compulsive disorder. Journal of Neurotherapy, 7(2), 25-52. DOI: 10.1300/J184v07n02_03

Hammond, C. (2005). Neurofeedback treatment of depression and anxiety. Journal of Adult Development, 12(2), 131–137. https://doi.org/10.1007/s10804-005-7029-5

Hammond, C., & Novian, A. (2016). The ISNR comprehensive bibliography of neurofeedback research. International Society For Neurofeedback and Research. https://isnr.org/isnr-comprehensive-bibliography

Hamza, M., Halayem, S., Bourgou, S., Daoud, M., Charfi, F., & Belhadj, A. (2019). Epigenetics and ADHD: Toward an integrative approach of the disorder pathogenesis. Journal of Attention Disorders, 23(7), 655–664. https://doi.org/10.1177/1087054717696769

Hartanto, T. A., Krafft, C. E., Iosif, A. M., & Schweitzer, J. B. (2016). A trial-by-trial analysis reveals more intense physical activity is associated with better cognitive control performance in attention-deficit/hyperactivity disorder. Child neuropsychology : a journal on normal and abnormal development in childhood and adolescence, 22(5), 618–626. https://doi.org/10.1080/09297049.2015.1044511

Harvey, C. J., Gehrman, P., & Espie, C. A. (2014). Who is predisposed to insomnia: A review of familial aggregation, stress-reactivity, personality and coping style. Sleep Medicine Reviews, 18(3), 237–247. https://doi.org/10.1016/j.smrv.2013.11.004

Hartley, L. (2004). Somatic psychology: Body, mind and meaning. Whurr Publishers.

Haschek, W.M., & Voss, K.A. (2013). Safety Assessment including Current and Emerging Issues in Toxicologic Pathology. Haschek and Rousseaux's Handbook of Toxicologic Pathology (Third Edition), 1187- 1258. https://www.sciencedirect.com/topics/agricultural-and-biological-sciences/mycotoxins

Hattapoğlu, E., Batmaz, İ., Dilek, B., Karakoç, M., Em, S., & Çevik, R. (2019). Efficiency of pulsed electromagnetic fields on pain, disability, anxiety, depression, and quality of life in patients with cervical disc herniation: a randomized controlled study. Turkish Journal of Medical Sciences, 49(4), 1095–1101. https://doi.org/10.3906/sag-1901-65

Hausenblas, H. A., Saha, D., Dubyak, P. J., & Anton, S. D. (2013). Saffron (Crocus sativus L.) and major depressive disorder: a meta-analysis of randomized clinical trials. Journal of Integrative Medicine, 11(6), 377–383. https://doi.org/10.3736/jintegrmed2013056

Hayes, S. A., & Watson, S. L. (2013). The impact of parenting stress: a meta-analysis of studies comparing the experience of parenting stress in parents of children with and without autism spectrum disorder. Journal of Autism and Developmental Disorders, 43(3), 629–642. https://doi.org/10.1007/s10803-012-1604-y

He, J., Hsuchou, H., He, Y., Kastin, A. J., Wang, Y., & Pan, W. (2014). Sleep restriction impairs blood-brain barrier function. The Journal of Neuroscience : The Official Journal of the Society for Neuroscience, 34(44), 14697–14706. https://doi.org/10.1523/JNEUROSCI.2111-14.2014

He, S., Wang, M., Si, J., Zhang, T., Cui, H., & Gao, X. (2018). Efficacy and safety of ginkgo preparations for attention deficit hyperactivity disorder: a systematic review protocol. BMJ open, 8(2), e020434. https://doi.org/10.1136/bmjopen-2017-020434

Healy-Stoffel, M., & Levant, B. (2018). N-3 (Omega-3) Fatty Acids: Effects on Brain Dopamine Systems and Potential Role in the Etiology and Treatment of Neuropsychiatric Disorders. CNS & neurological disorders drug targets, 17(3), 216–232. https://doi.org/10.2174/1871527317666180412153612

Hegvik, T. A., Instanes, J. T., Haavik, J., Klungsøyr, K., & Engeland, A. (2018). Associations between attention-deficit/hyperactivity disorder and autoimmune diseases are modified by sex: a population-based cross-sectional study. European Child & Adolescent Psychiatry, 27(5), 663–675. https://doi.org/10.1007/s00787-017-1056-1

Hewlings, S. J., & Kalman, D. S. (2017). Curcumin: A Review of Its' Effects on Human Health. Foods (Basel, Switzerland), 6(10), 92. https://doi.org/10.3390/foods6100092

Hezel, D. M., & Simpson, H. B. (2019). Exposure and response prevention for obsessive-compulsive disorder: A review and new directions. Indian journal of psychiatry, 61(Suppl 1), S85–S92. https://doi.org/10.4103/psychiatry.IndianJPsychiatry_516_18

Hidese, S., Ogawa, S., Ota, M., Ishida, I., Yasukawa, Z., Ozeki, M., & Kunugi, H. (2019). Effects of L-Theanine Administration on Stress-Related Symptoms and Cognitive Functions in Healthy Adults: A Randomized Controlled Trial. Nutrients, 11(10), 2362. https://doi.org/10.3390/nu11102362

Hinz, M., Stein, A., & Uncini, T. (2012). 5-HTP efficacy and contraindications. Neuropsychiatric disease and treatment, 8, 323–328. https://doi.org/10.2147/NDT.S33259

Hodges, R. E., & Minich, D. M. (2015). Modulation of metabolic detoxification pathways using foods and food-derived components: A scientific review with clinical application. Journal of Nutrition and Metabolism, 2015, 760689. https://doi.org/10.1155/2015/760689

Hoebert, M., van der Heijden, K. B., van Geijlswijk, I. M., & Smits, M. G. (2009). Long-term follow-up of melatonin treatment in children with ADHD and chronic sleep onset insomnia. Journal of pineal research, 47(1), 1–7. https://doi.org/10.1111/j.1600-079X.2009.00681.x

Hollis, F., van der Kooij, M. A., Zanoletti, O., Lozano, L., Cantó, C., & Sandi, C. (2015). Mitochondrial function in the brain links anxiety with social subordination. Proceedings of the National Academy of Sciences of the United States of America, 112(50), 15486–15491. https://doi.org/10.1073/pnas.1512653112

Hong, K. B., Park, Y., & Suh, H. J. (2016). Sleep-promoting effects of a GABA/5-HTP mixture: Behavioral changes and neuromodulation in an invertebrate model. Life Sciences, 150, 42-49. doi:10.1016/j.lfs.2016.02.086

Hoogendijk W. J., Lips, P., Dik, M. G., Deeg, D. J., Beekman, A. T., & Penninx, B. W. (2008). Depression is associated with decreased 25-hydroxyvitamin D and increased parathyroid hormone levels in older adults. Arch Gen Psychiatry, 65(5), 508–512. doi:10.1001/archpsyc.65.5.508

Hornyak, M., Voderholzer, U., Hohagen, F., Berger, M., & Riemann, D. (1998). Magnesium therapy for periodic leg movements-related insomnia and restless legs syndrome: An open pilot study. Sleep, 21(5), 501-505. doi:10.1093/sleep/21.5.50

Hosák, L. (2007). Role of the COMT gene Val158Met polymorphism in mental disorders: A review. European Psychiatry, 22(5), 276-281. doi:10.1016/j.eurpsy.2007.02.002

Hoseinzadeh, K., Daryanoosh, F., Baghdasar, P. J., & Alizadeh, H. (2015). Acute effects of ginger extract on biochemical and functional symptoms of delayed onset muscle soreness. Medical Journal of the Islamic Republic of Iran, 29, 261.

Hu, Z., Oh, S., Ha, T. W., Hong, J. T., & Oh, K. W. (2018). Sleep-aids derived from natural products. Biomolecules & Therapeutics, 26(4), 343–349. https://doi.org/10.4062/biomolther.2018.099

Huppert, J. D., Pasupuleti, R. V., Foa, E. B., & Mathews, A. (2007). Interpretation biases in social anxiety: response generation, response selection, and self-appraisals. Behaviour Research and Therapy, 45(7), 1505–1515. https://doi.org/10.1016/j.brat.2007.01.006

Hyman, S. E. (2000). The genetics of mental illness: implications for practice. Bulletin of the World HealthOrganization, 78(4), 455–463. https://www.ncbi.nlm.nih.gov/pmc/articles/PMC2560734/

Inoué, S., Honda, K., & Komoda, Y. (1995). Sleep as neuronal detoxification and restitution. Behavioural Brain Research, 69(1-2), 91-96. https://doi.org/10.1016/0166-4328(95)00014-K

Insel, T (2014). Are children overmedicated? National Institutes of Mental Health. https://www.nimh.nih.gov/about/directors/thomas-insel/blog/2014/are-children-overmedicated.shtml

Institute of Medicine (US) Committee on Sleep Medicine and Research; Colten HR, Altevogt BM, editors. Sleep Disorders and Sleep Deprivation: An Unmet Public Health Problem. Washington (DC): National Academies Press (US); 2006. 3, Extent and Health Consequences of Chronic Sleep Loss and Sleep Disorders. Available from: https://www.ncbi.nlm.nih.gov/books/NBK19961/

Ionescu J. G. (2014). Personalized anti-inflammatory diets for allergic and skin disorders. The EPMA Journal, 5(Suppl 1), A160. https://doi.org/10.1186/1878-5085-5-S1-A160

Itoh, T., Zang, Y. F., Murai, S., & Saito, H. (1989). Effects of Panax ginseng root on the vertical and horizontal motor activities and on brain monoamine-related substances in mice. Planta Medica, 55(5), 429–433. https://doi.org/10.1055/s-2006-962058

Jacobs, B. P., Dennehy, C., Ramirez, G., Sapp, J., & Lawrence, V. A. (2002). Milk thistle for the treatment of liver disease: a systematic review and meta-analysis. The American journal of medicine, 113(6), 506–515. https://doi.org/10.1016/s0002-9343(02)01244-5

Jagannath, V., Marinova, Z., Monoranu, C. M., Walitza, S., & Grünblatt, E. (2017). Expression of D-Amino Acid Oxidase (DAO/DAAO) and D-Amino Acid Oxidase Activator (DAOA/G72) during Development and Aging in the Human Post-mortem Brain. Frontiers in Neuroanatomy, 11, 31. https://doi.org/10.3389/fnana.2017.00031

Jagdish Singh, A. K. Upadhyay, Anant Bahadur & K. P. Singh (2004). Dietary antioxidants and minerals in crucifers. Journal of Vegetable Crop Production, 10(2), 33-41, DOI: 10.1300/J068v10n02_04

Jamshidi, N., & Cohen, M. M. (2017). The clinical efficacy and safety of tulsi in humans: A systematic review of the literature. Evidence-based Complementary and Alternative Medicine : eCAM, 2017, 9217567. https://doi.org/10.1155/2017/9217567

Jankord, R., & Herman, J. P. (2008). Limbic regulation of hypothalamo-pituitary-adrenocortical function during acute and chronic stress. Annals of the New York Academy of Sciences, 1148, 64–73. https://doi.org/10.1196/annals.1410.012

Jensen, M. P., Grierson, C., Tracy-Smith, V., Bacigalupi, S. C., & Othmer, S. (2007). Neurofeedback treatment for pain associated with complex regional pain syndrome type I. Journal of Neurotherapy, 11(1), 45-53, DOI: 10.1300/J184v11n01_04

Jessen, N. A., Munk, A. S., Lundgaard, I., & Nedergaard, M. (2015). The Glymphatic System: A Beginner's Guide. Neurochemical research, 40(12), 2583–2599. https://doi.org/10.1007/s11064-015-1581-6

Johnson, M. T., McCullough, J., Nindl, G., & Chamberlain, J. K. (2003). Autoradiographic evaluation of electromagnetic field effects on serotonin (5HT1A) receptors in rat brain. Biomedical Sciences Instrumentation, 39, 466–470. https://pubmed.ncbi.nlm.nih.gov/12724937/

Johnson, A., Hou, S., & Li, P. (2017). Inflammation and insulin resistance: New targets encourage new thinking: Galectin-3 and LTB4 are pro-inflammatory molecules that can be targeted to restore insulin sensitivity. BioEssays : News and Reviews in Molecular, Cellular and Developmental Biology, 39(9), 10.1002/bies.201700036. https://doi.org/10.1002/bies.201700036

Jones, D. E., Greenberg, M., & Crowley, M. (2015). Early social-emotional functioning and public health: The relationship between kindergarten social competence and future wellness. American Journal of Public Health, 105(11), 2283–2290. https://doi.org/10.2105/AJPH.2015.302630

Joseph, J. A., Bethapudi, B., Agarwal, A., & Kudiganti, V. (2014). An open-label study to elucidate the effects of standardized Bacopa monnieri extract in the management of symptoms of attention-deficit hyperactivity disorder in children. Advances in mind-body medicine, 28(2), 10–15.

Joshi, R. K. (2014). Chemical composition and antimicrobial activity of the essential oil of ocimum basilicum L. (sweet basil) from Western Ghats of North West Karnataka,

India. Ancient Science of Life, 33(3), 151–156. https://www.ncbi.nlm.nih.gov/pmc/articles/PMC4264302/

Kalueff, A. V., & Nutt, D. J. (2007). Role of GABA in anxiety and depression. Depression and anxiety, 24(7), 495–517. https://doi.org/10.1002/da.20262

Karl, J. P., Hatch, A. M., Arcidiacono, S. M., Pearce, S. C., Pantoja-Feliciano, I. G., Doherty, L. A., & Soares, J. W. (2018). Effects of psychological, environmental and physical stressors on the gut microbiota. Frontiers in Microbiology, 9, 2013. https://doi.org/10.3389/fmicb.2018.02013

Kawatra, P., & Rajagopalan, R. (2015). Cinnamon: Mystic powers of a minute ingredient. Pharmacognosy Research, 7(Suppl 1), S1–S6. https://doi.org/10.4103/0974-8490.157990

Khorasany, A. R., & Hosseinzadeh, H. (2016). Therapeutic effects of saffron (Crocus sativus L.) in digestive disorders: a review. Iranian journal of basic medical sciences, 19(5), 455–469.

Kiecolt-Glaser, J. K., Belury, M. A., Andridge, R., Malarkey, W. B., & Glaser, R. (2011). Omega-3 supplementation lowers inflammation and anxiety in medical students: a randomized controlled trial. Brain, Behavior, and Immunity, 25(8), 1725–1734. https://doi.org/10.1016/j.bbi.2011.07.229

Kim, M., Lim, H. S., Lee, H. H., & Kim, T. H. (2017). Role identification of passiflora incarnata linnaeus: A mini review. Journal of Menopausal Medicine, 23(3), 156–159. https://doi.org/10.6118/jmm.2017.23.3.156

Kim, H. G., Cheon, E. J., Bai, D. S., Lee, Y. H., & Koo, B. H. (2018). Stress and heart rate variability: A meta-analysis and review of the literature. Psychiatry Investigation, 15(3), 235–245. https://doi.org/10.30773/pi.2017.08.17

Kim, S., Jo, K., Hong, K. B., Han, S. H., & Suh, H. J. (2019). GABA and l-theanine mixture decreases sleep latency and improves NREM sleep. Pharmaceutical Biology, 57(1), 65–73. https://doi.org/10.1080/13880209.2018.1557698

Kimura, K., Ozeki, M., Juneja, L. R., & Ohira, H. (2007). L-Theanine reduces psychological and physiological stress responses. Biological Psychology, 74(1), 39–45. https://doi.org/10.1016/j.biopsycho.2006.06.006

Kitts, D., Yuan, Y., Joneja, J., Scott, F., Szilagyi, A., Amiot, J., & Zarkadas, M. (1997). Adverse reactions to food constituents: allergy, intolerance, and autoimmunity. Canadian Journal of Physiology and Pharmacology, 75(4), 241–254.

Knüppel, A., Shipley, M. J., Llewellyn, C. H., & Brunner, E. J. (2017). Sugar intake from sweet food and beverages, common mental disorder and depression: prospective findings from the Whitehall II study. Scientific reports, 7(1), 6287. https://doi.org/10.1038/s41598-017-05649-7

Ko, H. J., Kim, I., Kim, J. B., Moon, Y., Whang, M. C., Lee, K. M., & Jung, S. P. (2014). Effects of Korean red ginseng extract on behavior in children with symptoms of inattention and hyperactivity/impulsivity: a double-blind randomized placebo-controlled trial. Journal of Child and Adolescent Psychopharmacology, 24(9), 501–508. https://doi.org/10.1089/cap.2014.0013

Kolb B. (2009). Brain and behavioural plasticity in the developing brain: Neuroscience and public policy. Paediatrics & child health, 14(10), 651–652. https://doi.org/10.1093/pch/14.10.651

Kozielec, T., & Starobrat-Hermelin, B. (1997). Assessment of magnesium levels in children with attention deficit hyperactivity disorder (ADHD). Magnesium Research, 10(2), 143–148. https://pubmed.ncbi.nlm.nih.gov/9368235/

Kumperscak, H. G., Gricar, A., Ülen, I., & Micetic-Turk, D. (2020). A Pilot Randomized Control Trial With the Probiotic Strain Lactobacillus rhamnosus GG (LGG) in ADHD: Children and Adolescents Report Better Health-Related Quality of Life. Frontiers in psychiatry, 11, 181.
https://doi.org/10.3389/fpsyt.2020.00181

Lakhan, S. E., & Vieira, K. F. (2008). Nutritional therapies for mental disorders. Nutrition Journal, 7, 2. https://doi.org/10.1186/1475-2891-7-2

Lammert, C. R., Frost, E. L., Bolte, A. C., Paysour, M. J., Shaw, M. E., Bellinger, C. E., Weigel, T. K., Zunder, E. R., & Lukens, J. R. (2018). Cutting edge: Critical roles for microbiota-mediated regulation of the immune system in a prenatal immune activation model of autism. Journal of Immunology (Baltimore, Md. : 1950), 201(3), 845–850. https://doi.org/10.4049/jimmunol.1701755

Lanphear, B. P. (2015). The impact of toxins on the developing brain. Annual Review of Public Health, 36, 211-230. https://doi.org/10.1146/annurev-publhealth-031912-114413

Lau, B. W. (2002). Stress in children: Can nurses help? Pediatric Nursing, 28(1), 13–9. Google Scholar

Lawrence, T. (2009). The nuclear factor NF-kappaB pathway in inflammation. Cold Spring Harbor Perspectives in Biology, 1(6), a001651. https://doi.org/10.1101/cshperspect.a001651

Lazar, S. W., Kerr, C. E., Wasserman, R. H., Gray, J. R., Greve, D. N., Treadway, M. T., McGarvey, M., Quinn, B. T., Dusek, J. A., Benson, H., Rauch, S. L., Moore, C. I., & Fischl, B. (2005). Meditation experience is associated with increased cortical thickness. Neuroreport, 16(17), 1893–1897. https://doi.org/10.1097/01.wnr.0000186598.66243.19

Leblanc, M., & Ritchie, M. (2001) A meta-analysis of play therapy outcomes. Counselling Psychology Quarterly, 14(2), 149-163. DOI: 10.1080/09515070110059142

Lerner, A., & Matthias, T. (2015). Changes in intestinal tight junction permeability associated with industrial food additives explain the rising incidence of autoimmune disease. Autoimmunity Reviews, 14(6), 479–489. https://doi.org/10.1016/j.autrev.2015.01.009

Levine J. (1997). Controlled trials of inositol in psychiatry. European neuropsychopharmacology : the Journal of the European College of Neuropsychopharmacology, 7(2), 147–155. https://doi.org/10.1016/s0924-977x(97)00409-4

Lewis, J. E., Tiozzo, E., Melillo, A. B., Leonard, S., Chen, L., Mendez, A., Woolger, J. M., & Konefal, J. (2013). The effect of methylated vitamin B complex on depressive and anxiety symptoms and quality of life in adults with depression. ISRN psychiatry, 2013, 621453. https://doi.org/10.1155/2013/621453

Lichstein, K. L., Payne, K. L., Soeffing, J. P., Heith Durrence, H., Taylor, D. J., Riedel, B. W., & Bush, A. J. (2007). Vitamins and sleep: an exploratory study. Sleep Medicine, 9(1), 27–32. https://doi.org/10.1016/j.sleep.2006.12.009

Lidral, A. C., & Moreno, L. M. (2005). Progress toward discerning the genetics of cleft lip. Current Opinion in Pediatrics, 17(6), 731–739. https://doi.org/10.1097/01.mop.0000185138.65820.7f

Liew, W. P., & Mohd-Redzwan, S. (2018). Mycotoxin: Its impact on gut health and microbiota. Frontiers in Cellular and Infection Microbiology, 8, 60. https://doi.org/10.3389/fcimb.2018.00060

Lim, S. Y., Kim, E. J., Kim, A., Lee, H. J., Choi, H. J., & Yang, S. J. (2016). Nutritional factors affecting mental health. Clinical Nutrition Research, 5(3), 143–152. https://doi.org/10.7762/cnr.2016.5.3.143

Liou, S. (2010). Brain-derived neurotrophic factor (BDNF). HOPES. https://hopes.stanford.edu/brain-derived-neurotrophic-factor-bdnf/

Logan, A.C. (2004). Omega-3 fatty acids and major depression: A primer for the mental health professional. Lipids Health Disease 3(25). https://doi.org/10.1186/1476-511X-3-25

Lopes Sakamoto, F., Metzker Pereira Ribeiro, R., Amador Bueno, A., & Oliveira Santos, H. (2019). Psychotropic effects of L-theanine and its clinical properties: From the management of anxiety and stress to a potential use in schizophrenia. Pharmacological research, 147, 104395.

Lu, K., Gray, M. A., Oliver, C., Liley, D. T., Harrison, B. J., Bartholomeusz, C. F., Phan, K. L., & Nathan, P. J. (2004). The acute effects of L-theanine in comparison with alprazolam on anticipatory anxiety in humans. Human Psychopharmacology, 19(7), 457–465. https://doi.org/10.1002/hup.611

Lyon, M. R., Cline, J. C., Totosy de Zepetnek, J., Shan, J. J., Pang, P., & Benishin, C. (2001). Effect of the herbal extract combination Panax quinquefolium and Ginkgo biloba on attention-deficit hyperactivity disorder: a pilot study. Journal of Psychiatry & Neuroscience : JPN, 26(3), 221–228. https://pubmed.ncbi.nlm.nih.gov/11394191/

Lyon, M. R., Kapoor, M. P., & Juneja, L. R. (2011). The effects of L-theanine (Suntheanine®) on objective sleep quality in boys with attention deficit hyperactivity disorder (ADHD): a randomized, double-blind, placebo-controlled clinical trial. Alternative medicine review : a journal of clinical therapeutic, 16(4), 348–354.

Ma, X., Yue, Z. Q., Gong, Z. Q., Zhang, H., Duan, N. Y., Shi, Y. T., Wei, G. X., & Li, Y. F. (2017). The effect of diaphragmatic breathing on attention, negative affect and stress in healthy adults. Frontiers In Psychology, 8, 874. https://doi.org/10.3389/fpsyg.2017.00874

Mah, L., Szabuniewicz, C., & Fiocco, A. J. (2016). Can anxiety damage the brain?. Current Opinion In Psychiatry, 29(1), 56–63. https://doi.org/10.1097/YCO.0000000000000223

Mahmood, L. (2014). The metabolic processes of folic acid and Vitamin B12 deficiency. Journal of Health Research and Reviews,1(1), 5-9. http://www.jhrr.org/article.asp?issn=2394-2010;year=2014;volume=1;issue=1;spage=5;epage=9;aulast=Mahmood

Maintz, L., Schwarzer, V., Bieber, T., van der Ven, K., & Novak, N. (2008). Effects of histamine and diamine oxidase activities on pregnancy: a critical review. Human Reproduction Update,14(5), 485–495. https://doi.org/10.1093/humupd/dmn014

Malhotra, R. K. (2018). Neurodegenerative disorders and sleep. Sleep Medicine Clinics, 13(1), 63–70. https://doi.org/10.1016/j.jsmc.2017.09.006

Malsch, U., & Kieser, M. (2001). Efficacy of kava-kava in the treatment of non-psychotic anxiety, following pretreatment with benzodiazepines. Psychopharmacology, 157(3), 277–283. https://doi.org/10.1007/s002130100792

Mangin, M., Sinha, R., & Fincher, K. (2014). Inflammation and vitamin D: the infection connection. Inflammation Research : Official Journal of the European Histamine Research Society ... [et al.], 63(10), 803–819. https://doi.org/10.1007/s00011-014-0755-z

Manzel, A., Muller, D. N., Hafler, D. A., Erdman, S. E., Linker, R. A., & Kleinewietfeld, M. (2014). Role of "Western diet" in inflammatory autoimmune diseases. Current allergy and asthma reports, 14(1), 404. https://doi.org/10.1007/s11882-013-0404-6

Mariotti, A. (2015). The effects of chronic stress on health: New insights into the molecular mechanisms of brain-body communication. Future Science OA, 1(3), FSO23. https://doi.org/10.4155/fso.15.21

Martin. C., Hales, C., Gu, Q., Ogden, C. (2019). Prescription drug use in the United States, 2015–2016. NCHS Data Brief, no 334. Hyattsville, MD: National Center for Health Statistics.

Maroon, J. C., Bost, J. W., & Maroon, A. (2010). Natural anti-inflammatory agents for pain relief. Surgical neurology international, 1, 80. https://doi.org/10.4103/2152-7806.73804

Martin, C., & Zhang, Y. (2005). The diverse functions of histone lysine methylation. Nature Reviews Molecular Cell Biology, 6, 838–849. doi:10.1038/nrm1761

Martiny, K. (2017). Novel Augmentation Strategies in Major Depression. Danish medical journal, 64(4), B5338. https://pubmed.ncbi.nlm.nih.gov/28385173/

Mascarenhas, M. R. (2019). Pediatric Anti-Inflammatory Diet. Pediatric Annals, 48(6), e220–e225. https://doi.org/10.3928/19382359-20190515-02

Mata, J., Thompson, R. J., & Gotlib, I. H. (2010). BDNF genotype moderates the relation between physical activity and depressive symptoms. Health psychology : official journal of the Division of Health Psychology, American Psychological Association, 29(2), 130–133. https://doi.org/10.1037/a0017261

Maydych, V. (2019). The interplay between stress, inflammation, and emotional attention: Relevance for depression. Frontiers In Neuroscience, 13, 384. https://doi.org/10.3389/fnins.2019.00384

Mayer, E. A., Knight, R., Mazmanian, S. K., Cryan, J. F., & Tillisch, K. (2014). Gut microbes and the brain: paradigm shift in neuroscience. The Journal of neuroscience : the official journal of the Society for Neuroscience, 34(46), 15490–15496. https://doi.org/10.1523/JNEUROSCI.3299-14.2014

McCloskey S., Jeffries, B., Koprinska, I., Miller, C. B., & Grunstein, R. R. (2019). Data-driven cluster analysis of insomnia disorder with physiology-based qEEG variables.Knowledge-Based Systems, 183, 104863. https://doi.org/10.1016/j.knosys.2019.07.034.

McEwen, B. S. (2011). Effects of stress on the developing brain. Cerebrum : The Dana Forum On Brain Science, 2011, 14. https://www.ncbi.nlm.nih.gov/pmc/articles/PMC3574783/

McEwen, B. S. (2017) Allostasis and the epigenetics of brain and body health over the life course: The brain on stress. JAMA Psychiatry, 74(6), 551–552. doi:10.1001/jamapsychiatry.2017.0270

McKnight-Eily, L. R., Eaton, D. K., Lowry, R., Croft, J. B., Presley-Cantrell, L., & Perry, G. S. (2011). Relationships between hours of sleep and health-risk behaviors in US adolescent students. Preventive Medicine, 53(4-5), 271–273. https://doi.org/10.1016/j.ypmed.2011.06.020

McLeod, B. D., Weisz, J. R., & Wood, J. J. (2007). Examining the association between parenting and childhood depression: a meta-analysis. Clinical Psychology Review, 27(8), 986–1003. https://doi.org/10.1016/j.cpr.2007.03.001

McVoy, M., Lytle, S., Fulchiero, E., Aebi, M. E., Adeleye, O., & Sajatovic, M. (2019). A systematic review of quantitative EEG as a possible biomarker in child psychiatric disorders. Psychiatry Research, 279, 331–344. https://doi.org/10.1016/j.psychres.2019.07.004

Medline (June, 2020). Stress in Childhood. https://medlineplus.gov/ency/article/002059.htm

Meier-Ewert, H. K., Ridker, P. M., Rifai, N., Regan, M. M., Price, N. J., Dinges, D. F., & Mullington, J. M. (2004). Effect of sleep loss on C-reactive protein, an inflammatory marker of cardiovascular risk. Journal of the American College of Cardiology, 43(4), 678–683. https://doi.org/10.1016/j.jacc.2003.07.050

Meister A. (1991). Glutathione deficiency produced by inhibition of its synthesis, and its reversal; applications in research and therapy. Pharmacology & therapeutics, 51(2), 155–194. https://doi.org/10.1016/0163-7258(91)90076-x

Merete, C., Falcon, L. M., & Tucker, K. L. (2008). Vitamin B6 is associated with depressive symptomatology in Massachusetts elders. Journal of the American College of Nutrition, 27(3), 421–427. https://doi.org/10.1080/07315724.2008.10719720

Merikangas, K. R., He, J. P., Burstein, M., Swendsen, J., Avenevoli, S., Case, B., Georgiades, K., Heaton, L., Swanson, S., & Olfson, M. (2011). Service utilization for lifetime mental disorders in U.S. adolescents: results of the National Comorbidity Survey-Adolescent Supplement (NCS-A). Journal of the American Academy of Child and Adolescent Psychiatry, 50(1), 32–45. https://doi.org/10.1016/j.jaac.2010.10.006

Michigan Medicine - University of Michigan. (2020, May 26). Children may not always grow out of being picky eaters: Being overly restrictive with children's diets might not be the best strategy; most finicky eaters maintain a healthy childhood weight. ScienceDaily. www.sciencedaily.com/releases/2020/05/200526091408.htm

Michl, L. C., McLaughlin, K. A., Shepherd, K., & Nolen-Hoeksema, S. (2013). Rumination as a mechanism linking stressful life events to symptoms of depression and anxiety: longitudinal evidence in early adolescents and adults. Journal of Abnormal Psychology, 122(2), 339–352. https://doi.org/10.1037/a0031994

Minich, D. M., & Brown, B. I. (2019). A Review of Dietary (Phyto)Nutrients for Glutathione Support. Nutrients, 11(9), 2073. https://doi.org/10.3390/nu11092073

Minihane, A. M., Vinoy, S., Russell, W. R., Baka, A., Roche, H. M., Tuohy, K. M., Teeling, J. L., Blaak, E. E., Fenech, M., Vauzour, D., McArdle, H. J., Kremer, B. H., Sterkman, L., Vafeiadou, K., Benedetti, M. M., Williams, C. M., & Calder, P. C. (2015). Low-grade inflammation, diet composition and health: current research evidence and its translation. The British journal of nutrition, 114(7), 999–1012. https://doi.org/10.1017/S0007114515002093

Minocha A. (2009). Probiotics for preventive health. Nutrition in Clinical Practice : Official Publication of the American Society for Parenteral and Enteral Nutrition, 24(2), 227–241. https://doi.org/10.1177/0884533608331177

Misiak, B., Łaczmański, L., Słoka, N. K., Szmida, E., Piotrowski, P., Loska, O., Ślęzak, R., Kiejna, A., & Frydecka, D. (2016). Metabolic dysregulation in first-episode schizophrenia patients with respect to genetic variation in one-carbon metabolism. Psychiatry Research, 238, 60-67. https://doi.org/10.1016/j.psychres.2016.01.077.

Mitchell, R. H., & Goldstein, B. I. (2014). Inflammation in children and adolescents with neuropsychiatric disorders: a systematic review. Journal of the American Academy of Child and Adolescent Psychiatry, 53(3), 274–296. https://doi.org/10.1016/j.jaac.2013.11.013

Mokhtari, V., Afsharian, P., Shahhoseini, M., Kalantar, S. M., & Moini, A. (2017). A Review on Various Uses of N-Acetyl Cysteine. Cell journal, 19(1), 11–17. https://doi.org/10.22074/cellj.2016.4872

Moll, S. & Varga, E. A. (2015). Homocysteine and MTHFR mutations. Cardiology Patient Page: American Heart Association, e6-e9. DOI: 10.1161/CIRCULATIONAHA.114.013311

Montag, C., Jurkiewicz, M., & Reuter, M. (2012). The role of the catechol-O-methyltransferase (COMT) gene in personality and related psychopathological disorders. CNS & neurological disorders drug targets, 11(3), 236–250. https://doi.org/10.2174/187152712800672382

Mottaghi, T., Khorvash, F., Kheirollahi, M., Maracy, M., & Askari, G. (2019). The MTHFR C677T polymorphism influences the efficacy of folic acid supplementation on the nerve conduction studies in patients with diabetic polyneuropathy; A randomized, double blind, placebo-controlled study. Journal of Research in Medical Sciences : The Official Journal of Isfahan University of Medical Sciences, 24, 36. https://doi.org/10.4103/jrms.JRMS_774_18

Moore, L. D., Le, T., & Fan, G. (2013). DNA methylation and its basic function. Neuropsychopharmacology : official publication of the American College of Neuropsychopharmacology, 38(1), 23–38. https://doi.org/10.1038/npp.2012.112

Morey, J. N., Boggero, I. A., Scott, A. B., & Segerstrom, S. C. (2015). Current directions in stress and human immune function. Current Opinion In Psychology, 5, 13–17. https://doi.org/10.1016/j.copsyc.2015.03.007

Moslehi, N., Vafa, M., Rahimi-Foroushani, A., & Golestan, B. (2012). Effects of oral magnesium supplementation on inflammatory markers in middle-aged overweight women. Journal of Research in Medical Sciences : The Official Journal of Isfahan University of Medical Sciences, 17(7), 607–614.

Moura, F. A., de Andrade, K. Q., dos Santos, J. C., & Goulart, M. O. (2015). Lipoic Acid: its antioxidant and anti-inflammatory role and clinical applications. Current Topics In Medicinal Chemistry, 15(5), 458–483. https://doi.org/10.2174/1568026615666150114161358

Munoz, T., Patel, J., Badilla-Porras, R., Kronick, J., & Mercimek-Mahmutoglu, S. (2015). Severe scoliosis in a patient with severe methylenetetrahydrofolate reductase deficiency. Brain & Development, 37(1), 168–170. https://doi.org/10.1016/j.braindev.2014.03.003

Nagele, P., Zeugswetter, B., Wiener, C., Burger, H., Hüpfl, M., Mittlböck, M., & Födinger, M. (2008). Influence of methylenetetrahydrofolate reductase gene polymorphisms on homocysteine concentrations after nitrous oxide anesthesia. Anesthesiology, 109(1), 36–43. https://doi.org/10.1097/ALN.0b013e318178820b

Nan, Y., & Li, H. (2015). MTHFR genetic polymorphism increases the risk of preterm delivery. International Journal of Clinical and Experimental Pathology, 8(6), 7397–7402.

Nathan, P. J., Lu, K., Gray, M., & Oliver, C. (2006). The neuropharmacology of L-theanine(N-ethyl-L-glutamine): a possible neuroprotective and cognitive enhancing agent. Journal of Herbal Pharmacotherapy, 6(2), 21–30. https://pubmed.ncbi.nlm.nih.gov/17182482/

National Scientific Council on the Developing Child. (2004). Children's emotional development is built into the architecture of their brains" Working Paper No. 2. https://developingchild.harvard.edu/resources/childrens-emotional-development-is-built-into-the-architecture-of-their-brains/

National Alliance on Mental Illness - NAMI (2019). Mental health by the numbers. https://www.nami.org/mhstats

National Institutes of Health. COMT gene - Genetics Home Reference - NIH. U.S. National Library of Medicine. https://ghr.nlm.nih.gov/gene/COMT.

National Institutes of Health. MTR gene - Genetics Home Reference - NIH. U.S. National Library of Medicine. https://ghr.nlm.nih.gov/gene/MTR

National Institutes of Health. MTRR gene - Genetics Home Reference - NIH. U.S. National Library of Medicine. https://ghr.nlm.nih.gov/gene/MTRR

National Institutes of Health. CBS gene - Genetics Home Reference - NIH. U.S. National Library of Medicine. https://ghr.nlm.nih.gov/gene/CBS

National Institutes of Health - Office of Dietary Supplements (2020). Omega 3 Fatty Acids - - NIH. U.S. National Library of Medicine. https://ods.od.nih.gov/factsheets/Omega3FattyAcids-HealthProfessional/

National Institutes of Health - Office of Dietary Supplements (2020). Magnesium - - NIH. U.S. National Library of Medicine. https://ods.od.nih.gov/factsheets/Magnesium-HealthProfessional/

National Institutes of Health - Office of Dietary Supplements (2020). Vitamin D - - NIH. U.S. National Library of Medicine. https://ods.od.nih.gov/factsheets/vitamind-HealthProfessional/

Nazrun, A. S., Norazlina, M., Norliza, M., & Nirwana, S. I. (2012). The anti-inflammatory role of vitamin e in prevention of osteoporosis. Advances In Pharmacological Sciences, 2012, 142702. https://doi.org/10.1155/2012/142702

Nelson, F. R., Zvirbulis, R., & Pilla, A. A. (2013). Non-invasive electromagnetic field therapy produces rapid and substantial pain reduction in early knee osteoarthritis: a randomized double-blind pilot study. Rheumatology International, 33(8), 2169–2173. https://doi.org/10.1007/s00296-012-2366-8

Nemeroff, C. B. (2002). The role of GABA in the pathophysiology and treatment of anxiety disorders. Psychopharmacology Bulletin, 37(4), 133-146. https://europepmc.org/article/med/15131523

Neugebauer, R. (2005). Accumulating evidence for prenatal nutritional origins of mental disorders. JAMA, 294(5), 621–623. https://doi.org/10.1001/jama.294.5.621

Nicolas, G., Nicolas, F., & Rozo, L. (1976). Problèmes posés par l'anesthésie chez l'hypertendu traité par les bêta-bloquants [Problems posed by anesthesia in the hypertensive treated with beta-blockaders]. Archives des maladies du coeur et des vaisseaux, 69(12), 1311–1314. https://pubmed.ncbi.nlm.nih.gov/12725/

Nielsen, C. H., Balachandran, P., Christensen, O., Pugh, N. D., Tamta, H., Sufka, K. J., Wu, X., Walsted, A., Schjørring-Thyssen, M., Enevold, C., & Pasco, D. S. (2010). Enhancement of natural killer cell activity in healthy subjects by Immulina®, a Spirulina extract enriched for Braun-type lipoproteins. Planta Medica, 76(16), 1802–1808. https://doi.org/10.1055/s-0030-1250043

Niess, J. H., Mönnikes, H., Dignass, A. U., Klapp, B. F., & Arck, P. C. (2002). Review on the influence of stress on immune mediators, neuropeptides and hormones with relevance for inflammatory bowel disease. Digestion, 65(3), 131–140. https://doi.org/10.1159/000064933

Newmark, S. (2017, September 15). Just breathe: Diaphragmatic breathing for ADHD. Additude. https://www.additudemag.com/just-breathe-diaphragmatic-breathing-for-adhd/

Nogovitsina, O. R., & Levitina, E. V. (2006). Eksperimental'naia i Klinicheskaia Farmakologiia, 69(1), 74–77. https://pubmed.ncbi.nlm.nih.gov/16579066/

Novak, T. E., Babcock, T. A., Jho, D. H., Helton, W. S., & Espat, N. J. (2003). NF-kappa B inhibition by omega -3 fatty acids modulates LPS-stimulated macrophage TNF-alpha transcription. American journal of physiology. Lung Cellular and Molecular Physiology, 284(1), L84-L89. DOI: 10.1152/ajplung.00077.2002

Nuss P. (2015). Anxiety disorders and GABA neurotransmission: a disturbance of modulation. Neuropsychiatric Disease and Treatment, 11, 165–175. https://doi.org/10.2147/NDT.S58841

Oades, R. D. (2008). Dopamine-serotonin interactions in attention-deficit hyperactivity disorder (ADHD). Progress in Brain Research, 172, 543–565. https://doi.org/10.1016/S0079-6123(08)00926-6

Ooi, S. L., Henderson, P., & Pak, S. C. (2018). Kava for Generalized Anxiety Disorder: A Review of Current Evidence. Journal of alternative and complementary medicine (New York, N.Y.), 24(8), 770–780. https://doi.org/10.1089/acm.2018.0001

Orlando, P. C., & Rivera, R. O. (2004). Neurofeedback for elementary students with identified learning problems. Journal of Neurotherapy, 8(2), 5-19. DOI: 10.1300/J184v08n02_02

Ortiz, R. A., & Barnes, K. C. (2015). Genetics of allergic diseases. Immunology and Allergy Clinics of North America, 35(1), 19–44. https://doi.org/10.1016/j.iac.2014.09.014

Osborne, D. M., Pearson-Leary, J., & McNay, E. C. (2015). The neuroenergetics of stress hormones in the hippocampus and implications for memory. Frontiers In Neuroscience, 9, 164. https://doi.org/10.3389/fnins.2015.00164

Owens, J., Adolescent Sleep Working Group, & Committee on Adolescence (2014). Insufficient sleep in adolescents and young adults: an update on causes and consequences. Pediatrics, 134(3), e921–e932. https://doi.org/10.1542/peds.2014-1696

Pandi-Perumal, S. R., Srinivasan, V., Spence, D. W., & Cardinali, D. P. (2007). Role of the melatonin system in the control of sleep: therapeutic implications. CNS Drugs, 21(12), 995–1018. https://doi.org/10.2165/00023210-200721120-00004

Pardon, M. C., & Marsden, C. A. (2008). The long-term impact of stress on brain function: from adaptation to mental diseases. Neuroscience and biobehavioral reviews, 32(6), 1071–1072. https://doi.org/10.1016/j.neubiorev.2008.05.013

Pärtty, A., Kalliomäki, M., Wacklin, P., Salminen, S., & Isolauri, E. (2015). A possible link between early probiotic intervention and the risk of neuropsychiatric disorders later in childhood: a randomized trial. Pediatric research, 77(6), 823–828. https://doi.org/10.1038/pr.2015.51

Payne, P., Levine, P. A., & Crane-Godreau, M. A. (2015). Somatic experiencing: using interoception and proprioception as core elements of trauma therapy. Frontiers In Psychology, 6, 93. https://doi.org/10.3389/fpsyg.2015.00093

Peedicayil, J. (2012), Role of epigenetics in pharmacotherapy, psychotherapy and nutritional management of mental disorders. Journal of Clinical Pharmacy and Therapeutics, 37, 499-501. doi:10.1111/j.1365-2710.2012.01346.x

Pela I. (2012). How much vitamin D for children?. Clinical cases in mineral and bone metabolism : the official journal of the Italian Society of Osteoporosis, Mineral Metabolism, and Skeletal Diseases, 9(2), 112–117.

Penckofer, S., Quinn, L., Byrn, M., Ferrans, C., Miller, M., & Strange, P. (2012). Does glycemic variability impact mood and quality of life?. Diabetes Technology & Therapeutics, 14(4), 303–310. https://doi.org/10.1089/dia.2011.0191

Perlmutter, S. J., Leitman, S. F., Garvey, M. A., Hamburger, S., Feldman, E., Leonard, H. L., & Swedo, S. E. (1999). Therapeutic plasma exchange and intravenous immunoglobulin for obsessive-compulsive disorder and tic disorders in childhood. Lancet (London, England), 354(9185), 1153–1158. https://doi.org/10.1016/S0140-6736(98)12297-3

Peterson, C. T., Sharma, V., Uchitel, S., Denniston, K., Chopra, D., Mills, P. J., & Peterson, S. N. (2018). Prebiotic Potential of Herbal Medicines Used in Digestive Health and Disease. Journal of alternative and complementary medicine (New York, N.Y.), 24(7), 656–665. https://doi.org/10.1089/acm.2017.0422

Petkov, V. D., Yonkov, D., Mosharoff, A., Kambourova, T., Alova, L., Petkov, V. V., & Todorov, I. (1986). Effects of alcohol aqueous extract from Rhodiola rosea L. roots on learning and memory. Acta Physiologica Et Pharmacologica Bulgarica, 12(1), 3–16. https://pubmed.ncbi.nlm.nih.gov/3751623/

Pinquart, M. (2017). Associations of parenting dimensions and styles with externalizing problems of children and adolescents: An updated meta-analysis. Developmental Psychology, 53(5), 873–932. https://doi.org/10.1037/dev0000295

Pittenger, C., Bloch, M. H., & Williams, K. (2011). Glutamate abnormalities in obsessive compulsive disorder: neurobiology, pathophysiology, and treatment. Pharmacology & Therapeutics, 132(3), 314–332. https://doi.org/10.1016/j.pharmthera.2011.09.006

Pittenger, C., Adams, T. G., Jr, Gallezot, J. D., Crowley, M. J., Nabulsi, N., James Ropchan, Gao, H., Kichuk, S. A., Simpson, R., Billingslea, E., Hannestad, J., Bloch, M., Mayes, L., Bhagwagar, Z., & Carson, R. E. (2016). OCD is associated with an altered association between sensorimotor gating and cortical and subcortical 5-HT1b receptor binding. Journal of Affective Disorders, 196, 87–96. https://doi.org/10.1016/j.jad.2016.02.021

Pizzorno, J. (2014). Glutathione!. Integrative Medicine (Encinitas, Calif.), 13(1), 8–12. https://www.ncbi.nlm.nih.gov/pmc/articles/PMC4684116/

Plante, D. T., Jensen, J. E., & Winkelman, J. W. (2012). The role of GABA in primary insomnia. Sleep, 35(6), 741–742. https://doi.org/10.5665/sleep.1854

Poivre, M., & Duez, P. (2017). Biological activity and toxicity of the Chinese herb Magnolia officinalis Rehder & E. Wilson (Houpo) and its constituents. Journal of Zhejiang University-Science. B, 18(3), 194–214. https://doi.org/10.1631/jzus.B1600299

Prasad, A. S. (2014). Zinc is an antioxidant and anti-inflammatory agent: Its role in human health. Frontiers in Nutrition, 1, 14. https://doi.org/10.3389/fnut.2014.00014

Psychology today. (n.d.) Attention. https://www.psychologytoday.com/us/basics/attention

Pu, D., Shen, Y., & Wu, J. (2013). Association between MTHFR gene polymorphisms and the risk of autism spectrum disorders: A m eta-analysis. Autism Research, 6(5), 384-392. https://doi.org/10.1002/aur.1300

Ramasamy, K., & Agarwal, R. (2008). Multitargeted therapy of cancer by silymarin. Science Direct, 269(2), 352-362. https://doi.org/10.1016/j.canlet.2008.03.053

Ramos, C., Aguillon, D., Cordano, C., & Lopera, F. (2020). Genetics of dementia: insights from Latin America. Dementia & neuropsychologia, 14(3), 223–236. https://doi.org/10.1590/1980-57642020dn14-030004

Ramos, A., Jardim, S. R., & Silva Filho, J. F. (2004). Solvent-related chronic toxic encephalopathy as a target in the worker's mental health research. Anais da Academia Brasileira de Ciências, 76(4). https://doi.org/10.1590/S0001-37652004000400010

Rancour, P. (2016). Emotional Freedom Techniques: Finally, a unifying theory for the practice of holistic nursing, or too good to be true? Journal of Holistic Nursing. doi:10.1177/0898010116648456

Rao, T. S., Asha, M. R., Ramesh, B. N., & Rao, K. S. (2008). Understanding nutrition, depression and mental illnesses. Indian Journal of Psychiatry, 50(2), 77–82. https://doi.org/10.4103/0019-5545.42391

Rao, A. V., Bested, A. C., Beaulne, T. M., Katzman, M. A., Iorio, C., Berardi, J. M., & Logan, A. C. (2009). A randomized, double-blind, placebo-controlled pilot study of a probiotic in emotional symptoms of chronic fatigue syndrome. Gut Pathogens, 1(1), 6. https://doi.org/10.1186/1757-4749-1-6

Rao, P. V., & Gan, S. H. (2014). Cinnamon: a multifaceted medicinal plant. Evidence-Based Complementary and Alternative Medicine : eCAM, 2014, 642942. https://doi.org/10.1155/2014/642942

Rashidian, A., Mehrzadi, S., Ghannadi, A. R., Mahzooni, P., Sadr, S., & Minaiyan, M. (2014). Protective effect of ginger volatile oil against acetic acid-induced colitis in rats: a light microscopic evaluation. Journal of Integrative Medicine, 12(2), 115–120. https://doi.org/10.1016/S2095-4964(14)60011-X

Ratnaseelan, A. M., Tsilioni, I., & Theoharides, T. C. (2018). Effects of mycotoxins on neuropsychiatric symptoms and immune processes. Clinical Therapeutics, 40(6), 903–917. https://doi.org/10.1016/j.clinthera.2018.05.004

Rauh, V. A., & Margolis, A. E. (2016). Research Review: Environmental exposures, neurodevelopment, and child mental health - new paradigms for the study of brain and behavioral effects. Journal of child psychology and psychiatry, and allied disciplines, 57(7), 775–793. https://doi.org/10.1111/jcpp.12537

Razak, M. A., Begum, P. S., Viswanath, B., & Rajagopal, S. (2017). Multifarious Beneficial Effect of Nonessential Amino Acid, Glycine: A Review. Oxidative medicine and cellular longevity, 2017. https://doi.org/10.1155/2017/1716701

Rehman, K., Akash, M.S.H. Mechanisms of inflammatory responses and development of insulin resistance: how are they interlinked?. J Biomed Sci 23, 87 (2016). https://doi.org/10.1186/s12929-016-0303-y

Reifen R. (2002). Vitamin A as an anti-inflammatory agent. The Proceedings of the Nutrition

Society, 61(3), 397–400. https://doi.org/10.1079/PNS2002172

Riise, E. N., Kvale, G., Öst, L. G., Skjold, S. H., & Hansen, B. (2018). Concentrated exposure and response prevention for adolescents with obsessive-compulsive disorder: A replication study. Journal of Obsessive-Compulsive and Related Disorders, 19, 15-22. https://doi.org/10.1016/j.jocrd.2018.07.002.

Rod, N. H., Dissing, A. S., Clark, A., Gerds, T. A., & Lund, R. (2018). Overnight smartphone use: A new public health challenge? A novel study design based on high-resolution smartphone data. PloS One, 13(10), e0204811. https://doi.org/10.1371/journal.pone.0204811

Rodenburg, R., Benjamin, A., de Roos, C., Meijer, A. M., & Stams, G. J. (2009). Efficacy of EMDR in children: a meta-analysis. Clinical psychology review, 29(7), 599–606. https://doi.org/10.1016/j.cpr.2009.06.008

Rokot, N. T., Kairupan, T. S., Cheng, K. C., Runtuwene, J., Kapantow, N. H., Amitani, M., Morinaga, A., Amitani, H., Asakawa, A., & Inui, A. (2016). A Role of Ginseng and Its Constituents in the Treatment of Central Nervous System Disorders. Evidence-based complementary and alternative medicine : eCAM, 2016, 2614742. https://doi.org/10.1155/2016/2614742

Rondanelli, M., Opizzi, A., Monteferrario, F., Antoniello, N., Manni, R., & Klersy, C. (2011). The effect of melatonin, magnesium, and zinc on primary insomnia in long-term care facility residents in Italy: a double-blind, placebo-controlled clinical trial. Journal of the American Geriatrics Society, 59(1), 82–90. https://doi.org/10.1111/j.1532-5415.2010.03232.x

Rosen, J. B., & Donley, M. P. (2006). Animal studies of amygdala function in fear and uncertainty: relevance to human research. Biological psychology, 73(1), 49–60. https://doi.org/10.1016/j.biopsycho.2006.01.007

Roundtable on Environmental Health Sciences, Research, and Medicine; Board on Population Health and Public Health Practice; Institute of Medicine. Identifying and Reducing Environmental Health Risks of Chemicals in Our Society: Workshop Summary. Washington (DC): National Academies Press (US); 2014 Oct 2. 2, The Challenge: Chemicals in Today's Society. Available from: https://www.ncbi.nlm.nih.gov/books/NBK268889/

Rubia, K. (2009). The neurobiology of meditation and its clinical effectiveness in psychiatric disorders. Biological Psychology, 82(1), 1–11. https://doi.org/10.1016/j.biopsycho.2009.04.003

Ryan, R. M., Deci, E. L., Grolnick, W. S., & La Guardia, J. G. (2006). The significance of autonomy and autonomy support in psychological development and psychopathology. In D. Cicchetti & D. J. Cohen (Eds.), Developmental psychopathology: Theory and method (p. 795–849). John Wiley & Sons, Inc..

Ryan, R., O'Farrelly, C., & Ramchandani, P. (2017). Parenting and child mental health. London Journal of Primary Care, 9(6), 86–94. https://doi.org/10.1080/17571472.2017.1361630

Sadeghiyeh, T., Dastgheib, S. A., Mirzaee-Khoramabadi, K., Morovati-Sharifabad, M., Akbarian-Bafghi, M. J., Poursharif, Z., Mirjalili, S. R., & Neamatzadeh, H. (2019). Association of MTHFR 677C>T and 1298A>C polymorphisms with susceptibility to autism: A systematic review and meta-analysis. Asian Journal of Psychiatry, 46, 54–61. https://doi.org/10.1016/j.ajp.2019.09.016

Saha, T., Chatterjee, M., Sinha, S., Rajamma, U., & Mukhopadhyay, K. (2017). Components of the folate metabolic pathway and ADHD core traits: an exploration in eastern Indian probands. Journal of Human Genetics, 62(7), 687–695. https://doi.org/10.1038/jhg.2017.23

Sah, A. K., Shrestha, N., Joshi, P., Lakha, R., Shrestha, S., Sharma, L., Chandra, A., Singh, N., Kc, Y., & Rijal, B. (2018). Association of parental methylenetetrahydrofolate reductase (MTHFR) C677T gene polymorphism in couples with unexplained recurrent pregnancy loss. BMC Research Notes, 11(1), 233. https://doi.org/10.1186/s13104-018-3321-x

Salimi, S., Saravani, M., Yaghmaei, M., Fazlali, Z., Mokhtari, M., Naghavi, A., & Farajian-Mashhadi, F. (2015). The early-onset preeclampsia is associated with MTHFR and FVL polymorphisms. Archives of Gynecology and Obstetrics, 291, 1303–1312. https://doi.org/10.1007/s00404-014-3561-5

Salim, S., Chugh, G., & Asghar, M. (2012). Inflammation in anxiety. Advances in Protein Chemistry and Structural Biology, 88, 1–25. https://doi.org/10.1016/B978-0-12-398314-5.00001-5

Sanders, M., Kirby, J., Tellegen ,C., & Da.y J. (2014). The Triple P-Positive Parenting Program: a systematic review and meta-analysis of a multi-level system of parenting support. Clinical Psychology Review: 34(4): 337-357

Sandi, C., & Pinelo-Nava, M. T. (2007). Stress and memory: Behavioral effects and neurobiological mechanisms. Neural Plasticity, 2007, 78970. https://doi.org/10.1155/2007/78970

Sarris, J. (2007). Herbal medicines in the treatments of psychiatric disorders: a systematic review. Phytotherapy Research : PTR, 21(8), 703-716. https://doi.org/10.1002/ptr.2187

Sarris, J., Logan, A. C., Akbaraly, T. N., Amminger, G. P., Balanzá-Martínez, V., Freeman, M. P., Hibbeln, J., Matsuoka, Y., Mischoulon, D., Mizoue, T., Nanri, A., Nishi, D., Ramsey, D., Rucklidge, J. J., Sanchez-Villegas, A., Scholey, A., Su, K. P., Jacka, F. N., & International Society for Nutritional Psychiatry Research (2015). Nutritional medicine as mainstream in psychiatry. The Lancet Psychiatry, 2(3), 271–274. https://doi.org/10.1016/S2215-0366(14)00051-0

Saxena, R. C., Singh, R., Kumar, P., Negi, M. P., Saxena, V. S., Geetharani, P., Allan, J. J., & Venkateshwarlu, K. (2012). Efficacy of an Extract of Ocimum tenuiflorum (OciBest) in the Management of General Stress: A Double-Blind, Placebo-Controlled Study. Evidence-based complementary and alternative medicine : eCAM, 2012, 894509. https://doi.org/10.1155/2012/894509

Sayyah, M., Boostani, H., Pakseresht, S., & Malaieri, A. (2009). Efficacy of aqueous extract of Echium amoenum in treatment of obsessive-compulsive disorder. Progress in Neuro-Psychopharmacology & Biological Psychiatry, 33(8), 1513–1516. https://doi.org/10.1016/j.pnpbp.2009.08.021

Schaeffer, J. (2014). Diet and detoxification. Today's Dietitian, 16(3), 34. https://www.todaysdietitian.com/newarchives/030314p34.shtml

Schwahn, B.C., & Rozen, R. (2000-2013). Methylenetetrahydrofolate reductase polymorphisms: Pharmacogenetic effects. In: Madame Curie Bioscience Database [Internet]. Austin (TX): Landes Bioscience. https://www.ncbi.nlm.nih.gov/books/NBK5968/

Schwarz G., Belaidi A.A. (2013) Molybdenum in Human Health and Disease. In: Sigel A., Sigel H., Sigel R. (eds) Interrelations between Essential Metal Ions and Human Diseases. Metal Ions in Life Sciences, vol 13. Springer, Dordrecht. https://doi.org/10.1007/978-94-007-7500-8_13

Sears, M. E. (2013). Chelation: harnessing and enhancing heavy metal detoxification--a review. The Scientific World Journal, 2013, 219840. https://doi.org/10.1155/2013/219840

Sebastian, B., & Nelms, J. (2017). The effectiveness of emotional freedom techniques in the treatment of posttraumatic stress disorder: A meta-analysis. Explore (New York, N.Y.), 13(1), 16–25. https://doi.org/10.1016/j.explore.2016.10.001

Sedlmeier, P., Eberth, J., Schwarz, M., Zimmermann, D., Haarig, F., Jaeger, S., & Kunze, S. (2012). The psychological effects of meditation: a meta-analysis. Psychological bulletin, 138(6), 1139–1171. https://doi.org/10.1037/a0028168

Segerstrom, S. C., & Miller, G. E. (2004). Psychological stress and the human immune system: a meta-analytic study of 30 years of inquiry. Psychological Bulletin, 130(4), 601–630. https://doi.org/10.1037/0033-2909.130.4.601

Segerstrom, S., Miller, G., (2006) Psychological stress and the human immune system: A meta-analytic study of 30 years inquiry. Psychological Bulletin, 130(4), 601-630. https://www.ncbi.nlm.nih.gov/pmc/articles/PMC1361287/

Seppälä, E. M., Nitschke, J. B., Tudorascu, D. L., Hayes, A., Goldstein, M. R., Nguyen, D. T., Perlman, D., & Davidson, R. J. (2014). Breathing-based meditation decreases posttraumatic stress disorder symptoms in U.S. military veterans: a randomized controlled longitudinal study. Journal of Traumatic Stress, 27(4), 397–405. https://doi.org/10.1002/jts.21936

Selmi, C., Leung, P. S., Fischer, L., German, B., Yang, C. Y., Kenny, T. P., Cysewski, G. R., & Gershwin, M. E. (2011). The effects of Spirulina on anemia and immune function in senior citizens. Cellular & Molecular Immunology, 8(3), 248–254. https://doi.org/10.1038/cmi.2010.76

Sharif, M. R., Madani, M., Tabatabaei, F., & Tabatabaee, Z. (2015). The relationship between serum vitamin D level and attention deficit hyperactivity disorder. Iranian Journal of Child Neurology, 9(4), 48–53. https://www.ncbi.nlm.nih.gov/pmc/articles/PMC4670977/

Shakibaei, F., Radmanesh, M., Salari, E., & Mahaki, B. (2015). Ginkgo biloba in the treatment of attention-deficit/hyperactivity disorder in children and adolescents. A randomized, placebo-controlled, trial. Complementary Therapies in Clinical Practice, 21(2), 61–67. https://doi.org/10.1016/j.ctcp.2015.04.001

Sharma, A., Madaan, V., & Petty, F. D. (2006). Exercise for mental health. Primary care companion to the Journal of clinical psychiatry, 8(2), 106. https://doi.org/10.4088/pcc.v08n0208a

Shay, N. F., & Mangian, H. F. (2000). Neurobiology of zinc-influenced eating behavior. The Journal of nutrition, 130(5S Suppl), 1493S–9S. https://doi.org/10.1093/jn/130.5.1493S

Shih, C. M., Cheng, S. N., Wong, C. S., Kuo, Y. L., & Chou, T. C. (2009). Antiinflammatory and antihyperalgesic activity of C-phycocyanin. Anesthesia and Analgesia, 108(4), 1303–1310. https://doi.org/10.1213/ane.0b013e318193e919

Shreiner, A. B., Kao, J. Y., & Young, V. B. (2015). The gut microbiome in health and in disease. Current Opinion In Gastroenterology, 31(1), 69–75. https://doi.org/10.1097/MOG.0000000000000139

Shupak, N. M., McKay, J. C., Nielson, W. R., Rollman, G. B., Prato, F. S., & Thomas, A. W. (2006). Exposure to a specific pulsed low-frequency magnetic field: a double-blind placebo-controlled study of effects on pain ratings in rheumatoid arthritis and fibromyalgia patients. Pain Research & Management, 11(2), 85–90. https://doi.org/10.1155/2006/842162

Silberstein, R. B., Pipingas, A., Song, J., Camfield, D. A., Nathan, P. J., & Stough, C. (2011). Examining brain-cognition effects of ginkgo biloba extract: brain activation in the left temporal and left prefrontal cortex in an object working memory task. Evidence-based Complementary and Alternative Medicine : eCAM, 2011, 164139. https://doi.org/10.1155/2011/164139

Simkin, D. R., Thatcher, R. W., & Lubar, J. (2014). Quantitative EEG and neurofeedback in children and adolescents. Child and Adolescent Psychiatric Clinics, 23(3), 427- 464.

https://www.childpsych.theclinics.com/article/S1056-4993(14)00029-7/abstract

Simopoulos A. P. (2002). Omega-3 fatty acids in inflammation and autoimmune diseases. Journal of the American College of Nutrition, 21(6), 495–505. https://doi.org/10.1080/07315724.2002.10719248

Singh, U., Devaraj, S., & Jialal, I. (2005). Vitamin E, oxidative stress, and inflammation. Annual Review of Nutrition, 25, 151–174. https://doi.org/10.1146/annurev.nutr.24.012003.132446

Singh, M. K., & Chang, K. D. (2012). The neural effects of psychotropic medications in children and adolescents. Child and adolescent psychiatric clinics of North America, 21(4), 753–771. https://doi.org/10.1016/j.chc.2012.07.010

Slote, C., Luu, A., George, N., & Osier, N. (2019) Ways you can protect your genes from mutations with a healthy lifestyle. Frontiers for Young Minds, 7(46). doi: 10.3389/frym.2019.00046

Smetana J. G. (2017). Current research on parenting styles, dimensions, and beliefs. Current opinion in psychology, 15, 19–25. https://doi.org/10.1016/j.copsyc.2017.02.012

Smith, S. B., Reenilä, I., Männistö, P. T., Slade, G. D., Maixner, W., Diatchenko, L., & Nackley, A. G. (2014). Epistasis between polymorphisms in COMT, ESR1, and GCH1 influences COMT enzyme activity and pain. Pain, 155(11), 2390–2399. https://doi.org/10.1016/j.pain.2014.09.009

Snyder, S. M., Quintana, H., Sexson, S. B., Knott, P., Haque, A. F., & Reynolds, D. A. (2008). Blinded, multi-center validation of EEG and rating scales in identifying ADHD within a clinical sample. Psychiatry Research, 159(3), 346–358. https://doi.org/10.1016/j.psychres.2007.05.006

Spasov, A. A., Wikman, G. K., Mandrikov, V. B., Mironova, I. A., & Neumoin, V. V. (2000). A double-blind, placebo-controlled pilot study of the stimulating and adaptogenic effect of Rhodiola rosea SHR-5 extract on the fatigue of students caused by stress during an examination period with a repeated low-dose regimen. Phytomedicine : International Journal of Phytotherapy and Phytopharmacology, 7(2), 85–89. https://doi.org/10.1016/S0944-7113(00)80078-1

Spellicy, C. J., Northrup, H., Fletcher, J. M., Cirino, P. T., Dennis, M., Morrison, A. C., Martinez, C. A., & Au, K. S. (2012). Folate metabolism gene 5, 10-methylenetetrahydrofolate reductase (MTHFR) is associated with ADHD in myelomeningocele patients. Plos One, 7(12), https://doi.org/10.1371/journal.pone.0051330

Srivastava, J. K., Shankar, E., & Gupta, S. (2010). Chamomile: A herbal medicine of the past with bright future. Molecular medicine reports, 3(6), 895–901. https://doi.org/10.3892/mmr.2010.377

Staiano, A. E., Broyles, S. T., & Katzmarzyk, P. T. (2015). School term vs. school holiday: Associations with children's physical activity, screen-time, diet and sleep. International Journal of Environmental Research and Public Health, 12(8), 8861–8870. https://doi.org/10.3390/ijerph120808861

Stalp, M., Rohde, F., Bock, D., & Krettek, C. (2001). Glycine reduces the inflammatory response and organ damage in a two-hit sepsis model in rats. Shock (Augusta, Ga.),

16(2), 116–121. https://doi.org/10.1097/00024382-200116020-00006

Starobrat-Hermelin, B., & Kozielec, T. (1997). The effects of magnesium physiological supplementation on hyperactivity in children with attention deficit hyperactivity disorder (ADHD). Positive response to magnesium oral loading test. Magnesium Research, 10(2), 149–156. https://pubmed.ncbi.nlm.nih.gov/9368236/

Steiger, A. (2002). Sleep and the hypothalamo-pituitary-adrenocortical system. Sleep Medicine Reviews, 6(2), 125–138. https://doi.org/10.1053/smrv.2001.0159

Stein, M. B., Fallin, M. D., Schork, N. J., & Gelernter, J. (2005). COMT polymorphisms and anxiety-related personality traits. Neuropsychopharmacology : official publication of the American College of Neuropsychopharmacology, 30(11), 2092–2102. https://doi.org/10.1038/sj.npp.1300787

Steptoe, A., & Kivimäki, M. (2012). Stress and cardiovascular disease. Nature Reviews. Cardiology, 9(6), 360–370. https://doi.org/10.1038/nrcardio.2012.45

Stojanovich, L., & Marisavljevich, D. (2008). Stress as a trigger of autoimmune disease. Autoimmunity Reviews, 7(3), 209–213. https://doi.org/10.1016/j.autrev.2007.11.007

Stuart, S., Cox, H.C., Lea, R.A. and Griffiths, L.R. (2012). The role of the MTHFR gene in migraine. Headache: The Journal of Head and Face Pain, 52, 515-520. doi:10.1111/j.1526-4610.2012.02106.x

Stubbs, B., Vancampfort, D., Rosenbaum, S., Firth, J., Cosco, T., Veronese, N., Salum, G. A., & Schuch, F. B. (2017). An examination of the anxiolytic effects of exercise for people with anxiety and stress-related disorders: A meta-analysis. Psychiatry research, 249, 102–108. https://doi.org/10.1016/j.psychres.2016.12.020

Su, S., Duan, J., Chen, T., Huang, X., Shang, E., Yu, L., Wei, K., Zhu, Y., Guo, J., Guo, S., Liu, P., Qian, D., & Tang, Y. (2015). Frankincense and myrrh suppress inflammation via regulation of the metabolic profiling and the MAPK signaling pathway. Scientific Reports, 5, 13668. https://doi.org/10.1038/srep13668

Su, K. P., Matsuoka, Y., & Pae, C. U. (2015). Omega-3 polyunsaturated fatty acids in prevention of mood and anxiety disorders. Clinical Psychopharmacology and Neuroscience : The Official Scientific Journal of the Korean College of Neuropsychopharmacology, 13(2), 129–137. https://doi.org/10.9758/cpn.2015.13.2.129

Taha, H., Elsheshtawy, E., Mohamed, S. I., Al-Azazzy, O., Elsayed, M., & Ibrahim, S. A. (2017). Correlates of brain derived neurotrophic factor in children with attention deficit hyperactivity disorder: A case-control study. Egyptian Journal of Psychiatry, 38(3), 159-163. DOI: 10.4103/ejpsy.ejpsy_17_17

Talge, N. M., Neal, C., & Glover, V. (2007). Antenatal maternal stress and long-term effects on child neurodevelopment: how and why?. Journal of Child Psychology and Psychiatry, 48, 245-261. doi:10.1111/j.1469-7610.2006.01714.x

Tatomir, A., Micu, C., & Crivii, C. (2014). The impact of stress and glucocorticoids on memory. Clujul medical (1957), 87(1), 3–6. https://doi.org/10.15386/cjm.2014.8872.871. at1cm2

Tausk, F., Elenkov, I., & Moynihan, J. (2008). Psychoneuroimmunology. Dermatologic Therapy, 21(1), 22–31. https://doi.org/10.1111/j.1529-8019.2008.00166.x

Tang, Y. Y., Ma, Y., Wang, J., Fan, Y., Feng, S., Lu, Q., Yu, Q., Sui, D., Rothbart, M. K., Fan, M., & Posner, M. I. (2007). Short-term meditation training improves attention and self-regulation. Proceedings of the National Academy of Sciences of the United States of America, 104(43), 17152–17156. https://doi.org/10.1073/pnas.0707678104

Taylor, S. (2018). Association between COMT Val158Met and psychiatric disorders: A comprehensive meta-analysis. American Journal of Medical Genetics. Part B, Neuropsychiatric Genetics : The Official publication of the International Society of Psychiatric Genetics, 177(2), 199–210. https://doi.org/10.1002/ajmg.b.32556

Telle-Hansen, V. H., Holven, K. B., & Ulven, S. M. (2018). Impact of a healthy dietary pattern on gut microbiota and systemic inflammation in humans. Nutrients, 10(11), 1783. https://doi.org/10.3390/nu10111783

Thienemann, M., Park, M., Chan, A., & Frankovich, J. (2021). Patients with abrupt early-onset OCD due to PANS tolerate lower doses of antidepressants and antipsychotics. Journal of psychiatric research, 135, 270–278. https://doi.org/10.1016/j.jpsychires.2021.01.022

Thompson, A., Hollis, C., & Dagger, D. R. (2003). Authoritarian parenting attitudes as a risk for conduct problems Results from a British national cohort study. European child & adolescent psychiatry, 12(2), 84–91. https://doi.org/10.1007/s00787-003-0324-4

Toda, K., Hitoe, S., Takeda, S., Shimizu, N., & Shimoda, H. (2017). Passionflower extract induces high-amplitude rhythms without phase shifts in the expression of several circadian clock genes in vitro and in vivo. International Journal of Biomedical Science : IJBS, 13(2), 84–92. https://www.ncbi.nlm.nih.gov/pmc/articles/PMC5542920/

Tomás-Camardiel, M., Rite, I., Herrera, A. J., de Pablos, R. M., Cano, J., Machado, A., & Venero, J. L. (2004). Minocycline reduces the lipopolysaccharide-induced inflammatory reaction, peroxynitrite-mediated nitration of proteins, disruption of the blood–brain barrier, and damage in the nigral dopaminergic system. Neurobiology of Disease, 16(1), 190-201. https://doi.org/10.1016/j.nbd.2004.01.010

Trompetter, I., Krick, B., & Weiss, G. (2013). Herbal triplet in treatment of nervous agitation in children. Wiener medizinische Wochenschrift (1946), 163(3-4), 52–57. https://doi.org/10.1007/s10354-012-0165-1

Truax, A. D., Chen, L., Tam, J. W., Cheng, N., Guo, H., Koblansky, A. A., Chou, W., Wilson, J. E., Brickey, W. J., Petrucelli, A., Liu, R., Cooper, D. E., Koenigsknecht, M. J., Young, V. B., Netea, M. G., Stienstra, R., Sartor, R. B., Montgomery, S. A., Coleman, R. A., & Ting,

J. (2018). The Inhibitory Innate Immune Sensor NLRP12 Maintains a Threshold against Obesity by Regulating Gut Microbiota Homeostasis. Cell Host & Microbe, 2 (3): 364 DOI: 10.1016/j.chom.2018.08.009

University of British Columbia. (2018, December 3). Importance of good sleep routines for children. ScienceDaily. www.sciencedaily.com/releases/2018/12/181203080327.htm

University of California - Berkeley. "Vitamin C Lowers Levels Of Inflammation Biomarker Considered Predictor Of Heart Disease." ScienceDaily. ScienceDaily, 14 November 2008. <www.sciencedaily.com/releases/2008/11/081113091630.htm>.

University of California - Davis Health System. (2015, June 11). Movement in ADHD may help children think, perform better in school. ScienceDaily. Retrieved March 13, 2021 from www.sciencedaily.com/releases/2015/06/150611082116.htm

University of Pittsburgh. (2020, May 18). Brain-to-gut connections traced. ScienceDaily. Retrieved May 31, 2020 from www.sciencedaily.com/releases/2020/05/200518154939.htm

U.S. Department of Health and Human Services, Health Resources and Services Administration, Maternal and Child Health Bureau, The Health and Well-Being of Children: A Portrait of States and the Nation, 2011-2012. Rockville, Maryland: U.S. Department of Health and Human Services, 2014.

U.S. Department of Health and Human Services. (2019)."Detoxes" and "Cleanses": What you need to know. National Center for Complementary and Integrative Medicine. https://www.nccih.nih.gov/health/detoxes-and-cleanses-what-you-need-to-know

U.S. Department of Health and Human Services. Homeopathy. National Center for Complementary and Integrative Health. https://www.nccih.nih.gov/health/homeopathy

U.S. Department of Health and Human Services. Homocystinuria due to MTHFR deficiency. Genetic and rare diseases information center. https://rarediseases.info.nih.gov/diseases/2734/homocystinuria-due-to-mthfr-deficiency

U.S. Department of Health and Human Services. Folate fact sheet for consumers. National Institutes of Health. https://ods.od.nih.gov/factsheets/folate-Health%20Professional/

U.S. Department of Health and Human Services. Vitamin B12 fact information. National Institutes of Health. https://ods.od.nih.gov/factsheets/vitamin%20B12-HealthProfessional/

U.S. National Library of Medicine. (2019). Effects of 800mg of rhodiola rosea in attention in adults with attention-deficit/hyperactivity disorder. https://clinicaltrials.gov/ct2/show/NCT02737033#contacts

U.S. National Library of Medicine. (2020). What is a Gene? https://ghr.nlm.nih.gov/primer/basics/gene

Usenko G. A., Usenko A. G., & Vasendin, D. V. (2015). Features of oxygen utilization by the body of patients with arterial hypertension in the days of magnetic storms depending on the psychosomatic status and treatment options. Rossiiskii Fiziologicheskii Zhurnal Imeni I.M. Sechenova, 101(1), 123-133. https://europepmc.org/article/med/25868333

Valenzuela, A., & Garrido, A. (1994). Biochemical bases of the pharmacological action of the flavonoid silymarin and of its structural isomer silibinin. Biol Res, 27, 105-112. https://pdfs.semanticscholar.org/1116/c8b2d288a7096bbe2ea8ee846f45e94db307.pdf

Valizadeh, L., Farnam, A., & Rahkar Farshi, M. (2012). Investigation of stress symptoms among primary school children. Journal of Caring Sciences, 1(1), 25–30. https://doi.org/10.5681/jcs.2012.004

van Maanen, A., Meijer, A. M., Smits, M. G., van der Heijden, K. B., & Oort, F. J. (2017). Effects of melatonin and bright light treatment in childhood chronic sleep onset insomnia with late melatonin onset: A randomized controlled study. Sleep, 40(2), zsw038. https://doi.org/10.1093/sleep/zsw038

Van Petegem, S., Zimmer-Gembeck, M. J., Soenens, B., Vansteenkiste, M., Brenning, K., Mabbe, E., Vanhalst, J., & Zimmermann, G. (2017). Does general parenting context modify adolescents' appraisals and coping with a situation of parental regulation? The case of autonomy-supportive parenting. Journal of Child and Family Studies, 26(9), 2623–2639. https://doi.org/10.1007/s10826-017-0758-9

van Rooij, I., Vermeij-Keers, C., Kluijtmans, A., Ocké, M. C., Zielhuis, G. A., Goorhuis-Brouwer, S. M., van der Biezen, J., Kuijpers-Jagtman, A., & Steegers-Theunissen, R. Does the interaction between maternal folate intake and the methylenetetrahydrofolate reductase polymorphisms affect the risk of cleft lip with or without cleft palate? American Journal of Epidemiology, 157(7), 583–591. https://doi.org/10.1093/aje/kwg005

Verlaet, A., Maasakkers, C. M., Hermans, N., & Savelkoul, H. (2018). Rationale for dietary antioxidant treatment of ADHD. Nutrients, 10(4), 405. https://doi.org/10.3390/nu10040405

Vogel, S., & Schwabe, L. (2016). Learning and memory under stress: implications for the classroom. NPJ Science Of Learning, 1, 16011. https://doi.org/10.1038/npjscilearn.2016.11

Wan, L., Li, Y., Zhang, Z., Sun, Z., He, Y., & Li, R. (2018). Methylenetetrahydrofolate reductase and psychiatric diseases. Translational Psychiatry, 8(1), 242. https://doi.org/10.1038/s41398-018-0276-6

Wang, W., Wu, Z., Lin, G., Hu, S., Wang, B., Dai, Z., & Wu, G. (2014). Glycine stimulates protein synthesis and inhibits oxidative stress in pig small intestinal epithelial cells. The Journal of Nutrition, 144(10), 1540–1548. https://doi.org/10.3945/jn.114.194001

Webster Marketon, J. I., & Glaser, R. (2008). Stress hormones and immune function. Cellular Immunology, 252(1-2), 16–26. https://doi.org/10.1016/j.cellimm.2007.09.006

Weiss, M. D., Wasdell, M. B., Bomben, M. M., Rea, K. J., & Freeman, R. D. (2006). Sleep hygiene and melatonin treatment for children and adolescents with ADHD and initial insomnia. Journal of the American Academy of Child and Adolescent Psychiatry, 45(5), 512–519.

Weisz, J. R., McCarty, C. A., & Valeri, S. M. (2006). Effects of psychotherapy for depression in children and adolescents: A meta-analysis. Psychological Bulletin, 132(1), 132–149. https://doi.org/10.1037/0033-2909.132.1.132

Weitz, E., Kleiboer, A., van Straten, A., & Cuijpers, P. (2018). The effects of psychotherapy for depression on anxiety symptoms: a meta-analysis. Psychological Medicine, 48(13), 2140–2152. https://doi.org/10.1017/S0033291717003622

Whittal, M. L., Robichaud, M., Thordarson, D. S., & McLean, P. D. (2008). Group and individual treatment of obsessive-compulsive disorder using cognitive therapy and exposure plus response prevention: A 2-year follow-up of two randomized trials. Journal of Consulting and Clinical Psychology, 76(6), 1003–1014. https://doi.org/10.1037/a0013076

Wilkins, C. H., Sheline, Y. I., Roe, C. M., Birge, S. J., & Morris, J. C. (2006). Vitamin D deficiency is associated with low mood and worse cognitive performance in older adults. The American Journal of Geriatric Psychiatry, 14(12), 1032-1040. DOI: https://doi.org/10.1097/01.JGP.0000240986.74642.7c

Wilson V, Peper E, Moss D. (2007). "The Mind Room" in Italian soccer training: The use of biofeedback and neurofeedback for optimum performance. Biofeedback.;34(3):79–81

Wolf, O. T. (2007). Stress, Memory and Aging: Relevance for the Peri- and Post-menopausal Woman. Menopause Management. https://www.menopausemgmt.com/stress-memory-and-aging-relevance-for-the-peri-and-post-menopausal-woman/

World Health Organization (2018). Mycotoxins. https://www.who.int/news-room/fact-sheets/detail/mycotoxins

Xie, L., Kang, H., Xu, Q., Chen, M. J., Liao, Y., Thiyagarajan, M., O'Donnell, J., Christensen, D. J., Nicholson, C., Iliff, J.J., Takano, T., Deane, R., & Nedergaard, M. (2013). Sleep drives metabolite clearance from the adult brain. Science, 342(6156), 373-377. DOI: 10.1126/science.1241224

Xiong, Z., Shi, S., & Xu, H. (2005). A controlled study of the effectiveness of EEG biofeedback training on-children with attention deficit hyperactivity disorder. Journal of Huazhong University of Science and Technology, 25(3), 368–370. https://doi.org/10.1007/BF02828171

Yalcin, B., Willis-Owen, S., Fullerton, J., Meesaq, A., Deacon, R. M., Rawlins, J. N., Copley, R. R., Morris, A. P., Flint, J., & Mott, R. (2004). Genetic dissection of a behavioral quantitative trait locus shows that Rgs2 modulates anxiety in mice. Nature Genetics, 36, 1197-1202. https://doi.org/10.1038/ng1450

Yan, W. J., Tan, Y. C., Xu, J. C., Tang, X. P., Zhang, C., Zhang, P. B., & Ren, Z. Q. (2015). Protective effects of silibinin and its possible mechanism of action in mice exposed to chronic unpredictable mild stress. Biomolecules & Therapeutics, 23(3), 245–250. https://doi.org/10.4062/biomolther.2014.138

Yang, H. C., Liu, C. M., Liu, Y. L., Chen, C. W., Chang, C. C., Fann, C. S., Chiou, J. J., Yang, U. C., Chen, C. H., Faraone, S. V., Tsuang, M. T., & Hwu, H. G. (2013). The DAO gene is associated with schizophrenia and interacts with other genes in the Taiwan Han Chinese population. PloS one, 8(3), e60099. https://doi.org/10.1371/journal.pone.0060099

Yang, B., Fan, S., Zhi, X., Xia, R., Wang, Y., Zheng, Q., & Sun, G. (2017). Geographical and ethnic distribution of MTHFR gene polymorphisms and their associations with diseases among Chinese population. Clinical Genetics, 92(3), 243–258. https://doi.org/10.1111/cge.12929

Yaribeygi, H., Panahi, Y., Sahraei, H., Johnston, T. P., & Sahebkar, A. (2017). The impact of stress on body function: A review. EXCLI Journal, 16, 1057–1072. https://doi.org/10.17179/excli2017-480

Yurcheshen, M., Seehuus, M., & Pigeon, W. (2015). Updates on nutraceutical sleep therapeutics and investigational research. Evidence-based Complementary and Alternative Medicine : eCAM, 2015, 105256. https://doi.org/10.1155/2015/105256

Zachariae, R. (2009). Psychoneuroimmunology: a bio-psycho-social approach to health and disease. Scandinavian Journal of Psychology, 50(6), 645–651. https://doi.org/10.1111/j.1467-9450.2009.00779.x

Zadeh, S. S., & Begum, K. (2011). Comparison of nutrient intake by sleep status in selected adults in Mysore, India. Nutrition Research and Practice, 5(3), 230-235. https://doi.org/10.4162/nrp.2011.5.3.230

Zhao, H., Li, Q., Zhang, Z., Pei, X., Wang, J., & Li, Y. (2009). Long-term ginsenoside consumption prevents memory loss in aged SAMP8 mice by decreasing oxidative stress and up-regulating the plasticity-related proteins in hippocampus. Brain Research, 1256, 111–122. https://doi.org/10.1016/j.brainres.2008.12.031

Zheng, W. (2001). Neurotoxicology of the brain barrier system: new implications. Journal of Toxicology. Clinical Toxicology, 39(7), 711–719. https://doi.org/10.1081/clt-100108512

Zintzaras, E. (2006). C677T and A1298C methylenetetrahydrofolate reductase gene polymorphisms in schizophrenia, bipolar disorder and depression: a meta-analysis of genetic association studies. Psychiatric Genetics, 16(3), 105–115. doi: 10.1097/01.ypg.0000199444.77291.e2.

Zwanzger, P., & Rupprecht, R. (2005). Selective GABAergic treatment for panic? Investigations in experimental panic induction and panic disorder. Journal of Psychiatry & Neuroscience : JPN, 30(3), 167–175. https://www.ncbi.nlm.nih.gov/pmc/articles/PMC1089777/

Dr. Roseann-Capanna-Hodge

Dr. Roseann-Capanna-Hodge

Made in the USA
Coppell, TX
29 March 2023

14951355R00142